My Lord Brother
　　　The Lion Heart

Books by Molly Costain Haycraft

My Lord Brother the Lion Heart
The Lady Royal
The Reluctant Queen
Too Near the Throne

My Lord Brother
The Lion Heart

Molly Costain Haycraft

J. B. LIPPINCOTT COMPANY

PHILADELPHIA & NEW YORK

For Howard

CHAPTER

I

As our tall, clumsy carrack neared the harbor, I found myself stepping back into the shade of the canvas shelter. There was still enough breeze to take us over the water, but the closer we came to shore the hotter the sun grew, and Tripoli's mass of huddled white buildings, clearly visible now, seemed to shimmer in its glare. We had been spoiled by the deliciously cool days and nights at sea; they had almost made us forget the summer months in Palermo and the blistering weeks in Messina while we waited for our fleet to provision and to undergo the inevitable last-minute repairs.

I would have been content to have this long voyage from Sicily to the peninsula of Al-Mina, our last halt on the way to Acre, go on forever; but my lord husband, King William, standing nearer the rail of the deck on the forecastle, was eager to have it end. Nothing, I knew, could dampen the ardor of a true Crusader; heat, insects, disease, death—all these horrors were considered mere annoyances to be endured and overcome on the difficult road to the Holy Land. And, as if to prove it, my lord and our fellow Crusaders were already clad in their glittering chain mail and the white hauberks with the large red crosses that they would wear into battle. I, of course, was more comfortable in my thinnest cote and lightest mantle, with a soft veil tossed over my crown and around my face to protect it from the sun's rays.

Pulling the veil a little farther over my forehead I sighed, wondering, as I often did, why I, like my brother Duke Richard, had inherited the red-gold Plantagenet hair, blue eyes, and that aggravating skin which tended to freckle and peel. Our mother, Queen Eleanor, was dark and had a beautiful creamy complexion that never needed any care. In justice, however, I had to admit that neither in her beloved Aquitaine nor in our lord father's England was she exposed to the kind of heat I had endured for the last twelve summers. Indeed, for many a long year now she had been confined to the damp, thick-walled old castle at Winchester, where one might shiver in any season.

Why *had* my father imprisoned her there? I remembered hearing them quarrel hotly, it is true, when I was a small girl. But I also remembered the story of their passionate love for each other that began while she was Queen Eleanor of France, wife of King Louis VII, and he was the young Henry, heir to the crown of England. I had asked myself this question often since hearing of her incarceration, and on this particular day it crossed my mind again, here on the deck of my good William's ship—perhaps because she, too, had gone on Crusade. Her adventure, however, had taken place more than forty years ago, back in 1148; her Crusade was the second, mine and William's the third.

The deck under my feet dipped suddenly, bringing my wandering thoughts back to the present. A brisk, favorable breeze filled the sails over my head, sending our awkward vessel swiftly across the harbor and setting the flags and banners on the other carracks, the smaller dromonds, galleys, and ships of all sizes that made up our fleet, to fluttering wildly on their masts and rigging.

A sense of mounting excitement welled up in me, and I heard

loud bursts of talk and laughter around us. My lord, his long fair curls blowing on his shoulders, moved right to the high rail so that he could be seen by the milling crowd of Crusaders and seamen on the deck below, then turned and motioned to me. It seemed to me that my husband, always an unusually handsome man, had never appeared to greater advantage. His thirty-six years had not thickened the delicately chiselled features or added more than an inch or two to his girth, and as he welcomed me with his usual affectionate smile I found myself trying hopelessly to purse my own mouth into the tiny pink rosebud that it should have been. It was no use. My mouth was too wide for beauty, just as my eyes were too deep-set; by closing one of them I could see, too, that all my precautions had come to naught. There, on the bridge of my nose, the only good feature I had inherited from my lady mother, was a fresh spattering of freckles.

For a long, breathless moment we stood side by side, our nobles grouping themselves behind us. A hush fell over the whole ship, and all eyes were on my lord, my dear lord—King William the Good, as our people back home in Sicily had begun to call him.

Raising his hand high, he broke the silence with a loud shout. "Help!" His voice rang out so that everyone could hear him. "Help for the Holy Sepulchre!"

"Help! Help for the Holy Sepulchre!" The answering call from the other decks was the cry that was rousing every loyal Christian heart these days, the cry that was making friends of enemies and halting all quarrels, large or small, public or private, until Jerusalem had been rescued from the Infidel.

From the two ships on either side of our royal carrack came the same stirring words; then I heard it spread over the whole fleet as it sailed closer together into the crowded harbor. Everyone was still shouting when the anchors began to splash into the clear emerald water and the sails drop from the tall masts, and by the time our beautiful gilded and painted barge was lowered and William and I were seated under its richly embroidered canopy I actually found myself so moved that I was fighting back tears.

While I was wondering whether William felt the same emotion he reached over and took my hand in his; his was trembling, which both answered my unspoken question and reminded me of his wild grief when we learned that Saladin had captured Jerusalem. I was frightened for his reason at the time, for he hid himself away for four long days and nights, clad in sackcloth and ashes. He would not see anyone—me, or even our beloved Archbishop Walter.

"This is one of the great moments, Joan," he murmured now in my ear. "However our adventure fares, I shall always remember this."

Our oarsmen, as he spoke, were drawing us swiftly to the shore. Behind us came other barges filled with our lords and ladies; ahead of us, only a few rods away, a cheering crowd stood on the sand waiting for us to land. As we came closer my lord pointed out our host, Count Bohemund, in the center of the welcoming party, but my eyes were on a young man wading out through the foaming waves toward our barge. All I saw at first was that he was wearing the Crusader's cross on his hauberk, but when he reached us and held out his arms to carry me to shore I realized, suddenly, that this was no stranger. Where, I asked myself, had I seen this thick-browed, square-jawed face before? His voice, as he asked my lord's permission to take me in his strong arms, was familiar, too.

"If you will allow an old friend of her Grace the privilege—" was what he said, and as I clutched him around the neck with one hand and held up the tail of my cote with the other I tried hard to think who he might be. It came to me while we splashed through the last little curling wave and just before he set me down on the beach.

"You are Count Raimond of St. Gilles," I said. "My brother Richard's singing companion. I remember now, my lord! You were very kind to me many, many years ago when I was a timid little maid just twelve years old—and on my way to a husband I had never seen."

"Yes, I am Raimond," he replied, smiling down into my eyes as I disentangled my train and arranged the folds of my light mantle. "And I have never forgotten the pleasant days we spent together in my small castle at St. Gilles. Nor have I forgotten Rick's unhappiness after he said farewell to his favorite sister."

His last words, reminding me much too vividly of that parting with my brother, brought the color up into my cheeks. I was ashamed even now when I remembered how I had thrown myself into Richard's arms, sobbing that I was afraid, pleading with him to take me and hide me in Aquitaine, begging him to send King William's noblemen and ships back to Sicily without me.

Before either Count Raimond or I could say anything more, however, my lord was beside me and Count Bohemund was moving rapidly toward us over the sand. Rarely have I seen a less prepossessing man; he was cursed with large protruding ears, long front teeth, and wispy whiskers. To make matters worse he twitched his nose constantly while he was greeting us, and this unfortunate habit, added to the ears and teeth, made him look so much like a hare Richard had caught and tamed for me, when I was a child, that it was all I could do to keep from laughing.

But nothing could have been more gracious than his welcome, which he immediately followed by a speech of gratitude.

"By sending your powerful fleet to cruise our waters, my lord King, you made it possible for me to greet you here today. Saladin was planning to lay siege to Tripoli the spring after capturing Jerusalem—but your ships and armed knights frightened him away."

"It is my great hope that *we* will soon lay siege to Jerusalem and free you from Saladin's shadow forever," was William's reply.

The sun, as they talked, seemed to grow hotter and hotter, and I wondered how much longer it would be before we set out for Count Bohemund's palace. A curtained litter, standing a few feet away, looked most inviting and I was sure it was waiting to carry me to our destination.

Count Bohemund, either noticing my glance or reading my mind, rather hastily presented Count Raimond of St. Gilles, heir of Toulouse, to my lord.

"We must not keep your gracious lady in the heat," he said as my brother's friend knelt at William's feet, "but Count Raimond has letters for her and for you, my lord King, that should have reached you many weeks ago."

Raimond rose and signalled to a squire, who brought him two rolls of parchment. I saw Richard's seal on mine and turned to my lord. "Should we not wait to read them until we reach the palace?"

Before he could answer me young Raimond shook his head and spoke in a voice that somehow frightened me. "They contain grave news," he said.

Without more delay I broke the seal, unrolled the parchment, and saw Rick's large, carelessly scrawled signature at the bottom: *Ricardus Rex.* Ricardus Rex? Ricardus Rex!

I think I read the words aloud. I know I clutched William with my free hand.

Looking up from his letter, which he had been scanning swiftly, my lord took my trembling fingers in his and held them comfortingly.

"Yes, my love," he said. "Yes. Your father is dead and Duke Richard is now the King of England."

CHAPTER

II

Dazed by this word of my father's death, I was only half aware of what was said and done until they helped me into the litter and escorted my ladies to a large wooden chariot. I do remember William telling me that something in his letter from Richard made it necessary for him to summon those in charge of our fleet and our army and that he would join me at the first possible moment. And I also remember someone drawing the curtains tight because we would have to ride through the bazaar and the camel market to reach the palace, but I must have been carried halfway at least over the cobbled streets before I could think clearly enough to study Richard's letter.

Even then I could decipher only a bit at a time, for the litter was swaying and jolting so much that it made me queasy; I was, however, soon bewildered to find that our father, King Henry II, had died in July. July? And this was late in the month of September!

Another sentence or two answered part of my question. Rick had wanted to write me himself, he said, to assure me that our lady mother would be released immediately from her imprisonment in Winchester Castle and given all the rights and privileges of dowager Queen. "This I have done," he continued, "and now I am setting about the task of raising money for the Crusade. Plans for my coronation keep me occupied as well. I must be crowned before sailing from England to fight the Infidel, and I must also arrange for our mother to reign as Regent during my absence."

There was no date on his missive, but unless my dear brother had greatly changed his ways in the last twelve years I could picture the days slipping by while he attended to everything else. Then another thought struck me, and I counted on my fingers the weeks that had elapsed since my husband and I left Sicily. Our voyage was slow; we halted at Corinth, Crete, and Rhodes, and, altogether, we had been so long on the way that only by chance could we have heard of my father's death.

I had just come to this conclusion when a sudden jolt almost threw me out of the cushioned litter. Drawing aside the curtains, I saw that we were standing in front of a huge, leather-covered, nail-studded door, guarded by two swarthy black-bearded giants. At least they looked like giants to me as I peered up into their dark faces. The door swung open, and, to my astonishment, Count Bohemund stepped out and hurried over to help me out of the litter.

Seeing my bewilderment he smiled slightly and twitched his nose about four times. "I rode on ahead, my lady, to make sure that all was in readiness for you. Aware of the sad news in your letter, I assumed you would want to be alone with your ladies." While he talked he led me down a long, long corridor, blessedly cool after my stifling ride.

Open arches gave me glimpses of a green courtyard; then we turned, climbed a few steps, and entered another corridor. "Your apartments are at the very end here," Bohemund told me. "You may be sure of quiet and absolute seclusion. You will have your own kitchens, your own garden, and my promise that no one will visit you without permission. Your grief, I know, must indeed be deep."

I made some answer, but his last words disturbed me. Perhaps I would feel the sorrow I should, after a little while alone; at the moment I found it difficult to remember my father's face or even to think of him with any tenderness. He had, after all, spared little of his time for his daughters, and I, like Rick, had bitterly resented his treatment of our much-loved mother. Some people whispered that he had shut her up because she poisoned the Fair Rosamond, his favorite mistress; others said it was because she incited my brothers to rise against him. The first I knew was a lie; the second could well be true. But true or false, my sympathy still lay with my mother.

Hearing footsteps on the tiled floor behind us, I glanced over my shoulder. My ladies, led by one of Bohemund's servants, were following us. Even at a distance I could see that poor Lady Caterina, the oldest, kindest, and most faithful of my maids of honor, was white and shaken. If my ride in the little curtained litter had been rough, I could imagine what hers must have been in that lumbering wooden chariot. She had been woefully ill for much of our voyage and must, by now, be wishing herself dead.

For her sake as well as for mine I decided to be grateful for Count Bohemund's arrangements. We would both, at this particular time, accept the peaceful existence that was the usual way of life in Tripoli, where the ladies idled away the hours under the watchful eyes of their eunuchs and saw no one but their lord and master. Not for them the seat of honor at the high table, the merry evenings of dancing and song when lords and ladies mingled freely seeking mutual enjoyment and often romance, as was the custom in the courts of England, France, and—since my William had come to the throne—of Sicily. He was the first of its Norman kings to deny himself the pleasures of the harem, seraglio, or whatever it should be called; unlike him, his father, William the Bad, and the two Rogers, his grandfather and great-grandfather, had all three kept their women in seclusion and had not limited themselves to one or even two.

How my husband amused himself before I was old enough to share his bed I still do not know. I do know, however, that for the nine years during which I have been truly his wife we have rarely spent a night apart, and I have had no reason to suspect him of infidelity. Nor do I think he can, in the past, have fathered any bastards. If he had we would both welcome the child into our home, for our one little son died some years ago and we have by now almost given up hope of another.

A pair of eunuchs stood at the end of the corridor, and our host's steward, who was waiting in the doorway to my apartments, led us inside. The series of dim chambers opening into a sheltered arcade encircling a charming garden were very much alike, and as each one was furnished with a deeply cushioned divan, a low table, and a heavily carved chest, I could make my own decision as to which would be my sleeping chamber, my presence chamber, and my dining salon.

Count Bohemund remained only long enough to present Lady Caterina to his steward and interpret her few requests for additional comforts before making his bow.

"You are most kind, my lord Count," I said, realizing that he was as eager to leave my presence as I was to have him gone. "I know that I will feel very much at home here, and I shall look forward to what I hope will be your frequent visits."

*　*　*

The soft evening shadows were falling on the garden when a bustle at the entrance heralded the arrival of my lord. He entered alone and made his way through my busy ladies, who were still scurrying here and there, setting our possessions in order as best they could. They would have retired but I stopped them.

"No, no," I said. "Go on with your work, please. We will walk in the garden. Or are you too weary, my lord?" I could see that his face was drawn and tired, and his step slower than usual.

He shook his head. "After that steaming harbor your little garden looks most inviting. Especially the bench under the fig tree. Come, my love, and I'll tell you what kept me for so long."

When we were seated in the comfortable shade he took my hand in his.

"Forgive me for leaving you at such a time," he said tenderly. "But as Richard's letter to me means we must return to Sicily just as soon as possible, I had to inform all my people before leaving the waterfront."

"Return *home?*" I could not believe my ears.

"Even though it means making the journey all over again later," he replied. "When you hear why, my love, you will understand! Your brother and Philip of France plan to meet at Messina, so that we three may join hands and fight our Crusade as one great army, an army led by a triumvirate of kings. Think of it, Joan— King Richard of England, King Philip of France, and King William of Sicily, fighting under one banner to free the Holy Land! Is it any wonder that I am willing to retrace our steps and delay our own campaign? No, no, we must go home and prepare a warm welcome for our friends."

His weariness was forgotten. It was obvious that he was, at this very moment, picturing himself already back in Messina and greeting Rick and King Philip. For my part, I could think only of the joy of seeing my favorite brother, something I had longed for over the years. Indeed, one reason for my desperate unhappiness at our parting back in 1176 was the fear that we might never meet again: I knew only too well that when a king's daughter weds the ruler of a distant land it is likely she will never again lay eyes on any member of her own family, and I had schooled myself accordingly.

"Rick coming to Sicily!" I think I almost sang the words, my father's death, the Crusade, and all else forgotten. "Yes, yes, dear lord! We must turn back immediately—let me call my ladies and tell them not to unpack another thing."

As I rose to my feet William reached out and drew me down on the bench again. "It's not that simple, my dear child. You must remember that we have our army and our fleet with us. To provision five hundred vessels for another voyage is a lengthy task. Many of them fell into difficulties on the way here and need repairs, and several of our best men need time to recover from a virulent fever they caught in Rhodes. It may be some weeks, my love, before we set sail again."

* * *

My lord soon discovered that the heat in Tripoli was another problem. With the best will in the world his men could work for only an hour or two in the morning and for another short period when the sun began to climb down out of the sky; any attempt to perform the heavy labor asked of them during the remainder of the day made even the strongest faint. We were, it is true, accustomed to a limited work period all through the summer months in Sicily, but this, after all, was now October.

In the circumstances William was proved right in telling me that it might be weeks before we set sail, but set sail we finally did, with our ships heading northwest and the weather improving rapidly. Our stay in Tripoli, during which time I saw Count Bohemund rarely and the other noblemen at his court only when we said farewell, was a dull, restful interval for me and my ladies. For my lord it was otherwise; fretted by the continuous delays and forced to indulge in rich, spice-laden food and heavy, sweet wines, he was feeling so out of sorts that he slept long hours after we embarked and, when awake, was unreasonably concerned over our progress.

Try as I might, I was unable to convince him that we would reach home long before either Richard or Philip could arrive there with their armies, and finally, as we drew nearer our destination, I fell prey to some of his anxiety and joined him when he paced the decks, watching for the first glimpse of land.

As it happened, we were both near the rail when a loud shout from the lookout sent most of the crew running to the side of the carrack. All that we saw at first was a long purple streak in the distance, then William pointed out Etna to me, our kingdom's ancient enemy, looming up against the brilliant blue sky. Although it last erupted in 1169, completely devastating our city of Catania, Sicily lives always in the shadow of its constant threat. Today—tomorrow? We never know when the boiling lava will suddenly pour down our hillsides, killing the grapevines, olive trees, orange and lemon groves and covering and smothering our villages and precious pieces of pasture land.

Instead of abating, my lord's impatience grew as we sailed slowly up the coast past Taormina, perched high on its cliffs, then on to the seaport of Messina, guarding the Straits of Faro. While we were approaching the harbor, however, it looked as if it held only the usual amount of shipping; and when we were close enough in to count the masts of what seemed to be a few foreign ships, a handful of our own trading vessels, and a huddle of fishing boats, we were certain we were not too late to welcome the other two kings.

Messengers, sent ashore, returned to say that no word of their coming had been received, and we sailed around the tip of our island toward Palermo, feeling both relieved and disappointed. But as we came safely into harbor at Palermo and knew we were home, the sense of relief was uppermost for me, and I found myself catching my breath over the beauty of our beloved city. The majestic mountains cradling it, the fertile plain called the Conca d'Oro spread out at their feet, and, lying between that lush green plain and the harbor, the rooftops and cupolas of Palermo itself, nestled in the curve of the bright blue water—all were so lovely that they brought a rush of proud tears to my eyes. I blinked them away and, a moment later, saw the familiar trio of rosy red domes that top San Cataldo and, a stone's throw away from it, the more elaborately designed church of La Mortorana. Straight ahead, where we would pass it on the way to our palace, was our handsome new cathedral, built by my lord and Archbishop Walter who, I was sure, would be awaiting us on the quay.

He was. Just before we stepped ashore William pointed to him, standing not far away. A lowly born Englishman, he was in fact the son of a miller and was now called Walter Ofamillia by our people. He came to Sicily originally to be William's tutor, continuing on through the years as my dear lord's closest friend and adviser on both temporal and spiritual matters and growing in well-earned power until he became our archbishop.

I need hardly say that he has been my greatest source of comfort and strength, too, for never did a frightened, lonely little damsel, facing marriage with a stranger in a far-away land, ever find the understanding and counsel that I did when I arrived in Palermo in 1176.

Extremely tall and thin, he towered over the shouting, waving crowds of townspeople. His bushy white eyebrows and hair and his long, arched, hawklike nose would have made him easily recognizable in the surging mass of swarthy, dark-haired Sicilians no matter what his attire, but today he was garbed in his richest embroidered robes and his most glittering jewelled mitre.

"Welcome home, my dear lord, my dearest lady!" His voice and smile were as warm as an embrace, and his eyes, beaming down on us, were wet. "What a happy day for me, to have you return so unexpectedly soon!"

"It is a happy day for us all," replied my lord. "Come with us to the palace and I will tell you what brought us back."

*　　*　　*

Later I was to remember the day of our return and our reunion with our dear friend as the last happy one for us all. I saw little of William on the day following, for he was deeply immersed in arranging ceremonies and banquets both at Palermo and Messina to celebrate the arrival of my brother and King Philip; I, thinking it early days for such preparations, busied myself with my own household.

I remember that he seemed very weary that night and slept heavily. I did, too, and awoke refreshed. My lord, however, did not, and

I was distressed to hear him lose his temper over some minor mistake that was actually no one's fault. This was so unusual that I began to think he must be ill, and his irritation, when he assured me that he was quite well, did not set my fears at rest. I waited, after that, until a restless night added to my concern; then I summoned our physician to my privy chamber.

After listening to my story he admitted that he, too, had been watching my lord. "His color is too high," he told me in worried tones, "and his eyes overbright. But he will not let me examine him, or even question him about his health."

I rose. "Come," I said firmly. "We will seek him out, you and I. I will take the blame if it angers him."

My lord needed so little persuasion to return to bed and swallow a foul-looking draught that my anxiety grew. I remained at his side until he fell asleep, then returned to my favorite retreat where, a short time later, the physician rejoined me.

"You were quite right, your Grace," he said. "My lord King *is* ill. He confesses that he has had chills and fevers for some days now and has an odd, light-headed feeling. I think it may be the same pestilent disease that laid many of our company low in Tripoli, but, although I would be happier had he allowed me to help him earlier, I have no doubt we will soon have him well again."

Moving to my side, he first took my hand in his then felt my cheek and forehead. "I shall bring you a draught," he added, "just to make sure that you remain well. Rest, do not fret, and leave my lord in my hands."

* * *

I remembered his confident words the following evening, but they brought me little comfort. Every time I visited my lord's bedside he seemed worse, for, although he chatted quite naturally with me at first, he grew confused as the day waned and frightened me by talking incoherently about the mosaics at Monreale. The artisans must work more swiftly, he said; the panels depicting Adam and

Eve were far from completed—he would ride out himself—

I tried to calm him, assuring him that our beautiful cathedral on the hill had been finished long since. But he merely looked through me, his eyes wild, and slipped even farther into the past. A sleep-inducing potion quieted him finally, and I agreed to accompany Walter, who had been watching over William since morning, down to the royal chapel.

"We do no good here," he whispered to me, his voice suddenly that of a very old man, "so let us retire and pray for our lord's recovery."

I think we were both fighting back tears as we slipped out of the chamber and made our way to the chapel. Built many years before by my husband's grandfather, Roger II, it, like Monreale and Roger's bedchamber, which was now my beautiful privy chamber, blazed with golden mosaics. Time had not touched them; still as bright as the day they were made, they gleamed like sunshine in the window-less room. But instead of taking my usual pleasure in them I kept my eyes on the inlaid marble floor; my dear lord's wild words about Monreale had distressed me so much that I found I could not bear to look at them.

Walter's prayers helped me to regain my composure, however, and I was grateful when he assured me that he would not quit the palace until William was out of danger. I doubt if either of us slept that night—probably not many in the palace did—and shortly after dawn I threw on a chamber robe and crept back to my lord's chamber. Walter was there already and our chancellor, Matthew d'Ajello, stood beside him.

William was sleeping heavily and his face, on the pile of silken pillows, was that of a stranger. The flesh was drawn tightly over its delicately modelled bone structure, the closed eyes were deep in their sockets, and his color was a terrifying purple.

Again Walter led me away to the chapel, and again we knelt together.

The hours that followed were agony. I paced up and down my

retreat until the noonday sun lit up the frescoes and drove me away. Each gay scene on those walls and vaulted ceiling tore at my heart. The deer took me to woods at Monreale where my lord and I had spent so many happy summer months; the peacocks meant La Ziza, the small pleasure palace where I first lived in Palermo, awaiting my wedding day; the lions made me long for the arrival of my brother, the Lion Heart, to sustain and comfort me.

Where I went then or what I did is mostly lost in the great fear that rode with me. My ladies accompanied me, I suppose, and I think I was several times turned away from William's door.

Whether it was evening, midnight, or another dawn when Walter came to me at last, his grey face betraying what he had come to tell me, I do not know. Nor did I care.

CHAPTER

III

The long ceremony was over at last, and as Walter and Chancellor Matthew led me back down the aisle of Monreale Cathedral, where we had just laid my husband to rest, I clung to the remnants of the strength and control that had, somehow, brought me through the wearying ordeal. My first agony of grief had had its way during the days when his body lay in state in our other cathedral at Palermo. While his people crowded in to say their farewells I had wept and prayed in privacy, but today, riding slowly up the hillside behind the elaborate *catafalco* and, later, standing in the beautiful house of God that my dearest William had built with such love and care and now would never leave again, I had only my veil to hide my sorrow.

I was shaken, at first, by the noisy tears of the lords and ladies grouped behind me; then the very sound stiffened me and I resolved to keep my own sobs at bay until I could be alone. The dimness inside the cathedral helped. Only occasionally did a burst of sunshine light up the mosaics overhead, and when it did I refrained from looking at the two panels where my dear lord was pictured. . . .

As we emerged from the great doorway the clouds parted again, and Walter suggested that we retire to the cloister for a few moments of quiet before descending the hill to the city. I assented and Matthew, never a great favorite of mine, had enough acuity to remain with the other nobles. Having told Lady Caterina and my ladies to do the same, I walked with just the Archbishop into the enclosure.

"I feel very close to my lord here," I said to him as we strolled around the cloisters to the loggia surrounding the fountain. "We planned so much of this together. He allowed me the pleasure of helping him choose all these different columns—" I paused, placing my hand first on the most exquisite of them, a column carved to resemble the finest ivory lace, then on another that glittered with bands of mosaic inlay. "And the fountain was our particular pride and joy. I wonder how many hours we spent here both before and after it was completed."

"The world will never forget King William the Good while Monreale stands." Walter's eyes were dim. We stood beside the wide circular basin, watching the water drip down out of the mouths of the stone lions and sparkle in the sun.

For a long moment we were silent, the only sounds the splash of the fountain and the far-off voices of monks in their dormitory on the other side of the flower-studded garden. Then, with its customary suddenness, a wild, hot sirocco broke the peace, setting the palm fronds rattling noisily, bending the tall scarlet blossoms down until they touched the grass, and blowing the spray directly into my face, dampening my veil and white mourning cloak.

"Take me to the palace, dear sir," I said sadly, stepping back into the arcade. "Take me home."

*　　*　　*

In the weeks that followed I found, to my growing distress, that the palace no longer seemed like home to me. For the first time in many years I felt a stranger in a strange land, alone and unhappy, although everyone around me was almost too kind. Torn between grief for my husband and an increasing anxiety over my future, I was restless during the day and slept brokenly at night, my one comfort the thought that soon or late my royal brother would arrive in Sicily and settle the questions disturbing me. He, I was confident, would tell me whether I should remain here in Palermo as the dowager Queen, content to live out my life in the shadow of the court of Queen Costanza and her German husband Prince Henry; or return to England and my lady mother; or, perhaps, retire to my own vast holdings in the county of St. Angelo, the property deeded to me by William when we wed.

I had never made the journey to see it; crossing the Straits of Faro and then the mainland to the coast of the Adriatic where the property lies, just a little north of Bari, would have been arduous. But William had often described it to me, telling me that much of it jutted out into the sea and that there were beautiful castles at both Viesta and Liponti, the two largest towns.

Walter, to whom I one day confided my anxieties, reminded me that there were two other things I might do.

"You could seek the peaceful shelter of a nunnery, dear child," he said. "Or, when time has dulled your grief—as I assure you it will—you might marry again. Then, God willing, you might fill your empty arms with the children denied you and our dear lord."

I shook my head over his first suggestion and protested violently at the very thought of the second. As if anyone could take William's place! "He was so good to me! And, as you know, we found a very rare contentment together. No, no—I am much too old to consider such a thing."

"Too old at twenty-three—or is it twenty-four years of age?" My old friend smiled down at me. "That might be true of some women, my daughter, but not, I think, of you."

He changed the subject then, wondering as we both did frequently these days why our summons had not brought the Lady

Costanza and the Lord Henry to claim their inheritance. "There is an unsettled feeling among our people that I do not like," he went on, his face grave. "And an empty throne places more power in our Chancellor's hands than I fear is entirely wise."

We said nothing more, although I shared his concern and he knew it. A strong man, Matthew d'Ajello and, with my lord's guidance, one of the best chancellors we had ever had. But his personal ambition and love of power, carefully held in check until now, might lead us all into difficulties. Unfortunately, as dowager Queen I had little or no authority over him.

For all these reasons it was not surprising that, as time dragged on, I rarely passed my windows without looking hopefully over the rooftops to the harbor, hoping to see the arrival of my brother's or my Aunt Costanza's ships. The possibility that either of them might choose to travel overland from Messina was always in my mind, too, and I kept a watch on the road leading to the palace.

Despite my vigilance, however, and despite the couriers that Walter and I sent to and from Messina seeking word of Rick or Lady Costanza, I was startled one afternoon when the Lady Caterina awoke me from my siesta.

"A large party has just arrived in the city, my lady," she told me, her face flushed and her voice shrill with excitement. "They say it is our new King."

Still half asleep, I stared at her with bewildered eyes. "Our new King? Lady Costanza's husband?"

She threw up her hands. "It is all confusion below," she told me. "I have already heard a dozen stories. Some think it is your lord brother, others King Philip of France."

Wide awake now, I leaped off the bed and ran into my little privy chamber that overlooked the roadway. Lady Caterina followed me and we hung out as far as we dared, trying to see the banners carried by the great band of horsemen already in sight. They were a mass of bright color in the breeze, but I could not tell what arms they bore. In any case they were approaching so swiftly that I realized I must ready myself without any further delay, and by the time I had scrambled back into my mourning robes and tidied my long red braids we could hear the clatter of hooves on the cobbled courtyard and much loud shouting.

"Send someone below to discover who it is," I said to Caterina. "Tell my usher I will receive our visitor here, in private." For this I was grateful; my recent bereavement forbade any public greeting, and, whether it was Henry, Philip, or my dearest Rick, our first meeting could take place here in my own apartments.

I waited, then, my heart pounding, but although I wanted it to be my lord brother I hardly dared hope. He would surely have sent word ahead to me—or would he? Was he, perhaps, intent on surprising me?

No message came back to me, and still I waited. Then there was the sound of many footsteps on the stairs and in the corridors and a babel of voices. I thought I heard my usher protesting, but I was not sure. Were they speaking the French tongue? Even that I could not tell. My ladies grouped themselves around me, our eyes fixed on the door. Out of our sight, at the entrance to the antechamber, I heard my guards questioning someone. The answer must have satisfied them for two swarthy men-at-arms, in strange livery, marched through a moment later and halted, facing me.

Lady Caterina looked to me for guidance. Such a thing had never happened before. Where was my usher? Our royal chamberlain? Why had the guards allowed these men to approach my privy chamber unannounced?

Before either of us could say anything we heard more footsteps, lighter ones this time, and a most extraordinary figure walked past the two men-at-arms and entered my chamber. I stared at him. He was certainly not my Lord Henry, whom I had met long ago, or my brother the Lion Heart. Could it be Philip of France? But no one had ever told me that France's king was a dwarf!

Less than five feet tall, even counting the jewelled crown set high on his shaggy black locks, the man before me might, except for the thick beard that hid his chin, have been a small boy playing king. The richly embroidered mantle looked much too heavy for his narrow shoulders, and the hands holding the sparkling scepter were actually tinier than those of my daintiest maid of honor.

It flashed through my mind that this might be a jest—had Rick sent his dwarf ahead, clad in royal robes? Then I realized that this odd little apparition bore a strong resemblance to King Roger II, my lord's grandfather.

He bowed, his beady black eyes fixed on mine.

"Forgive me for what may seem an intrusion," he said, "but, as both a kinsman and Sicily's new King, I thought it only proper to present myself without a moment's delay."

As he spoke I saw that the antechamber behind him was filling with more men-at-arms, and I was swept by a sudden fear. Perhaps he saw it in my face. I do not know. Stepping forward swiftly, he took my hand in his. "I am your late lord's cousin Tancred," he explained. "I am here to claim my throne."

His words merely bewildered me at first; then I remembered hearing William mention a baseborn cousin named Tancred who lived in Lecce, a bastard grandson of Roger II.

Freeing my fingers, I looked down at him with incredulity and some disdain. "I am afraid that your journey can end in nothing but disappointment," I replied coldly. "The Lady Costanza was recognized as my lord's heir some years ago. Our people swore their fealty to her then and are awaiting her arrival. And even if my lord had not expressed his wishes long before his death, you must surely realize that the unfortunate circumstances of your birth would make your claim impossible."

He was about to answer me when the entrance of Chancellor Matthew and Archbishop Walter caused him to pause. I was overjoyed to see them and glad that they were garbed in their most elaborate ceremonial robes; I wanted the full authority of state and church beside me to send this odd little man about his business.

"Here, my lords, is King William's baseborn cousin Tancred—

come, he tells me, to claim our throne." I set the matter forward in the fewest words possible, leaving it to them to destroy his ridiculous dream.

Walter looked at Matthew, obviously expecting him to speak first. When he said nothing, my dear old friend raised his white eyebrows as if in surprise.

"We welcome you to our city as King William's kinsman." His voice was courteous, hiding the anger I knew he must be feeling. "But there can be no question, certainly, as to who will ascend his throne. The Lady Costanza is now King Roger's only living descendant born in wedlock, and our late lord and master named her and her husband his heirs some five years ago. The nobles of Sicily swore fealty to them at that time, without exception, and await them now with undiminished love and loyalty."

"They will wait for some time," was Tancred's smiling reply. "Both the lady and her German prince took the Cross and sailed for Acre before my cousin's death. I know, for I watched their fleet leave Brindisi harbor. Their whereabouts, however, has nothing to do with my right to be King of Sicily. I base that on the facts that I am the only *male* descendant of the great Roger, that the good people of Sicily are reluctant to crown a woman—particularly one wed to a German—and, finally, that I have reason to believe His Holiness the Pope will be sympathetic to my cause."

I waited for Chancellor Matthew to say what I was thinking. None of Tancred's "facts" meant anything in the face of his bastardy, and he was a fool to think they could. To my astonishment, Matthew advanced toward the black-bearded dwarf and bowed.

"I am sure you will agree, my lord," he began, in offensively placating tones, "that the Queen's privy chamber is not the place to discuss a matter of such great import to us all. Especially at this sad time when, by custom and her own wish, she remains in the strictest seclusion. With her permission, we will lead you, my lord, to a more suitable apartment."

Horrified, I turned to Walter. I had never, it is true, been very fond of Matthew—but this sounded to me like absolute treachery. Our Archbishop, his face pale, touched my hand with gentle fingers.

"It is true, dear daughter, that we should not be intruding on your grief. Allow me, please, to return to you later."

"Come to me at any time, dear lord. I will be waiting! I am confident that you and I are one in our views, and it is my wish that you will be my voice in this"—here, I must confess, I had some trouble in controlling my vehemence—"this matter."

*　*　*

It was very late before my old friend, looking more weary than I had ever seen him, came again to my chamber. A gesture sent my ladies away and I led him to a cushioned seat.

"Before you say a word, dear lord," I commanded him, "I shall give you some wine. Sit quietly while I pour it."

With a nod and a sigh he sank down and, as I busied myself with a silver cup and flagon, rested with his eyes closed and his hands folded in his lap. He roused himself to sip the heartening red wine, but his whole attitude—his haggard face, his reluctance to speak—filled me with great fear for the future. I had told myself, during the hours of his absence, that Tancred's arrival here in Palermo was something to laugh over. Or to pity, perhaps; the hopeless dream of a man born both bastard and dwarf. And that our Chancellor's incomprehensible response was merely a ruse to ease me of his distasteful presence. Suddenly I was no longer so confident.

Settling down on the soft divan beside Walter I took the empty cup from his long thin fingers and placed it on the low table in front of us. Some color had returned to his cheeks, but I could see, in the flickering light, that his lips were quite blue.

His eyes met mine and he tried to smile. "I came because you were expecting me, my daughter. Not, I regret to say, because I can in any way set your mind at rest. I find it difficult to believe, but almost every one of our nobles who joined us at the council

31

table is willing to consider Tancred's claim. And before I had recovered from that blow, Tancred produced a letter from the Holy Father that destroyed my strongest arguments against his right to the crown."

"And Matthew?"

"Is supping in private with him at this very moment. Planning his new master's coronation, I have no doubt. Our loyal Chancellor"—his voice was grim, his face bitter—"made us a long speech in which he declared himself willing to swear fealty to Tancred. Neither he nor the people of Sicily, or so he said several times, want the oldest son of Frederic Barbarossa on our throne. According to Matthew, our lord should not have wed the Lady Costanza to a German prince—not, certainly, if she was to be designated his heiress. That was his final word, and nothing that I found to say swayed him even a trifle."

"Oh!" I buried my face in my hands. "Why did my little son die? Why was I unable to give my dear lord more children? He was so good, so kind, so wise—and to have his place usurped by this ridiculous pretender, this bastard—"

"Well, we are not defeated yet, dear child. We must think of this as the first skirmish only. If necessary I will go to Rome, to the Vatican, and before I sleep tonight I shall dispatch letters to Costanza and Henry and speed a courier on his way to the Emperor Frederic."

As he spoke a fresh and cheering thought struck me. "My brother Richard!" I said. "We have forgotten Richard! Ah, there is our strongest weapon, surely. King Richard of England will have something to say when he lands on our shores with his army. And perhaps Philip of France will aid us, too." I bent and kissed Walter's hand. "There, dear lord, there! All will be well. I had forgotten Richard. Go home, sleep peacefully, and tomorrow you and I will laugh together at this silly little man."

* * *

As it turned out we did indeed laugh at Tancred the following day, but I must confess that I wondered, for a long time afterwards, whether I had not made a serious mistake in allowing myself that pleasure. Perhaps it caused his unfeeling attitude toward me later —I just do not know; Walter thought so, and I have great faith in his judgment. But by then it was too late. The damage, if damage it was, was done.

My belief that Rick would soon arrive and set everything right having carried me through the wakeful hours of the night, I rose on the morning after Tancred's unheralded appearance determined to prove to him that I, at least, was not prepared to accept him as King of Sicily. I had no particular plan at first, but when my ladies told me that the palace, its courtyard, and its gardens were all swarming with his men-at-arms, and that no one could come and go without being questioned, my anger increased.

It grew even hotter as I listened to the story of our chamberlain, an excitable man at best. He seemed on the verge of tears, and his hands, as he spread them wide, were trembling.

"All is confusion," he told me. "And no one knows who is master here now. Will you help us, your Grace? Although our lord Chancellor says we must obey the Lord Tancred, there are many of us unwilling to do so, and we have all agreed to accept your decision in the matter."

"I will tell you frankly," I replied, "that I consider the lord Tancred's claim to the throne an insult. But until the question is settled, and certainly while his men-at-arms keep us at a disadvantage, I am afraid you must do as he demands. Has he given you any particular orders?"

He nodded his grizzled head. "Orders, my lady, that sicken me. He plans to sit in our dear lord's seat at dinner with his nobles around him and wants all prepared as for a great feast." The tears were visible in his eyes now, and his voice thickened with emotion. "Our dear lord's seat!"

I thought for a moment and smiled to myself as an idea began to shape itself in my mind. There might be difficulties in carrying it out, but it was, I decided, worth trying.

"Do what he asks," I said. "Bring in the solid gold table and set it for twelve with the silver cups and the gilt plates. See to this at once, let a few of his men have a glimpse of your preparations so he will know you are obeying his orders, then, when all is in place, close the door and have our own guards on duty to prevent anyone's entering the hall until the dinner hour. Say we always do this to protect our most valuable treasures." Although there was no one near us, I now lowered my voice and spoke directly into his ear. "Listen carefully, please, while I tell you what I shall do. . . ."

* * *

The day was pleasant, for which I was grateful. An important part of my plan was for five of my ladies to stroll with me shortly before dinner in a garden near the kitchens, and had it been raining I do not know what I should have done. As it was, we donned our long mantles, I draped a thick veil to hide the glittering crown on my red braids, and we made our way through the corridors and down the staircase. Whenever one of Tancred's men barred the way, my Caterina explained that we were in search of a little fresh air before our meal and siesta. This seemed to satisfy them, and once we were safely inside the small garden, with its wealth of fruit trees spread against the walls, and had begun walking up and down the path, they were content to leave us to our own devices.

There were, fortunately, no strange men-at-arms anywhere around when we slipped out of the gate and hurried through the busy kitchens; my own people watched us with astonished faces, but a word from the chamberlain, who met us there and escorted us swiftly to the tall carved screen that hid the servitors' entrance to the dining hall, was enough to send them back to their tasks.

Six cloaked and hooded figures awaited us on the other side of the screen, one being Walter Ofamillia and the others five nobles I could still trust. Our Archbishop's face was grave and a little worried, but he had come and I was satisfied. As we all threw off our mantles I told them, in whispers, why I had summoned them.

There are, I am sure, certain incidents in anyone's life that impress themselves so clearly that they can never be forgotten. Certainly I shall always remember every detail of Tancred's ceremonious entrance into our dining hall that day. I can still hear the sound of the trumpets as his heralds advanced before him, I still see the obsequiousness of my chamberlain, bowing low in the wide doorway before stepping aside to usher him in, and, just behind him, I glimpse over his diminutive crowned head his band of richly garbed nobles. But even more deeply carved in my memory is the unbelieving expression on Tancred's face when he first caught sight of me at the glittering gold high table, sitting in my dead husband's chair. Walter was beside me, occupying the seat that had been mine for so many years, and our lords and ladies filled the other ten places.

He stood, for a long, stunned moment, staring down the long hall at us, then marched furiously along behind the chamberlain until he reached our dais.

"The Lord Tancred," announced my chamberlain loudly, at last breaking the hush that had fallen over the hall. "A guest from Lecce."

I leaned a little forward, smiling kindly down on the man before me.

"Welcome, my lord," I said swiftly, my voice condescending and my whole attitude that of the gracious queen. "Welcome to our palace. My good chamberlain will, I know, be happy to find places for you and your friends somewhere here in our hall. *Any* kinsman is always sure of a seat at our tables, even one who is not—" I let the rest of the sentence dwindle away, as if unwilling to distress him.

His face scarlet with anger, I saw him turn to Chancellor Matthew. But Matthew, obviously at a loss as to how to proceed against me, his widowed Queen, avoided Tancred's eye and, when our chamberlain led them to a nearby table where my lord's secretary and a few other members of our household were seated, seemed more than willing to take the place indicated.

Well, I had my triumph and I enjoyed it. I know only too well that I broke many rules of conduct in leaving the seclusion of my apartments so soon after William's death, but I did not care. For one night, at least, I had prevented this loathsome usurper from sitting in the chair of King William the Good.

As I watched our unwelcome intruders being seated I had a fresh and, I must confess quite honestly, a most malicious thought. A clap of my hands brought a page to my side.

"Find a cushion for our cousin to sit on," I told him in a voice that would reach the far end of the hall. Then, without lowering it, I spoke as if in confidence to the Archbishop beside me. "I think I shall call him 'Tancredulous,'" I said, laughing. "Little Cousin Tancredulous!"

CHAPTER

IV

Ripples of laughter breaking out here and there in the hall followed my jest. Walter, who had at first refused to take part in my scheme and had agreed finally with much reluctance, gave me a reproving frown.

"I feel that we must rid ourselves of this imposter," he said softly, his high forehead wrinkled, "but I cannot think you wise, my child, to make such an enemy of him at this time. I saw actual hate in his eyes then. Nor, and I tell you this because you have always allowed me the privilege of an occasional rebuke, was it a fitting thing for a queen to do."

I flushed and dropped my eyes. He was right, of course. But who could have resisted such an opportunity? Nevertheless, I respected my old friend's judgment, and I found I was not enjoying my little victory as heartily as I had thought I would.

As a result, I rose at the first possible moment and retired to the seclusion of my apartments, leaving the others to linger at the table as long as they wished. There would be no music, with our court in deep mourning, but our wine was excellent, pressed from grapes grown on the slopes near Catania, and my cooks had prepared delicious jellies, pastries, crostates, a special gingerbread, and the saffron pudding with pounded almonds that I had taught them to make. With all these dishes to tempt their appetites, I was sure no one would be in a hurry to finish the meal.

I was soon proved wrong, however, for my tiring-women had barely lifted the crown off my aching head and removed the elaborate mourning robe when a servant came to my antechamber with a message from the Archbishop. Would I grant him a few words in private?

I was sure he was not coming to scold me further, and I knew that I would sleep better if I took this opportunity to admit that he was right. So I sent for him immediately and, before he could tell me the reason for his visit, I made my peace and received his blessing.

"Now that we are friends again," I said, "tell me what brings you here."

"Something I could not discuss at dinner," was his reply. "A morning of futile argument with Matthew and many of our nobles has made me realize that I must see His Holiness myself—and without wasting another day. I'm setting out for Rome at daybreak, dear daughter, and will not see you until I return."

My heart sank. My old friend should not take such an arduous journey at his age, and his going would leave me truly alone. I was, however, reluctant to say so and sought some other reason for protesting.

"But, surely, with my brother arriving soon—"

"If we had some word from him, I would wait. As we have not, I dare not delay. No, my child, I must go to the Pope *now* and make him realize that it would be a sacrilege for this baseborn little man to wear our crown. It is my duty as Archbishop, and I shall not shirk it."

He was right. And it was *my* duty to speed his departure, to send him on his way without adding my anxieties to his other burdens.

"Go, dear sir, and go with God," I said, kneeling before him. "Bless me again, if you will, and promise me that you will spare yourself when you can, that you will guard your health, and return to me safely."

* * *

After a restless night I awakened the next morning feeling even more desolate than before. Walter was gone. Would I ever see his white head again? And, in the meantime, what would happen to me?

My second question was answered by Tancred himself. He demanded an audience later that day, and having no way to prevent him from visiting me, then or at any other time, I agreed. Until Rick arrived I was in his power and must endure him.

The moment he entered my chamber I saw that Walter was right—I had made him hate me. It was written all over his bearded face, and his cold voice told the same story.

"You will order your women to pack your personal belongings," he said at once, "and ready yourself to leave the palace. I think I need not explain why I am sending you away. You have made it only too apparent that we are not to be friends, and in the circumstances I think it wise to move your household to La Ziza, where you may live in comfort and seclusion."

What could I say to that? La Ziza was one of our favorite retreats, a small pleasure palace set in the royal gardens a short distance beyond the city walls, and I could not deny that I would be very comfortable there. My first days and nights in Sicily were spent under its roof, there I had lived while the final preparations were made for my wedding to William, and he and I, in the years that followed, often rode out there to celebrate its anniversary.

On the other hand I rebelled against the thought that this bastard dwarf could order me out of my own palace. But with Walter on his way to Rome, Matthew and most of our nobles turned traitor, the building swarming with Tancred's followers, and his men-at-arms standing outside my very doors, I was utterly helpless.

Swallowing my protests, I inclined my head. I had no desire, certainly, to be dragged out of Palermo, kicking and screaming, nor would I give Tancred the satisfaction of seeing me lose my temper. No, I must accept my dismissal with what dignity I could. But when my lord brother arrived, I told myself, it would be my turn; Tancred would learn, to his sorrow, that Joan of England and Sicily knew how to punish her enemies.

It began to seem, however, as if my turn would never come. The winter dragged away day after day, week after week, month after month, while I, still mourning the loss of my dear William, waited in vain for some word of my brother. Realizing that I was a prisoner at La Ziza, I began to fret over the probability that Tancred was intercepting letters or messengers. This, of course, would explain the interminable delay, but there was not a thing I could do about it but pray. No news reached me of Walter's progress, either, and I was as shut off from the world as if I were in a nunnery. More so, actually: I was allowed to walk around the gardens and lakes, but only if accompanied by a guard; I had constant access to the roof of my pretty little palace, to its comfortable rooms and sunny courtyard, but I knew that someone was always watching me wherever I went.

La Ziza was tall and almost square, its exterior very like that of an English keep. It was built around a court, as are most of Sicily's palaces, and, there being no windows on the outside walls, I climbed to the roof once or twice every fair day to watch the harbor and the roads approaching the city. My hopes would rise as I mounted the stairs—surely this time I would see Richard's ships or a great band of his horsemen—and then would turn to despair as I returned to my apartments. Both Richard and Walter must be dead, I often told myself, and from now on my life would be nothing but this empty, useless existence.

In March, when Sicily bursts into the loveliest season of its year, the sun beneficent, the flowers turning the island into a paradise, I threw off my gloomy thoughts and allowed myself to think that Richard must soon arrive. He would want the summer weeks for his voyage to the Holy Land; this had to be his plan.

Confident that I was right, I set our servants the task of refurbishing La Ziza, beginning with the lower hall, the chamber where Richard and I would meet. My dear lord's father, who rebuilt the little palace, was, with good reason, prouder of that chamber than of anything else that he planned and carried out in his lifetime. It is unusual in shape, with three deep alcoves cutting it into a Greek cross, and he decorated it with the finest Moorish honeycomb work and many of our delightful mosaics. The high vaulted ceiling, dripping with stalactites, is carved to resemble a cave, and the mosaic panels on the back wall depict vivid palm trees, gaudy peacocks with their tails spread, and archers aiming their arrows at birds. Under the panels a fountain pours water down into two square pools, one after the other; *cipollino* marble covers most of the rest of the walls, its whiteness a striking contrast to the gleaming greens and blues and golds of the mosaics.

Everything was washed and polished, the pools were drained and cleaned, and the archers, because I thought they would amuse Rick, were given a final rub by one of my little fan-bearers. After that was done we turned our attention to the chambers he would occupy and to my own large *salone,* alcoved and columned in the same manner as the entrance hall directly below it. Both looked down into the inner courtyard, which was now a blaze of bright blossoms, one corner shaded by an orange tree, another filled with a small, lacy stone pavilion. Almost too soon we had everything inside and out in perfect order, and I again had nothing to do but wait.

April, May, June. The sun was so hot now that I made my rooftop vigils in the early morning and after vespers; even then the distant roads were dusty and deserted, and the blue waters of the harbor almost empty.

The wild fears that often kept me wakeful in the darkness just before dawn began to haunt me during the daylight hours. Were both my lord brother and dear Walter dead? I could not believe that they were still alive and had left me to languish here, friendless and imprisoned.

July. August. Our gardens were swept by sudden siroccos, the nights were as unbearably hot as the days, and my despair mounted. As I lay awake in the steaming dark I thought seriously of trying to escape. Perhaps I could disguise myself as a manservant, slip past the guards, steal a horse and ride to Messina.

My mother and her ladies had garbed themselves as Amazons and ridden off to join the second Crusade. She was, I remembered, called "the Dame of the Golden Boot," and her band was known as "Queen Eleanor's Guard." I was her daughter; was I so spiritless that I was going to allow Tancred to keep me here forever?

On the other hand, her ladies were daring young Frenchwomen; mine were far from young and much less than daring. In the twelve years since William and I were wed, my English maids of honor had all gone, some home to England, others to try another world, and, having grown increasingly fond of our warm-hearted Sicilians, I had filled each empty place from the nobility here. But they were born to live quietly in the shadows, protected, often shut away from the world, and subservient to their men. They were not, certainly, eager for adventure or willing to disturb the placid waters of their existence. They were easily frightened, too, and, in many cases, incapable of making a difficult decision. And from my grizzle-haired, over-plump, decorous Caterina down to our newest lady, the swarthy, spare Elizabetta, a scuttling little woman who had barely enough courage to touch what she considered my august person, there was not one in whom I could even confide.

In fact, the very thought of any one of them helping me to escape from La Ziza made me laugh. No, if I sought for assistance it must be among the gentlemen. Counting them off on my fingers I soon realized that this, also, might well prove impossible, for Tancred had allowed me to bring here only my confessor (who had been William's oldest secretary), a lame young vielle player, and two cooks from my kitchens at Palermo. It was, to say the least, a dispiriting list.

Added to this problem was the enervating effect of the constant heat. When the least exertion makes one burst into a sweat it is easy to sit quietly and plan for some time in the future. However, as August dragged away, the certainty that there could not be too many more weeks of such weather tended to raise my spirits a trifle. The nights, I told myself, would soon turn cool and surely then I could arrange something.

I was languidly considering what that "something" might be when the Lady Caterina surprised me by bringing Giorgio, one of our cooks, into the garden. He was followed by a pantry boy carrying a large silver platter on which lay a huge, brilliantly patterned fish, surrounded by a border of oranges and lemons, sprays of their dark glossy leaves, and some of their blossoms.

To my great annoyance I saw one of Tancred's guards walking close behind them, his eyes watchful. This was too much! I ordered him to leave in what I know was an angry voice. Surely, I said, I could speak to my own cook without someone hovering over us! When he shrugged his shoulders and moved away Giorgio gave a little sigh of relief, came closer, and pointed to the platter in the stripling's hands.

"A gift, Altissima," he announced, so loudly that the lurking guard could hear him. "From Giuseppi, a fisherman who has sold fish to our palace kitchens since he was a lad. He wanted to bring it to you himself, hoping for a coin or two, but the Lord Tancred's men barred the way."

Here he dropped his voice and whispered swiftly, "He is one of our old friends who may come to us here, your Grace, and as he knows that you are held a prisoner I have asked him to bring us what news he could gather."

Without a pause he spoke again, but in carrying tones. "If you wish I will make a special sauce for this special fish." Then, in a whisper, "A trading vessel from Marseilles reports that King Richard of England is there with his ships and army."

My heart leaped. Richard—at last! But still as far away as Marseilles? "What fish is it, Giorgio?" I asked calmly. I did not, however, listen to his answer.

Hiding my fingers in the folds of my soft linen cote, I pulled off two rings, one given me by Rick when he kissed me farewell at St. Gilles twelve years ago, the other a more costly one. As I did so I called Caterina to my side.

"Fetch my purse, if you please," I said. "So unusual a gift must not go unrewarded."

While we waited her return I spoke softly to Giorgio, barely moving my lips and keeping my head turned away from the guard who was still lingering in the loggia shadows. "I will hand you two rings with the money," I told him. "The plain one is for my lord brother, the gemmed circle to pay the ship's captain for carrying my message and ring to King Richard. He must tell my brother that Tancred has kept me a prisoner here at La Ziza for almost a year and that I beg his help. That is all."

He murmured his assent and I, reaching out with my other hand, took a spray of orange blossoms, fragrant and sweet, from the platter and placed it on the bench beside me. "Serve this handsome fish for my dinner, Giorgio, with whatever sauce you think suitable. Ah, here comes the Lady Caterina with my purse."

* * *

I did not allow myself to hope until I learned from Giorgio himself that the trading captain had the rings and was on his way back to Marseilles to deliver my message. After that I began to count the days and nights again; so many must elapse before the trading vessel could reach its destination, so many more before Rick could possibly arrive in Sicily. There would be delays, of course, and armies and fleets move slowly. Finally I came to the sensible conclusion that it was better not to count, and I gathered up what patience I had left for the ordeal of more waiting.

Life, for a while, went on in its usual dull fashion. No fresh news reached me from outside La Ziza's gardens, and, although I was tempted, I dared not summon Giorgio for another of our surreptitious exchanges. The last thing I desired was to lose my one link with the world, and it seemed to me, at the end of about a fortnight, that my enemies were growing increasingly vigilant. This, of course, could have been because my own mounting mixture of hopes and anxieties were making me more aware than usual of their eyes and ears, but I did begin to wonder whether Tancred had some reason for tightening his guard.

I was actually pondering the matter when he surprised me by appearing, unannounced, in my hot *salone*. I was lying, clad in my thinnest cote, on a pile of silken cushions. Two small slaves were waving peacock-feather fans over my head, but the breeze they stirred up made little difference, and when I saw the man whom I now always thought of as Tancredulous standing before me, I sat erect and motioned them to stop.

I had seen him rarely since the day of my expulsion from the royal palace at Palermo. His visits had been few and mercifully brief, and, as their only purpose was quite obviously to assure himself that everyone around me was obeying his orders, we never exchanged more than a few curt words.

Today, however, his manner was quite different, and although I could still see the hate in his black eyes he began to question me in an uneasy, conciliating way about my health and comfort.

"The city has been unbearably hot this summer," he said, when I answered him coldly. "You were fortunate to be here at La Ziza, my lady. I often envied you."

Staring at him with scornful disbelief, I made no reply. My silence seeming to add to his discomfort, he floundered around for a few minutes longer, commenting further on the weather and the advantages I had enjoyed. At last, with what I could see was a painful effort, he swallowed hard, shifted from one foot to another, sighed, and swallowed again.

"Two—ambassadors—arrived today with messages from your lord brother, King Richard of England. He is—established—at Messina." His hesitation over the words "ambassadors" and "established" told a story that made me want to laugh in triumph, but I controlled the impulse, watching his ugly little face flush and hearing his voice falter. "He would like you to join him there. If you decide to accept his invitation, I shall be happy to send you to him in my own galley."

This, of course, was what I had waited long months to enjoy. This was the moment I had thought would never come. Here, before me, stood the baseborn dwarf who had dared to usurp my dear lord's crown and throne, demeaning them, making them ridiculous, his arrogance gone and plain fright written all over his bearded countenance.

When he finished speaking, his voice dwindling away, I stared for a long, long moment into his eyes, savoring to the full what I read in them. I waited until his lids dropped over them and then, and only then, did I laugh!

CHAPTER

V

It was late in September when I set sail for Messina, after one of the busiest days and nights I have ever spent. Not a moment was wasted from the time when Tancred brought me Richard's message until, less than twenty-four hours afterwards, my household and I, accompanied by my brother's two ambassadors, Lord de Forz of Poitou and Richard de Templo, moved swiftly out of Palermo's harbor on board Sicily's two royal galleys. The sky was overcast but the wind was favorable, and our larger, more lightly loaded vessels soon left behind the little fleet of ships that followed us holding all my personal belongings.

"I cannot believe that I am not in a wonderful dream," I said to Lord de Forz. "After waiting for almost a year, to be actually sailing toward Messina and my brother! And to be carrying with me my clothing and jewels—and even the household furniture I brought from England so many years ago. I keep thinking I shall wake and find myself back in La Ziza."

Lord de Forz laughed. "I have never seen a more frightened man than that odd-looking monarch! He began shaking as he read our Lion Heart's letter and was still trembling, I swear, when we bade him farewell. Everything my lord King wanted would be done, he assured me. But how he achieved it in such a short time, I shall never know. When I count the weeks and months we have been on our way, encountering one obstacle after another, each delay more irritating than the last! I tell you, my lady, the King's temper has flared so often recently that I, for one, am happy that we found the small Tancred eager to placate him."

My attention had been caught by his mention of obstacles and delays. What, I asked, had prevented Richard from coming to Sicily long since? What had happened to his year-old plan to meet Philip of France at Messina? Did William's death change all that?

He shook his head. "No, I believe that has always been their intention. But the two kings first had to settle their differences; then winter set in. Finally, when all seemed propitious, King Philip's queen fell ill and died, and the usual period of mourning was observed."

"I heard nothing," I told him. "No news of any kind reached me until a friendly fisherman informed my cook that my brother was at Marseilles and then helped me send my message asking for deliverance."

"That message speeded us all on our way as nothing else could have done," said Richard de Templo, a tall, very thin young man with a scrubby beard and ink-stained fingers. I was to learn later that he was a great friend of Richard's and was acting as a chronicler of our Crusade; what I discovered now was that he could describe its progress as vividly in words as he did with his pen.

"We halted a day or two in Rome and then proceeded, with all haste, to Messina. And, oh, my lady!" His voice mounted as he began the story of their arrival. "You cannot imagine a more stirring scene! I landed early with some of the men sent ahead to prepare for King Richard's reception. We brought with us his own gallant steed, and those of the other nobles, and awaited him on the shore, surrounded by crowds of people who rushed down to the beach. From a distance the sea seemed cleft with innumerable oars, the loud voices of the triumpets and horns sounding clear and shrill! Then, on nearer approach, we could see the galleys rowing in order, adorned with various armor and with their pennons and banners floating on top of the spears. The beaks of the vessels were painted with the various devices of the knights they bore, and the hot rays of the sun glittered on the bright shields."

I could, indeed, see it all. De Templo smiled at me when I gave an appreciative gasp and, his own eyes rapt, continued his tale.

"The sea boiled with oars, the air trembled with the clang of the trumpets, and the excited crowds around me burst into tumultuous shouts. There he was! Our most magnificent King, loftier and more splendid than all the nobles behind him, standing erect on the prow. I shall never forget it. Never!"

Sighing, I said that I wished I, too, had been there to receive him. "We had planned it so, my dear lord and I," I told them. "King William and I, side by side, to embrace my lord brother as he set foot on our island."

"Our King had no reason to complain of his welcome," Lord de Forz assured me. "He arrived in true royal fashion and was received as a great monarch should be. King Philip, I regret to say, disappointed your people by slipping ashore a few hours earlier, unheralded and without the panoply fitting his high rank."

"For which some of the islanders actually dubbed him an arrant coward," de Templo broke in again. "But not the Lion Heart! I heard them all around me, before they rushed after him and followed him to his domicile. 'He is worthy of an empire,' one man said. 'He was rightly made king over people and kingdoms,' said another. 'What we have heard of him falls far short of what we see now!'"

My heart swelled with pride during this recital, and I beamed on the two men. Had the galley not now begun to roll in the heavier seas offshore, I would have asked them to tell me even more. As it was, I realized that we might all be more comfortable apart; if there was rough weather ahead, any one of us might succumb to the miseries of the *mal de mer*—and with a distressing suddenness. Lady Caterina, standing patiently nearby, had already turned a little green, and, meeting her agonized glance, I swiftly ended the conversation and hurried her below.

Long before we reached the shore at Messina I was ready to disembark; from the moment our galleys turned into the Straits of Faro, the choppy seas subsided and the decks steadied, making it possible for me to stand comfortably while my tiring-women helped me into my cote and mantle and then took their usual pains in dressing my long red braids. I did not, naturally, want my brother to think me grown old and ugly during the—what?— nearly fourteen years of our separation, and although I must still be garbed in plain white for another two months, a glimpse of myself in the precious small mirror that always dangled from Lady Caterina's girdle made me feel reasonably content. My pleated widow's cote was far from unbecoming, and the soft snowy veil under my crown was prettier with my hair than any other color I might have chosen. As always I sighed over the freckles on my nose and deplored the size of my mouth, but these were afflictions about which I could do nothing.

Shouts brought us up on the deck to find that we were near enough the harbor's sandy beach to see a large crowd awaiting our arrival. Towering over them was a tall, broad-shouldered man with a head even redder than mine. I waited impatiently until they set me down on the shore; then I forgot my rank and ran toward Rick, all but tripping over the tail of my cote as I did so.

Striding through the group around him, Rick advanced to meet me, catching me up in his great arms and swinging me off my feet.

"Jo, Jo!" he said, his voice booming; then he bent and kissed me on both cheeks, tickling me with a strange, luxuriant red beard. I laughed, cried, and reached up to pull it.

"Rick, Rick!" I put my other arm around his neck and gave him a squeeze. "But with a beard! Are you truly my brother Rick?"

The bright blue eyes smiling down into mine were unchanged, although the years that had reddened and coarsened his skin had added a few lines at their corners. Except for that and the hair covering the once clean-shaven chin he was my own reckless, lion-hearted Richard and, I am happy to say, seemed as delighted to see me as I was to see him.

Holding me out at arm's length, he looked me up and down. "Yes, truly your brother," he replied. "But can I be sure that this tall, beautiful queen is my scrawny, leggy, freckle-faced, carrot-topped chit of a sister? I confess, Jo, I was a little frightened of you for a moment before I saw you running wildly across the sand, with your train flapping around your feet!"

Our people, by this time, were gathering around us, and after straightening my veil, disarranged by my brother's bearlike embraces, I presented my lords and ladies to him and, in turn, received the obeisances of his. When these tedious ceremonies were concluded, he informed me that he had fitted up several comfortable apartments for me in the huge old hospital of St. John, which we could see from where we stood. It was the obvious place for me to stay, for the order was founded by the members of the first Crusade, and in the intervening years many of their hospitals had allowed women to rest within their walls.

"After you are established there," he told me, "I will visit you in private. We have many things to discuss—so many that I expect to spend most of the evening with you."

I was soon to discover that this was an unusual thing for my brother to do; he had grown out of the way of being in the company of women, even the ladies of his own family, preferring the free and easy manners of his male companions. And for him to devote a whole evening to me was proof enough that I was still what he had called me years before, his favorite sister.

In any event, knowing that we would soon meet again, I was content to put myself in the care of the shrivelled little abbess who ruled the women's portion of the ancient hospital. Mother Seraphina was a sharp-eyed and often sharp-tongued *religieuse* with more than a suspicion of a moustache adorning her upper lip. She welcomed me at the entrance, leading us swiftly through the damp pillared galleries, past the rows of straw pallets filled with sufferers, many of whom were only too audible about their pain and misery for my peace of mind, and, at last, into the remote part of the great stone edifice that was to be my home.

There, after a searching look around her, she left me alone with my ladies. Now we, too, looked at the arrangements made for our comfort and found them better than I had dared hope. Richard had sent in some of his own belongings: the embroidered bed hangings our mother's ladies had made for him before he left England for Aquitaine, a golden ewer and basin with his arms handsomely chased and bejewelled, richly woven lengths of French fabric to hide some of the grim walls, and, thrown over a cushioned, carved chair, something that made me purr with delight.

It was a cote of the sheerest sendal, the color of a ripe apricot, and as I picked it up and examined it I could see that it was made in some new French fashion. With it was a mantle of gleaming silk a few shades darker than the cote, with an embroidered border of golden blossoms and green leaves entwined together, and a pair of twisted girdles of the same green and gold thread. I could not wear these beautiful things for several more weeks, of course, but they made me eager, for the first time, to discard my mourning robes.

* * *

We had all enjoyed a short rest and a simple evening meal and were awaiting the arrival of our boxes from the harbor when Rick joined me and sent my ladies into another chamber. Before we said anything else I thanked him for my entrancing garments and for all he had done to make our gloomy apartments more livable. Then I laughed and told him that his letter to Tancred had frightened him so much that I had brought almost everything I owned with me and could, if necessary, furnish a dozen such chambers.

"Tell me," he said, sitting down beside me on a cushioned bench, "just how badly were you treated by that baseborn rascal? I want the whole tale, Jo, for all I had was your message that he was holding you prisoner."

Beginning with my dear lord's death, I did as he asked, not sparing myself in the recital of the story; I described fully my successful attempt to ridicule him before our court, and even Walter's disapproval of my behavior. "But if I was unwise, Rick, I paid a heavy price. I cannot claim that I was uncomfortable at La Ziza—I was not. What drove me almost mad was that I was not allowed to leave its walls; I was watched, day and night, by Tancred's guards, never seeing a friend or receiving a letter. I began to fear, as the months dragged on and on, that both you and my dear Walter must be dead."

A cloud darkened his face. He had smiled over the way I had tricked Tancred but that smile was gone. "While I was in Rome," he said, "I heard that Palermo's archbishop had been residing in the city for some time and was ill. They said he was English born and quite old."

"That would be Walter," I replied, my heart heavy. "He was my lord's dearest friend and adviser and my one source of strength in those dreadful hours when William was dying. I must send a courier to Rome, now that I am free."

"Give me your letter and I will dispatch it for you when I send on some of my own to the Pope. But tell me more about Tancred, Joan. Did he restore your dowry?"

"He did. The document is with my jewels. I own the county of St. Angelo, Rick, and I have been wondering whether I should live out the rest of my life there or return to England. It is beautiful country, they say, and I have several luxurious castles from which to choose."

"If you want to please me," said Richard, "you will forget your future for a while. There is something I want you to do, Joan— something that should not prove too difficult or disagreeable."

His face, as he spoke, puzzled me; the expression on it was odd: part resignation, part weariness. Or was it distaste?

"I want you to stay here until my bride arrives and then accompany us to the Holy Land," he explained. "I will be so occupied that she will need a companion, and who better than you? After your long years in this part of the world, you must know just how a queen's household should be arranged. I, certainly, know nothing."

"Your bride? So you are wedding the Lady Alys at last, Rick. It is time; I have wondered and wondered why you waited so long, and I've pitied the poor maid, living all these years in England, away from her own family."

"Well, you may stop pitying her, Jo, for she doesn't deserve it, and she will never be my wife, no matter what Philip of France says or does. But don't ask me why I'm breaking our betrothal. It's a shameful story, and no one, if I can help it, shall ever hear it. The blame lies on her, however, not on me—although I know only too well that I shall be a monstrously bad husband."

"Nonsense!" I smiled at him and patted his knee. "Your wife will be envied by every lady in Christendom. But if it is not to be Alys, who is it?"

"The Damsel Berengaria of Navarre. A daughter of Sancho the Wise."

I stared at him. How many more bewildering things was he going to tell me? His long, long betrothal to King Philip's sister broken for a reason so shameful that even I was not to know it. And now he was planning to wed a maiden from little Navarre. Surely the King of England could do better than that? Then I remembered hearing that Berengaria was an unusually beautiful girl, and I was sure I had the answer. It was a love match! My heart warmed at the thought.

"You have met the Damsel," I said delightedly, "and you love her!"

"I have seen the Damsel just once," he replied dryly, "and only from a distance. Her brother—my good friend Sancho—tells me she is the beauty of the family, and perhaps she is. I have a dim recollection of a small, dark-haired lass with wide-set eyes in a white, white face, watching us joust. In any case, she will do as well as anyone, or better, for she brings me money I need for our Crusade. That, I promise you, will ensure her welcome with me."

Poor Berengaria! She was not to be envied, after all. To be wed for her dowry to a man who felt she would "do as well as anyone" was a not too happy prospect, and I suspected Rick was right when he said she would need a companion.

"When do you expect the lady?" I asked.

"Not for some weeks, I'm afraid. Our mother has gone to Pamplona to arrange the business for me, and she will bring her here as soon as she can. But with winter setting in, the journey will not be an easy one."

"Our mother? At her age?"

Rick laughed at my astonishment. "She's younger at sixty-seven than many women of forty. Her hair is white now, but she's still beautiful—at least, she is to me. She's an amazing woman, our lady mother. And what a welcome we'll give her here, you and I!"

I would, certainly. This last surprise of Richard's was so wonderful that I hardly dared believe it—my mother, coming to Sicily! After all these years we would be together again, my mother, my brother, and me.

"Oh, Rick!" I said sadly. "Why did my lord have to die? He would have been so proud, so happy—"

"Then he was good to you, Joan? I've been afraid to ask. You were such a young and timid little bride, and I felt a very brute, sending you off on that galley with his strange, Sicilian nobles."

I shuddered, remembering only too vividly the day we parted, and the days that followed. "It was a most miserable voyage," I told him. "We ran into storms after we left Genoa, and I was so ill that I wanted to die. Perhaps I almost did. I know that my lord's ambassadors took me ashore at Naples and, after I had recovered, decided that we should abandon our ships and travel overland to the Straits of Faro."

"They sound very kind."

"They were, Rick. Very, very kind. And from the moment that my dear lord met me outside Palermo until Tancred appeared in the doorway of my privy chamber, I was guarded, loved, and cherished. We rode into the city together, after our meeting, at the head of a great band of nobles. It was late in the evening, and I have never seen such lights—thousands of them, and all in my honor. The people of Palermo shouted and cheered and crowded the streets, and William, seeing that I was timid and weary, made everything as comfortable and easy for me as he could. My dear lord!" The tears gathered in my eyes as I talked of him, trying to picture to my brother the years of contentment that my husband and I had enjoyed together and my deep grief at losing him.

"I am glad that you were so fortunate in your marriage. I thought of you and wondered—" Rick fell silent; then, making a wry face, he rose. "May the Damsel Berengaria find herself half so lucky in hers! Well, well, I shall try—I *must* try!" And, dropping a kiss on the top of my head, he left me, promising me that he would visit me, if possible, on the following day.

I lay awake for a while that night, thinking of all that Richard had told me. After my year in seclusion, the thought of seeing my mother again, of meeting my lord brother's bride, and of accompanying her on the Crusade was enough to keep even a travel-weary woman awake; and both our talk and the prospect of setting out a second time for the Holy Land brought back, inevitably, my last journey with William and its tragic ending. Weeping softly into my pillows, I saw his dying face much too clearly and I struggled, as I had struggled all through those first lonely months, to remember him when he was strong, handsome, and happy. I turned my mind, finally, to that moment in the harbor of Tripoli; that wonderful moment when, with the shore in sight, the wild shout of "Help! Help for the Holy Sepulchre!" had echoed from ship to ship. Then, and only then, was I able to see him smiling at me, his eyes alight with joyful anticipation.

Consoled, I fell into a deep sleep and awakened the next morning wonderfully refreshed and more than ready for whatever the day held. A message arrived from Rick informing me that he would be occupied until sundown or later, and, as my ladies and I, after the tedium of La Ziza and our many days at sea, were extremely tired of being idle, I summoned the abbess and asked whether we might not help her sisters ease some of the sick. With a rather surprised expression on her face, she led us back through the dim, damp, echoing corridors and set us to work. It was so far from pleasant that I must confess I almost regretted my impulsive suggestion; but, after our tasks were done and we had returned to our own distant part of the hospital, we felt delightfully virtuous.

"As a reward for my labors," I announced, "I shall slip on my new cote and mantle. If I cannot wear them yet I may surely see how this new fashion becomes me and decide whether we should try to alter our older garments."

Elizabetta obediently scuttled off and returned with the enticing apricot armful. Other ladies helped me out of the cote I was wearing, and I stood in my long linen chainse while Elizabetta dropped the apricot cote carefully over my head. Then she looked at it in bewilderment, for the bodice seemed to fasten in an unusual way, with lacings. A young novice, entering with a flagon of wine for us, paused, watched, then asked a little timidly if she might assist me.

"A lady from France who visited my parents' home wore cotes just like this one," she explained, her fingers busy. "That was before I came here, of course, but I have not forgotten." And she pulled the lacings, making the bodice cling so tightly to my breasts that I gasped. Looking down, I saw that it bloused over my belly in a most peculiar way, stressing it instead of concealing it as our customary garments did, and that the skirt was so long that it lay in crumpled heaps on the floor around my feet.

"It cannot have been made for me," I protested. "A giantess with no breasts or belly could wear it, perhaps. And," I added, laughing, "one with arms twice the length of mine!" I raised them, showing everyone how the sleeves extended away beyond my hands, hiding them completely.

The novice broke into a ripple of laughter that echoed mine and pushed the odd sleeves up over my wrists. "No, no, my lady," she said, "the cote is as it should be. You wear the sleeves so."

I took a step and tripped on the skirt. "How do I walk?"

"Like this!" And, as we all stared at her with fascinated eyes, the nun-to-be lifted the front of her long habit with one hand and, thrusting her stomach forward, pranced her way to the door, her stiff-legged gait, with knees held high, suggesting a horse showing its paces for a new master.

She turned, her eyes twinkling. "You see?"

I saw. Before Caterina could protest, I was trying it and was out in the long corridor with the little novice a step or two behind me, both of us holding up our skirts and raising our knees as she had shown me. Several of my other ladies streamed after us, laughing and imitating us.

We had almost reached the end of the passage when an usher wearing the royal arms of England appeared in the archway, followed by my lord brother and an ugly, meanly clad man with thin, straw-colored hair and a cast in one eye.

My impulse, when I saw the usher, had been to turn tail and run back to the shelter of my own chambers; but I saw now that Rick was sharing the joke with us, and, as he was alone except for the lowly clerk or scribe who would not dare criticize my behavior, I picked up my skirt again and pranced toward him.

He roared and waited for me. I knelt, spreading out the tail of my cote into a great fan around my feet, and laughed right back at him.

"Greetings, my lord brother," I said. "I have been peacocking, as you see, in the fine feathers you brought me from France. Do they not become me?"

"Indeed they do!" To my astonishment the answer came from Rick's companion, and when I swung around to face him, shocked by his affrontery, I realized that he was staring at me with openly admiring eyes, eyes that ran almost greedily over my breasts and belly. "In fact, my dear lady, as France's King, I must say that I have rarely seen our feathers adorn a more beautiful bird!"

CHAPTER

VI

When I scolded Rick later for placing me in such an awkward situation, he said it was all my fault. Had I remained in my own apartments his usher would have come in to me, as was proper, and given me warning of their visit.

"Not that it matters," he went on, still chuckling. "Philip was obviously much taken with you. He tends to be a dull dog, Jo, and has no idea of how a king should comport himself—but not too dull, apparently, to appreciate your better points."

While he laughed at his own coarse wit I felt my face flame and knew that he was right. If King Philip of France took liberties with me from now on I had only myself to blame; nor could I rail at his behavior as unbecoming to a man who had so recently lost his wife, for my own, certainly, had not been that of a grief-stricken widow.

Such giddiness was, in fact, shocking for any woman of twenty-five, mourning or no mourning, and I asked myself what had come over me. It was most unlike me to kick up my heels in such a fashion! I was not a girl any longer, and the more I tried to excuse myself, the greater my shame. There *was* no excuse!

As it turned out, however, I had nothing to do with the French king for many weeks. When it became apparent that we would all spend some months in this part of the world, my brother decided to provide me with a more suitable domicile. There being nothing around Messina, he crossed the Straits of Faro with a small force of his men-at-arms and, after a swift reconnaissance of the countryside on that side of the water, took possession of the monastery of La Baignare, a strongly fortified retreat where the monks practised perpetual devotion. Here, in their care and with a large retinue of servants and soldiers to wait on me and guard me, he established my household.

"You will be quite safe here, Jo," he told me, "and so will our mother and the Damsel Berengaria when they arrive. With luck I shall have settled the ugly business of Alys with Philip by then—I should have faced it long since, but I've been hoping for just the right moment to bring the matter up between us. He's touchy enough these days; I think he's jealous of me, the fool! Instead of acting the king, as I do, and winning the people here with a bit of royal display, he continues to sneak around on that worn-out nag of his, garbed meanly, as you saw him, and with that ill-trimmed, scraggly beard on his chin." He laughed and stroked his luxuriant red whiskers. "I hear they are calling him 'the Lamb.'"

This was all very amusing to listen to—I pictured "the Lamb" lying down with "the Lion" and chuckled with him—but in reality I thought it rather disturbing. These two kings had agreed to lead our Crusade together, their old differences set aside for the duration, and for them to be already at odds was more than unfortunate.

And so was the word that came back to me at La Baignare after my brother returned to Messina. The townspeople, in his absence, had become enraged by the licentious behavior of the English forces and had driven them out of its walls. Rick, never one to bow under what he considered an insult, marched back in, subdued the now hostile city, and set the English banners floating over its highest ramparts.

Philip, wilier and more level-headed, protested. If they were to remain in Sicily for some time, he said, they should not be at war with its people; it was foolhardy to throw away men, weapons, and gold that would be needed for the Crusade. Richard's flag must come down or he, Philip of France, would break their alliance.

I, still feeling deeply for my adopted land, could only agree with Philip. And I was very much relieved when Richard actually listened to him and arranged to have Messina governed by a group of knights from various countries until he could meet Tancred and settle matters to everyone's satisfaction. Where or when this was to take place I had no idea; but after my own dealings with the odious, baseborn dwarf I thought it wise to remind my brother of my suffering at his hands.

Rick's response was to bring Tancred himself to my new home and to make him wait alone while he and I had a private talk. He had, he told me, encountered the little man by chance; our ancient enemy, Mount Etna, had decided to erupt—not disastrously, but enough to draw them both to Catania to watch the boiling lava pour down the rocky slopes. And there, in the smoke and by the light of the flaming volcano, they met.

"There was no mistaking him, of course," said Rick. "Your description was vivid, Jo, and I knew him at once." My brother's eyes twinkled at me and he laughed. "Strangely enough, he seemed to recognize me, too. So we greeted each other with Judas kisses and lied like kings. Then, after our masterful show of unlikely affection, we retired to the cathedral and discussed our problems, and when he insisted that he had treated you well in every way I thought it best to bring him to you."

"I'm very glad you did," I replied. "I would like to hear him say that to my face!"

"I didn't argue—but it occurred to me that although he *has* returned all your possessions there might well be some of King William's treasures that he would have willed to me, his brother-in-law, had he known he was dying."

I looked back at my brother and gave an understanding chuckle. "There are indeed," I said. "Bring him in and I'll tell him what they are."

His face, when I did, and Richard's too, for that matter, were payment, in part, for my sufferings at Tancred's hands. They came to me at twilight, and a heavy rain was falling, making the monastery chill and damp. The monks, accepting physical discomforts as a necessary part of their dedicated lives, merely shook their heads over the ugly weather and shivered in their long habits. My steward, who was more resourceful, had moved me into the smallest of the vaulted, echoing rooms and found several brass utensils in which he had the servants place charcoal, a form of fuel that gives out heat without smoke.

As a result I was very snug despite the lack of sunshine and, it now being December and my period of mourning at an end, I was arrayed in the charming apricot costume Richard had given me—and in which I had played the fool. I was sitting in my solid gold queen's chair when they entered; I rose, of course, but Rick waved me back.

"We will not disturb you for long, my dear sister," he said blandly. "We came merely to settle, once and for all, this matter of your dowry and inheritance from your late lord."

Here Tancred broke in, sounding humble and eager to please. "I assured his Grace that I had returned to you everything—everything! Tell him that this is true."

Staring down on the little man, I paused for some moments before answering.

"The lord Tancred," I said at last, turning to Richard, "has truly done what he should about all the things that belong to *me*—but I shall not be happy, my lord brother, until he surrenders to you the grand pavilion made of rich silks, the golden table that is twelve feet in length, its trestles, the twenty-four silver cups and the twenty-four silver dishes, all beautifully gilt, which my lord the King bequeathed to you at his death."

As I named one treasure after another, Rick's eyes lighted up with amusement and Tancred's face darkened. Mine was impassive while I awaited the dwarf's protest.

Instead, he gulped. "I shall be happy to carry out King William's dying wishes," he said, his voice sounding anything but happy. "I will send word that these gifts must be brought to Messina immediately."

"Thank you." I nodded my approval. "But we must not forget the sixty thousand measures of corn, barley, and wine, the hundred galleys of weapons, and all the other food that was gathered for our Crusade. It was enough, if I remember, for two years, and had been set aside by my lord King to provision the French and English armies."

A smothered sound that emerged from Rick's throat as a kind of cough warned me that he, too, was enjoying my vengeance. Tancred flushed, paled, flushed again, opened his mouth, closed it, then sighed heavily. Finally he spoke directly to Richard, his voice trembling. "If the Queen has now mentioned *all* her lord's wishes, sir, I suggest that we retire from her presence and discuss between ourselves just how they should be carried out."

* * *

Although Rick and I later chuckled over his discomfiture, I did not learn the final outcome of this conversation until I joined my brother near Messina to observe the Christmas celebration. He had done great things to the monastery there, turning the buildings into a fortified castle, surrounding it with a deep moat, erecting a huge fort that overlooked the nearby meadows where his soldiers were encamped, and calling it all "Mategriffin."

"You will preside over our Christmas feast with me, Jo," he told me, soon after I arrived. "Philip joins us, of course, and Philip of

Flanders, with many of their nobles. We should have a merry time, for I have worked day and night seeing to the repairing of our ships and the building of catapults and other new weapons, and I now look forward to a pleasant interval of minstrelsy and good company. We shall forget our labors and show our guests how royally the King of England can entertain them when he so wishes! By the way," and he laughed, pinching my cheek, "your little enemy Tancred has promised me twenty thousand ounces of gold to satisfy your demands. But he stipulates that you must not discover any new codicils to your husband's will!"

* * *

That Christmas Day in the Year of Our Lord 1190 dawned bright and cool; but later, as the sun gained in strength, it turned delightfully warm, so warm, in fact, that our guests found their richest silks and velvets, donned in honor of the day, much too heavy. I, of course, was accustomed to sunny Yuletides, but many of my brother's nobles deplored the comfortable weather, complaining that they missed the roaring fires and the crunch of frost or snow underfoot. Richard, however, saw to it that they missed nothing else—even ordering steaming wassail bowls set about—and he played the host in a lavish fashion. For just this once he put the thought of the Crusade out of his mind and concentrated on making the day one we would never forget.

The rafters of the great banqueting hall were hung with hundreds of gay silken banners; the long tables gleamed with silver and silver-gilt utensils, some glittering with precious gems; the wall behind the high table was massed with Sicily's Christmas flower, a deep red, star-shaped blossom that runs wild at this time of year; and when we took our seats and the servants filed in from the distant kitchens, holding aloft platters heaped with meat, fish, and poultry, the company buzzed with admiration.

King Philip of France, on my right hand, had apparently made a valiant attempt to look the king today, for his awkward body was encased in the handsomest garments I had yet seen him wear and his sparse locks were surmounted by a jewelled circlet. Instead of arriving on his beloved old nag, accompanied by a handful of lackeys and a lord or two, he rode in great state, if rather nervously, on the back of a large white gelding, surrounded by fifty richly garbed noblemen and followed by Philip of Flanders and his retinue.

Before we had finished the sweetmeats I realized that our royal guest was behaving toward me with unusual warmth, his compliments and attentions so marked that I actually grew uncomfortable. I tried to tell myself at first that he was merely being gallant, in the ardent French manner; then, as his knee sought mine under the table and his remarks became more and more amorous, that he had indulged too freely in the wine; but when I saw several of my ladies watching us with wide eyes and whispering together behind their hands, I turned and gave my lord brother a silent plea for help.

His instant response proved that he, too, was aware of my predicament, and his slightly puzzled expression showed that he was not quite sure what were Philip's intentions. Clapping his hands, he summoned his musicians to the dais and, leaning across me, asked the French king to name his favorite song.

Courtesy demanded that Philip do so and then attend to the chanson he had requested, which was sung by Blondel de Nesle, Rick's most gifted minstrel, and before he had finished the last few verses I saw my lord brother send for his own vielle. What followed was sheer delight, and from that moment on no one in the great hall, including Philip, had eyes or ears for any but the two men singing together. Blondel, so called I think because of his silver-gilt hair, was a slender youth with a delicate, beardless face, as unlike Richard, with his huge frame, strong features, and red-gold locks as anyone could be. But for all that they appeared to be a most ill-assorted pair, I have never heard two voices blend together in greater harmony: Blondel's tones pure and flutelike, Rick's deep, full-throated, and rich.

We made them sing on and on until they had run through everything we could remember and turned to songs of their own inven-
tion, sometimes singing alternate verses, sometimes capping each
other's lines. When they grew hoarse at last and refused to answer
our calls of "More! More!" they stood for a minute or two and
laughed delightedly, my brother's arm around young Blondel's
shoulders, their faces flushed with the joy of the music they had
been making.

A silence fell, then Rick strode back to the high table and, after
resuming his seat under his royal canopy, took his jewelled cup
in his hands, beckoned to Blondel, and gave it to him. "A gift from
your King on Christmas Day," he said, and, with a smile, dismissed the lad. As Blondel retired, my brother turned to Philip of
France and waved at all the other treasures on the table. "Choose
what you will, my lord King," he told him, so that everyone
present could hear him, "and then it will please me if our other
guests will do the same."

Philip, smiling at me in an odious, simpering fashion, reached
over and lifted my goblet in both his hands, taking a sip from the
side where my lips had touched it. "A loving cup," he whispered
meaningly.

The moment he had made his choice the other nobles began
scrambling around the table, laughing and snatching at the precious
plates and cups. In the noise and confusion I sat quietly, moving
my leg away from Philip's encroachments. He spoke again softly,
but this time to Richard.

"A most happy day for us all, my lord. A day that makes me more
eager than ever to call you 'brother.' Send for Alys, Richard; put
an end to these delays! And, who knows? The lady Joan and I
might decide to make us doubly kin."

For the second time my eyes sought Rick's. He looked over at
Philip, forced his lips into a smile, and replied with what I knew
was false lightness.

"I cannot think the banquet table a fitting place to discuss a matter of such import—or Christmas Day a suitable time. Another day, my dear friend, another day, if you please."

Philip's hand tightened slowly on my jewelled cup. I saw his knuckles turn white and a large vein in his forehead begin to throb. "I begin to fear there *is* no fitting place or suitable time! I say we discuss it now—your evasions weary me!"

Suddenly aware of the curious and concerned glances of our guests, in particular those of Philip of Flanders, who was watching us from Richard's other side, I decided to interfere.

"Come to my privy chamber, my lord," I suggested. "You will be private there."

Richard shook his red head. "No, no," he protested. Then, his face resigned and a little drawn, he shrugged his shoulders and spread his hands wide. "I believe you are right, Philip," he said. "By God, I think my evasions begin to weary me, too. Accompany me to my council chamber and we will have at it at last."

As we all retired from the table, I determined to be either a participant or a spectator at their meeting. I had no way of knowing whether or not Richard favored Philip's suggestion that he and I might make them "doubly kin," and I was not, if I could help it, going to have Philip for a second husband. So, meeting Philip of Flanders and the Archbishop of Rouen nearing the doorway, we entered the room together. Once inside I settled myself in a far corner and watched the others take their places at the long table.

It was soon apparent that this question of Richard and Alys was not to be settled in private, for all the seats were rapidly filled with both French and English nobles; Philip of Flanders, I suppose because he was related to us by marriage and was also a high vassal of King Philip, began to act as arbiter.

At his suggestion, Richard spoke first. "We are here, my lords," he said, "at the request of King Philip of France. Several quarrels have sprung up between us recently, but the bitterest is of long standing—the matter of my betrothal to his sister, the Lady Alys. It is true that I have delayed our marriage, as my lord King contends. It is also sadly true that I have had good reason to do so; a reason so shameful that it makes our union impossible, and one that I would rather not reveal even in this chamber."

Philip, his face scarlet, leaped up and pounded on the table.

"I will not sit and listen to such evasive, palpably false talk! There can be only one reason, after all these years, to prevent the marriage, and that is that the royal bridegroom has changed his royal mind. So let the King of England know this, my lords, and know it for certain: if he puts my sister Alys aside and weds another woman, I will be the enemy of him and his as long as I live!"

Obviously Richard had waited too long. Some hint of his plan to marry the Damsel Berengaria had reached Philip's ears. I could tell, from Richard's face, that he realized it too, and as a deathly hush fell over the room he looked almost sadly at Philip and spoke again.

"Attend to me, my lord King—put aside your natural anger, if you can, and listen to me. For your sister's sake, for yours and mine, for the honor of both France and England, *listen* to me!"

Then, leaning forward, he stared right into Philip's infuriated eyes. "Free me from my contract but *do not* force me to state my reason!"

"State it!" screamed Philip. "State it—and be damned for a liar, for a liar you are!"

"My lords, my dear lords." Philip of Flanders, rising between them, put out a protesting hand. "As your chosen arbiter, I must beg you both to continue this dispute in a more reasonable fashion. After King Richard's warning, my lord of France, do I understand that you insist on hearing his reason for refusing to wed the Lady Alys, his betrothed?"

"I do."

"Then, my lord of England, state that reason."

Richard sighed heavily and dropped his eyes. "The Lady Alys," he said at last, in a reluctant voice, "was, for many years before his death, my royal father's mistress. I have witnesses here who will swear to this fact, my lords, and who will tell you that she bore him a child."

CHAPTER

VII

When Philip of France had finally conceded that Richard's story must be true, and the bishops and barons had agreed that the betrothal should be considered null and void, they began to argue over the return of Alys's dowry, and I slipped quietly away to my own apartments. During the heat of the altercation that had followed my lord brother's statement of the lady's guilt, I saw King Philip glance, more than once, in my direction, his face making it quite clear that I need fear no further attentions from him; not, certainly, until he had recovered from the shocking blow dealt him by the Plantagenets.

Actually, I was distressed and shocked myself, for, although I had not seen the Lady Alys for many years, we had in bygone days played together in the royal nurseries. I cannot say that we had ever had a deep affection for each other—our natures were too dissimilar—but, as Richard's future bride, she had been brought up as a member of our family, which made my father's behavior doubly shameful.

The more I thought of it, the more horrible it seemed, and I wondered how my mother had allowed such a thing to happen. Then I remembered that she had been more or less confined to the castle at Winchester during my father's latter years, and it occurred to me that his desire for this royal maid, living under his protection, might well have been his reason for sending his queen into seclusion.

I was pondering it again the following morning when Rick and our cousin of Flanders entered my room.

"I am off to the encampment, Jo," Rick told me, "but I must first bring you fresh news of our lady mother. According to Philip, here, who, I may now tell you, acted as her envoy for a great part of her journey, she and the Damsel of Navarre have crossed the Alps and are descending into the plains of Lombard. Even if all goes well, it will be some weeks before they reach Sicily, but as I am at last free of the Lady Alys I need no longer keep the purpose of my mother's travels a secret."

"I am certainly glad of that," said Philip. "I am weary of evading the questions of our friends."

"My lady mother is well?" I asked him.

"Well and very eager to see you, your Grace. What an amazing woman she is! My admiration increased every day as we toiled over those grim mountain passes, for she never allowed us to see her daunted. Always cheerful, always seemingly unwearied, always ready to mount her horse and set out again in fair or ugly weather, no matter how steep the trail or rough the road."

"And the Damsel Berengaria?" I was, I admit, extremely curious, having heard only Rick's vague description of the girl.

He hesitated. "A quiet and gentle maid. Perhaps a little in awe of Queen Eleanor, which was natural enough. But when she was not too shy to speak I thought her quick-witted, anxious to please, and most lovely to look at."

Quiet, gentle, shy—I glanced at Rick and wondered how he would fare with such a bride. My reckless, thoughtless, impatient brother!

Well, who could tell? She might be the very one to tame our Lion Heart.

* * *

January and February slipped away with only occasional word of my mother's progress. We learned, at last, that she had reached Milan, then Rome, and as I sat in my quiet apartments at La Baignare I remembered what Philip of Flanders had said about her and the Damsel Berengaria and compared their journey with mine, when I travelled from England to Sicily to wed a husband I had never seen. Was Rick's future wife suffering from those same fears and uncertainties? Was she longing for Navarre and missing the two Sanchos, her brother and her father? Was my lady mother's indomitable spirit a burden, perhaps; something impossible to emulate and a little aggravating to contemplate? And would this shy Berengaria be in awe of me, too, when we met?

I thought that some of these questions might have occurred to Richard, also, but I soon discovered that he had neither the time nor the inclination to think about or even to discuss his new betrothed. His visits to me at La Baignare were rare and brief; once he had ascertained that I was well and comfortable he would be off again, riding swiftly to the little harbor north of Reggio where his galley waited to row him back across the Straits of Faro to Messina. His army, his fleet of ships, his continuing difficulties with King Philip, and his eagerness to set out for Acre at the first possible moment completely occupied his thoughts.

* * *

Spring, always the most beautiful time of the year in this part of the world, wrought its usual magic, and although La Baignare, in March, was not as flower-filled as my beloved Sicily, it had its own way of delighting the senses. The countryside surrounding my temporary home was a mass of the same sweet chestnut trees that flourish on the slopes of Mt. Etna, providing us with the chestnut flour our cooks put to such good use; now they charmed our eyes

72

with their glossy dark-green leaves and starry white blossoms and our noses with their haunting scent.

Then, too, the monastery was situated so near the coast that many of our windows commanded magnificent views of the sea, the glorious water so blue as it sparkled in the warm March sun that it reminded me of the sapphires adorning William's crown. This comparison, which a few months earlier would have brought tears to my eyes, was no longer painful. The peaceful winter in this quiet spot, undisturbed except for my brother's hasty but enjoyable visits, seemed to have healed my grieving heart.

Freed as I now was of anxiety over my future, happy in the prospect of seeing my mother again, and anticipating the stirring adventure ahead when we would all set sail for the Holy Land—I had so much to look forward to that I could no longer mourn over the past. Instead of bewailing the death of my dear lord I found I was accepting it, that I was thanking God for the contented years we had spent together and remembering only the sunny hours.

Another realization that came to me at this time was that, had William not died, I might have become an older woman than my years necessitated. With his assumption that I would not bear him another child had grown the feeling that my young, fruitful days were over, and this at an age when most women can look forward to perhaps another fifteen years of motherhood.

I do not mean by this that I was thinking of marrying again; it was more a sense of quickening, of being very much alive and ready for a new way of life, whatever its problems or perils. And a message from Rick, informing me that our lady mother and the Damsel of Navarre had reached Brindisi and that he had dispatched a good stout dromond, with our best Sicilian admiral at the helm, to bring them around to us at Reggio, threw me into a most pleasant flutter and set me to counting the days that must intervene.

Finally I could restrain myself no longer, and despite Lady Caterina's disapproval I ordered a few boxes packed and rode along the coast to Reggio, to await my mother there. Well aware that I might not find a suitable dwelling in the small city, I was prepared, if necessary, to cross over to Messina. This, however, I was reluctant to do; King Philip was still there, nursing his grievance, and although we would undoubtedly meet in Acre, I saw no reason to hasten the evil day.

A courier, sent ahead, brought me back a friendly invitation from the nuns of a small convent that adjoined the church of Ottimati. It was situated in the ancient part of the town and, as nothing could have been more convenient, I ended my journey with a light heart.

I notified Richard of my arrival, of course, and two days later he crossed over to visit me. Looking absurdly large in my narrow white cell, he admitted that he was not only glad to see me but was more than content to find me here in Reggio.

"I was about to send for you, as it happens," he told me. "For unless our mother has encountered unusual weather en route she should reach here within the next few days, and if Philip will only do as he has been promising—set out for Acre ahead of us—I shall feel free to establish all of you in my castle at Messina. I know, although he has not said so, that he hopes to avoid both our lady mother and Berengaria, and I, I must confess, will be happier if he is not here to throw us into the glooms with his dark moods."

* * *

Before I retired that night a messenger came over with the word that King Philip was embarking the very next morning and that Richard would accompany him until he was a few miles out of the harbor. Realizing that their course would bring them close to the shore at Reggio, I rose early and, with two of my ladies, hurried down to the waterfront. Many of the townspeople were already there, waiting to watch the ships sail by, and we joined them, cheering as they did when we heard the chanting of the oarsmen and the steersmen calling their orders on their trumpets. These, of course, were the galleys; farther out, in the deeper water, the clumsy dromonds and carracks, like square arks, sailed awkwardly along, just barely visible against the line where the sky met the blue strait.

I returned to the convent and was sitting with the nuns when, an hours or two before vespers, one of the pages provided by my brother scurried in all out of breath, his small face aglow.

"King Richard's ship is in sight again," he announced shrilly. "He is heading straight in here to Reggio, my lady, and they say there is a dromond following him that must be bringing our gracious Queen Eleanor from Brindisi!"

By the time I had changed into a more suitable costume and returned to the waterfront, both Rick's galley with its red sails and the larger vessel were very close. My brother, standing on the prow, cupped his hands around his mouth and bellowed loudly that he was landing to take me on board. The upper deck of the dromond was crowded with ladies and gentlemen watching me embark, but it had moved ahead, continuing sluggishly on its way to Messina, and was just too far away for me to see whether my mother was among them.

Rick, after welcoming me and my ladies, gave orders to overtake the dromond and then lead the way. Philip, he told me, must have passed it.

"As for me," he said, "I could hardly believe my eyes when it loomed into sight. There I was, just idling along, about to change course and head back, for the French ships were safely on their way, mere dots in the distance. If I had turned a few minutes earlier, as I might well have, we would have reached Messina without knowing that my mother was following us. But now, Jo, you and I shall welcome her together."

I laughed. "Had we planned it this way, ten things would have gone wrong. Philip would have delayed his departure, our mother's ship would have been blown off its course, something would have kept me at La Baignare! But here we are, simply by chance. It's a miracle!"

While we talked the steersmen urged the chanting oarsmen to more and more speed, and we cut through the water so swiftly that we were soon abreast of the square, lumbering "dromedary of the sea," and a moment later left it behind. As we passed it I was

75

sure I saw a white-headed woman standing beside a small dark-haired girl. I pointed them out to Rick, and he agreed they must be our mother and the Damsel of Navarre.

"Will we reach Messina before dark?" I asked.

"Easily, if this favorable wind continues."

Eager as I was for the reunion with my mother, I soon found myself enjoying the ten-mile journey across the straits just for itself. The view was magnificent: first, of Reggio behind us, against the great mass that is Aspromonte; then, when we approached the other shore, of Messina harbor with the Peloritani Mountains in the background.

It grew cool as the sun set and twilight fell, so cool that I was grateful for the warm cloak that Lady Caterina had thought to bring with her when we rushed from the nunnery to the waterfront. She and the other ladies were more than content to seek the shelter of the cabin, but I wanted to remain on deck with my brother, for the oarsmen were resting now and we were skimming briskly along under sail, the dromond close behind us and Messina just ahead.

There was still time, however, after our galley set us on the shore, to dispatch messengers for horses and litters before the slower dromond dropped its anchor and then its sails. I stood, my heart beating furiously, and watched a small boat hurry out to it and return through the dusk. Richard waited beside me until the boat was nearly up on the sands, then strode out into the little curling waves breaking on the strand and held out his arms for one of its occupants.

My mother's voice reached me. It sounded weary, but there was joy in it, and laughter.

"Here is your bride, my son. Take her first, then return for me."

A moment later he was at my side, carrying what looked, in the dim light, like a large bundle of clothing. Setting her down, he presented Berengaria to me while I bent over and attempted to disentangle her feet from the folds of her mantle. They were very small feet, and, as I straightened up and smiled down into her heart-shaped face, telling her how happy I was to welcome a new sister,

I saw that the only large thing about her was a pair of soft black eyes. Her mouth was the rosebud mine would never be, her ears dainty shells set close to her head, and the hand that I took in mine so tiny that it might have belonged to a child.

When I felt it tremble and saw that her lips, as she answered my greeting in a few shy words, were unsteady, I leaned down again and kissed her warmly. "We are going to be the best of companions," I told her. "I am sure of it!"

If she replied I did not hear her, for Rick, who had splashed back into the water to fetch our mother, was bringing her to me in his arms as he had brought Berengaria. I ran to meet them and held her close, crying and laughing in a most absurd and undignified fashion. She laughed, too, and returned my kisses and embraces with fervor, her own cheeks glistening with tears.

Aware, suddenly, that the other lords and ladies were gathering around us and that our servants were holding torches and flares to light us to the waiting horses and litters, we broke apart and regained some of our decorum. She turned and greeted the nobles, many of whom were old friends, with a friendly little speech, then suggested that we make our way to Richard's castle without further delay.

"It has been a long journey and a long day," she said. "And I, for one, will be glad to climb into a bed that does not roll or pitch."

My own day had been so full that I found I was equally ready to see it end; tomorrow would be soon enough to cross the chasm of time between my lady mother and me, and to begin the pleasant task of setting Rick's betrothed at her ease. In fact, when we reached Mategriffin, having ridden through Messina, we refused my brother's suggestion that we sup together with him and retired, each to her own apartments.

All I wanted was some broth and my bed. I had soon drunk the first and was snugly settled into the latter, thinking drowsily of my mother and the changes that time had wrought in her appearance. It is true that she was no longer a young woman when we parted back in 1176, but her hair then, either by good fortune or the arts of her clever maid Amaria, was the dusky dark cloud that it had always been, the creamy skin of her face still taut, with only a hint of lines here and there, and her body slender and erect.

Now, in 1191, she was thin rather than slender and it seemed to me that she held herself erect by strength of will; the soft hair had turned snowy white, and the lines in her face were more deeply etched. What remained of her beauty was ageless and would be hers as long as she lived: the delicately chiselled nose, the high cheekbones, the bright eyes in their shadowed sockets.

As my thoughts moved on to Berengaria I smiled on my pillows, wondering what it was about her that had drawn me to her so quickly. She was not, certainly, the first shy and appealing little dark-eyed maiden that I had encountered. Sicily bred them that way and our court had been filled with them.

Was it, perhaps, because I had doubted Philip of Flanders's description and feared she might be a shrill-voiced, arrogant Navarrese, with a nose like a parrot and an upper lip framed in a black moustache? That, I decided, drifting off to sleep at last, must be the answer. And for Rick's sake—and my own—I was exceedingly grateful. . . .

* * *

Thinking my mother would rise late the following morning, I waited until midday before visiting her apartments. To my surprise and disappointment I found Amaria there alone. Queen Eleanor, she informed me, had been closeted with King Richard for the better part of two hours and had said that she might go directly from his privy chamber to the dining hall.

Amaria, much stouter than I remembered her, had been a young woman fresh from Rouen when she first entered my mother's household, whose clever fingers knew instinctively how to paint the cheeks and arrange the hair most becomingly. Enhancing and protecting her royal mistress's beauty was then a pleasure and a privilege and must be still, for I saw the same old array of brushes and the same forest of small pots filled with lotions, pomades, and salves, all set out tidily on a long chest.

After answering my question as to my lady mother's where-abouts, Amaria, who apparently regarded me even now as her mistress's child and not the widowed Queen of Sicily, tipped up my chin with a fat finger and clucked over my freckles.

"You would never pay any attention to my warnings, my lady, so now I find you spotted like a plover's egg! Here." Reaching over to the crowded chest, she took up one of the squat jars and handed it to me. "Give this to your tiring-woman, your Grace, and have her apply it every night. Every night, mind! And do try to keep your face veiled when you ride in the sun."

I laughed. It was so much like old times, being scolded by Amaria. "You must take me in hand for a while, Amaria," I told her. "I don't think the Damsel Berengaria will need your skill as much as I, do you?"

"Indeed she will not," replied Amaria severely. "Her ladyship's skin is beautiful—thick, creamy, and free of blemishes. *She* guards it! You won't see her with a freckled nose!"

Obediently clutching the pot in my hand, I left her there. She watched me go with a disapproving look, and as I strolled on to Berengaria's chambers I felt just like an awkward twelve-year-old child again.

What I saw, when I entered the solar, made me forget all about myself, and I stood quite still, wishing Rick was there to see it, too. Berengaria was seated in a golden chair—one from my palace at Palermo, I think—her glossy dark head bent over a brightly colored piece of needlework, and the tail of her rich, silken cote draped around her feet in graceful folds. Close beside her on a cushion crouched my brother's minstrel, Blondel, his fingers caressing the strings of his vielle and his blue eyes abstracted as he sang, very softly, some obviously only half-remembered chanson; in a small group nearer the open window sat her ladies in a row, busily sewing pearls on a long girdle that rested across their laps.

It was apparent that Berengaria was caught in the spell of Blondel's sweet singing, and I was glad this was so. A love of music would surely bring her close to Richard and that, now that I had observed her loveliness, was my dearest wish.

All in all, I was so delighted by this picture of beauty and tranquillity that I was almost sorry when Berengaria caught sight of me in the doorway and, dropping her skeins of silk on the floor, leaped to her feet. "Queen Joan!" she said, her face lighting up. "I have been hoping all the morning that you would visit us." Then, noticing the pot in my hand, she asked me what it was. "Something for me?"

Shaking my head, I set it down on the nearest table. "Amaria gave it to me a moment ago," I told her, laughing. "With stern orders to apply whatever is in it every night. I'm as freckled as a plover's egg, she says. And so I am, but I doubt that her lotion will drive them away."

"How ridiculous of Amaria! I see just a few—a faint sprinkling of gold dust. I like them!"

Her soft-voiced indignation made me laugh even more, and I told her how Amaria had scolded me years before about exposing my aggravating skin to the sun. "That's all very well in England," I said, "or even in Aquitaine, but I've lived for the last thirteen years in Sicily where the sun shines almost every day. Besides, why should an old widow of twenty-five summers care about a few blemishes?"

While we were talking Blondel, in response to a nod from Berengaria, pulled over a second chair for me, bowed, and slipped out of the room. And, as her ladies were too far away to join in our conversation, both the young Damsel and I seized this opportunity to chat easily and freely together.

"You must not call yourself old at twenty-five," said Berengaria, with her timid smile, "or I shall look for white hairs in my own head. I am well past twenty, you know."

Too astonished to hold my tongue, I blurted out the question that sprang into my mind. "Past twenty? And still unwed? A daughter of Navarre—and so beautiful?"

She flushed and dropped her eyes.

"My lord father refused several alliances. He hoped—he thought —he wanted. . . ."

As her voice trailed away I leaned over and took her hand in mine. "Then I am sure he must be very happy now. Your marriage to my brother the King should be everything he hoped and thought and wanted. And, loving Richard as I do, I trust that you are happy, too."

Her color deepened even more and her answer came haltingly. "Indeed—yes. Thank you, your Grace."

She sounded so uncertain, however, that I bent closer and asked her what was wrong. "Was there someone else you loved?"

This brought her head up. "No, no, never. It is nothing, dear lady. Nothing but a foolish feeling that will pass."

"Tell me."

"But it is nothing, truly. Just that his Grace frightens me a little."

"Frightens you? Richard?"

"I said it was foolish. And it is, I know. But they call him the Lion Heart and he seems so very much like a lion to me. Large and strong, rough, and—and ferocious!"

Tempted as I was to laugh, I had to admit that there was some truth in what she said. And I realized, as I watched her lips tremble and the color come and go in her cheeks, that she had undoubtedly dreamed of wedding a parfit gentil knight, who would court her with sighs and promises and sing songs about her beauty. Rick would sing songs, yes, but not about any woman's beauty; his songs were more likely to be about the joys of battle. And he might very well not take the trouble to court her at all. What had he said to me —that he would make a bad husband?

I was wondering whether I could explain Rick to her, make her see him as I did, when an usher entered and asked me to follow him to the Queen, my mother. This put an end to our talk, of course, but I was still pondering the matter while I made my way to my mother's presence chamber.

She held out her hand and drew me to a window.

"I want to see what the years have done to you, my child," she said, her eyes first searching my face, then dropping to my body. As I was wearing Rick's apricot cote she could tell at a glance that I was neither fat nor emaciated, so I stood still and waited for her to speak again.

After a moment she smiled and nodded her white head. "Still mostly Plantagenet, I see. And I am relieved to find that the luxurious life here did not plump you up as it seems to do to most of Sicily's women."

She looked down at her own spare frame with, I thought, some satisfaction, then led me back to a chair placed by hers.

"Now tell me. Were you reasonably content in your marriage?"

"I was," I replied instantly. "More than reasonably, my lady. My lord was kind, thoughtful, even tender—wanting me at his side, never reproaching me for our lack of an heir, constantly assuring me of his devotion. He was—gentle, when I was a timid young maid. . . ." My voice thickened and I faltered to a stop.

We were both silent for a little while; I, because I was too stirred by memories of my dear William to continue speaking and my lady mother because she seemed to be considering what I had said.

"I assume then," she said at last, "that you were never tempted to take a lover or two?"

Aghast, I stared at her.

"No, no," she answered her own question hastily. "I see you were not. I just wondered. You said your William was 'kind and gentle'—however, never mind that. I am glad you were so content, for we could not know, of course."

To my great relief she now changed the subject, asking me what I thought of Berengaria.

"A sweet child," I said warmly, forgetting that she was almost as old as I. "My heart went out to her the moment we met."

"Yes, I suppose so. But for Richard? A little too sweet, perhaps?"

It was my turn to think for a moment. What should I say? Confess that I had a few doubts?

"I don't know. Who can tell? She may be the perfect choice for him. If he shows her some of the consideration that my lord showed me—"

But my mother shook her head. "He won't. Not Richard. I shall talk to him—suggest it—warn him that she is shy, but I have no faith that he will listen. No, what he really needs is a wife who fears nothing, who would ride neck and neck with him and who would beg him to take her into battle."

I laughed, for my mother was describing herself. "A second Queen Eleanor of Aquitaine, in fact. Another Lady of the Golden Boot. I agree. But where will we find her? In the circumstances, our aim must be to make the Damsel easy with us, and, perhaps, if she and Rick have time to become friends before the wedding day, all may be well. When is it to be, by the way?"

Shrugging her thin shoulders, my mother said she did not know. "Not until after Lent, according to Richard. And that means I will not be present."

"But you cannot leave us so soon!" I protested. "I thought you would go on to Acre with us!"

"God knows I wish I could." She suddenly looked weary. "It seems I am needed both in England and in Aquitaine—and I must also have a talk with the Pope. The Archbishop of Ely grows dangerous, so dangerous that I need help in curtailing his power. And your brother John must be checked, too." Then, with what I could see was an effort, she smiled. "Never mind, I have done what I set out to do: I have brought Richard his bride and I have seen you again, my dear daughter. I must be satisfied with that."

*　*　*

Actually, we had only four days together; and as my mother and Rick spent most of the daylight hours discussing the problems that faced her as England's Regent, and as Berengaria and I were very busy preparing ourselves for the voyage to the Holy Land, my mother and I saw little of each other during that time. Philip's departure had speeded everything forward. The day of that departure and my mother's arrival was a Thursday, on the following Monday she and the Archbishop of Rouen set out for Rome, and early the next morning Berengaria and I sailed out of the harbor toward Acre, leaving Richard to follow us.

My hope that he and his bride would, in this interval, become friends was not realized. During those four days in Messina we saw him only in the dining hall, and rarely there, for whenever he was not conferring with our mother he was down at the harbor, overseeing the loading of the hundreds of busses, dromonds, and galleys with men and horses, fodder, provisions, mangonels and their stones, other siege machines—the countless things needed to fight our Holy War.

When they did meet, he and Berengaria were awkward and stiff. I watched and listened and felt like shaking both of them: Berengaria for keeping her eyes on the table and answering him in whispers, Richard for bellowing his cheerful commonplace comments at her as if she were a deaf, slightly stupid guest whose presence at his side must be tolerated.

I know my mother, who was annoyed with them also, tried to talk some sense into him. I did so myself, only to be told that he had already been sufficiently scolded and would try to play the gallant when he had more time.

After his indifferent behavior, I was almost surprised that he bothered to see us off. But he did, and actually brought young Blondel with him as a farewell gift.

"To make your voyage a tuneful one," he said to Berengaria, ruffling Blondel's silver-gilt hair with one of his large hands. "I shall miss my friend and his music, but I shall be happy knowing that he is with you and the lady Joan."

Then he released the lad and spoke to me. "Take care of my lady Berengaria for me, Jo," he said. "God willing, we will rendezvous at Crete. And when we are there, or someplace else on the way"— turning back to Berengaria, he smiled and raised her small fingers to his lips—"I will then claim my bride!"

CHAPTER

VIII

Berengaria and I left Messina on the fourth day of April with a favorable wind that took us directly out of the harbor and into the straits. According to Robert de Turnham, in whose care we were travelling, we, and two dromonds carrying most of my lord brother's treasures, were setting out first because we were the slowest vessels. The remainder of the fleet would follow, the order of their departure determined by their speed, the number increasing each day until all one hundred and eighty ships were under sail. Richard, in his swift war galley, the *Trenchmer*, would be the last. He would, however, soon overtake and pass every one of us and then lead the way.

We wallowed along alone for that first day and the next; then, at nightfall, the wind died and our three dromonds dropped anchor. It was a delightfully warm evening, and after we had finished our supper I suggested to Berengaria that we sit on the broad deck for an hour or two before retiring.

"Summon Blondel," I said to Lady Caterina. "Ask him to bring his vielle." As she obeyed and we were leaving the stuffy cabin, I told Berengaria that I thought he should teach us some of Richard's favorite songs. Actually I had made up my mind that she should learn them whether I did or not. It would pass the time pleasantly, and, I hoped, please my brother when we met again.

Robert de Turnham, a serious man whose interest lay in the law and not in music, saw us comfortably settled on cushioned benches carried out from the cabin, and then he disappeared below, quite content, I'm sure, not to be responsible for our entertainment. For the rest of us it was an evening we would never forget. The velvety sky over our heads was pierced with stars; the soft air, the gentle motion of our ship as it swung slowly at anchor, the glow of my old enemy Mt. Etna in the distance, the laughter of the men on the lower decks, and the harmony of our own voices, as we sang with Blondel, cast a spell over us all.

Berengaria, I am glad to say, overcame her shyness in an amazingly short time and was soon able to sing several of Rick's songs without missing a word or note. I took a little longer, but before we reluctantly retired for the night I had even mastered the one he and Blondel had made up together, capping each other's verses.

Early the following morning the wind freshened and we were overtaken by the vessels of the second line; by supper time, however, we were again becalmed and spent another happy evening with Blondel; this time, as we sang, we could see lanterns on the masts of many more ships anchored around us, bobbing in the darkness.

Every day after that brought more of our fleet into view, and as the stronger winds helped the smaller, swifter vessels to catch us, we watched for Rick's handsome war galley. As the *Trenchmer* had a boldly carved and gilded prow and bright red sails flaunting the leopards of Anjou, there would be no mistaking it when it came into sight, and I was standing out on our deck on Good Friday, my eyes raking the roughing waters behind us, hoping to see a bit of red against the blue.

Robert de Turnham suddenly appeared at my side, his face concerned.

"The weather is changing," he said. "Our master tells me we must ready ourselves for a storm."

Even as he spoke the wide deck tilted under our feet and a sharp gust of wind blew my veil into my eyes. The waves were rising and I heard, below us, the scampering of sailors' feet as they raced here and there preparing our clumsy old dromond for a bad blow.

Holding fast to the rail we watched for a few minutes longer; then, at de Turnham's insistence, I returned to the cabin, where our ladies and Berengaria were sitting. Poor Lady Caterina was reaching for a basin; Berengaria's attendants were praying in a corner, and those of mine who had sailed to Tripoli with me the year before were hastily stowing away all small articles to prevent them from being tossed around by the violent motion of our ship.

I shall not describe the hours—and days—that followed. Suffice to say that we suffered agonies of mind and body, some praying that the dromond would not sink and others praying that it would. Never a wholly intrepid sailor myself, although not as bad a one as Caterina, I succumbed eventually and prefer to forget my miseries. Berengaria, however, surprised and sometimes almost annoyed us all by remaining in excellent health and spirits. Through the worst of the tempest she worked tirelessly with a dwindling handful of other ladies and handmaidens, caring for the rest of us, a task that must have strained her patience.

When the wind dropped at last and the waves subsided, I dragged myself out of the odorous enclosure and tottered onto the deck, taking long, invigorating breaths of fresh salty air. Berengaria hurried after me and, seeing that my legs were quite shaky, clutched me firmly by the arm.

Two of our gentlemen reached us a moment later and helped us over to the rail, where Robert de Turnham and the master of our ship were surveying the empty seas around us. After they had greeted us, I asked where we were and what had happened to the rest of the fleet.

"I wish we knew," was de Turnham's reply. "Our master here thinks we must have passed Crete during the height of the storm."

"Shall we turn back?" I remembered Rick's plan to meet us there. The master shook his head. "If our King reached it himself he would not linger there very long. No, your Grace, we must sail on to Cyprus. With luck we may still encounter him along the way."

I looked at the blue water and wondered how any one vessel could find another in all that vastness. Then I told myself that it wasn't just one ship; almost two hundred would be nearby, and we must surely soon see some other sails.

Another day and night passed, and then we saw only a handful of much smaller ships and our other two dromonds, reminding me, as they moved sluggishly along, of the dromedaries for which they were named; just so had I seen camels lumber by on the desert near Tripoli.

The weather continued fair, the winds helping us steadily on our southern course. The low-ceiled cabin was a pleasant refuge again, sweetened by the sea breezes that poured through it during the day, and when the sun was too hot on deck we retired there and took up our needlework.

The pearled girdle was long since finished and would adorn Berengaria on her wedding day; now we were working on a mantle for my lord brother, embroidering it with rows of glittering golden suns and softly shining silver crescent moons. A pleasant enough task, although I suspected Berengaria was still dreading the hour when Richard would fling it around his great shoulders and lead her to the altar. Biddable and sweet, however, she hid her reluctance and stitched away beside me, willing always either to ply her needle or put the mantle aside and practise Rick's songs with Blondel.

As it happened, we were just threading our needles for a fresh start after our usual afternoon's rest when we heard one of the crew shout that land was in sight. His cry, and the sound of rushing feet, took us out on deck.

"Cyprus," said our sailing master, shading his eyes with one hand. "Cyprus at last! We will keep the vigil of good St. Mark in its harbor tonight and thank him for bringing us safely over the waters."

Smiling at him a little guiltily, for we had neglected our prayers rather shamefully after weathering that dreadful storm, I promised him that we would all do so. As we watched the island begin to emerge from the shadows, Berengaria, coming closer to my side, slipped her small hand in mine; it trembled enough to tell me what she was thinking, so I gave it a comforting squeeze.

There, ahead of us, was the kingdom of Isaac Comnenus who years ago, I had recently learned from Berengaria, after his wife's death had asked for her hand and been refused. Within the next twenty-four hours we would set foot on his island and be welcomed by him—and, perhaps, by my brother also, who could very well be awaiting us there. In any event, our peaceful voyage was to be interrupted and she, before many days had passed, might be wed and in her royal husband's arms, my little sister-in-law in fact, as she now was in my heart.

Our ship was, I noticed, moving more swiftly than it had for some time and the water slapped noisily against her stout sides, frothing into a lacy blue-green foam that was fascinating to see from our high rail. How long we all stood there, watching it, the mass of land coming closer and closer and the screaming gulls wheeling around us, I do not know.

Just before sunset, however, I began to feel cold and saw a knot of excited sailors on the wide deck below us, pointing to a black cloud. It was small at first; then, as we sailed toward the entrance of the harbor and saw a range of mountains some distance inland, the sky turned black and several of our smaller ships heeled over in a sharp gust of wind.

I watched sailors climbing up the rigging on the other two dromonds ahead of us, and heard the loud shouts of their masters giving what sounded like desperate orders. But they were too late. Before my eyes, and I was so horrified that I was hardly aware of the need to clutch our own rail with both hands to remain upright, the usually slow-moving vessels cut through the water at frantic speed and crashed against the rocky promontory of the harbor.

A groan went up on our ship. Robert de Turnham, appearing from somewhere, cried out that we must return to the cabin. I ignored this, thinking, if I was thinking at all, that we were safer on deck. Berengaria, still close beside me, was holding tightly to the rail, too, her dark hair blowing wildly and her mantle whipping out behind her in the wind.

"Joan, oh, Joan!" she cried to me. "Look, they are lowering their boats!"

As we headed for the rocks ourselves, we saw many of the little vessels fill with scrambling men and set out for shore. Several of them must have been overloaded, for they sank while we watched and the turbulent water was dotted with bobbing heads. But our own doom was upon us now; prayers were being babbled and screamed all around me and I was vaguely aware that our ship's master was shouting, shouting, shouting. . . .

While we swooped down on the jutting promontory and the two wrecked dromonds my thoughts ran wild. Would we run on the rocks or smash into one of the ships? My heart pounded. I saw Rick's treasures spilling into the sea, Rick's treasures and my dear lord's golden chair and table, my own throne. . . .

Robert de Turnham had forced his way in between Berengaria and me and was holding us firmly against the rail with an arm around each of us. How he kept his footing I will never know.

Now, I thought, as we stared right up at the face of the rocks— now—

Suddenly everything was very quiet. Even the women had stopped screaming. Then, while we braced ourselves for the impact, our master shouted another order and, at the last possible moment, we came about and skimmed past the jagged point.

Some time later when we were safely out to sea again, the freakish wind fallen and the sun long set, we dropped our anchors for the night. Robert de Turnham, joining us in our cabin, suggested that we retire early.

I'm afraid I laughed a little hysterically. "Indeed we will, sir," I assured him. "We are tired enough, certainly. But"—and I sobered quickly—"we may not be able to sleep. Those poor men on our other ships."

He nodded. "I know, my lady, I know. With luck, however, many—perhaps even most—of them may be safely on the island. And in the morning King Isaac will surely send his galleys out to guide us into the harbor. So try to rest. It will be a long and weary-ing day."

*   *   *

It was hard to believe, when we rose the following morning and saw the quiet bright-blue water, the sunny sky, and the sails flapping gently overhead, that the violence of that sudden storm was not merely a bad dream. But there in the distance was the rocky point and one of the two wrecked dromonds, still afloat, to prove that it really had happened. And, as we approached the entrance to the harbor again, barely moving in the soft breeze, a small sailing vessel crept up beside us, carrying a sailor of our own fleet.

He climbed aboard and, after talking to him for a few minutes, Robert de Turnham brought him to me.

"Our friend has disturbing news, my lady," Robert said. "He has on his ship a wounded sailor from the dromond that sank."

"Wounded?"

The man nodded. "He reached the shore in a small boat, your Grace, but he says Isaac's men met them there, disarmed all of them —even the knights—and marched them off under guard. Young Jack was the only one who escaped, and although he was hurt in the scuffle he managed to swim out to us. He heard one of the Cypriots say that their emperor (Isaac calls himself that) is in league with Saladin and has promised to imprison any Crusaders who set foot on the island."

"Then"—I looked at Robert, a dozen questions on my lips— "what should we do, my lord? Does this mean my brother has come and gone? Will Isaac take us prisoner, too?"

"Not while I am alive," he replied grimly. "And we must find out more about the situation before we venture any closer."

"Indeed we must!" I added just as grimly. "Much more."

We were still discussing the problem when we heard that two handsome galleys were rowing toward us from the harbor. Berengaria and I donned our mantles, settled our gemmed circlets carefully over our veils, and accompanied Robert out on deck. It was obvious, even from a distance, that these must be Isaac's royal vessels; they were more elaborately carved, painted, and gilded than either Richard's or my dear William's, and as one of them drew alongside we saw a richly dressed man standing on the prow with a glittering crown on his dark head.

This could be only Isaac himself, and I moved to where I could look directly down on him. He bowed and called up to me.

"Welcome, your Grace. Will you descend and allow me to take you to my palace, to rest and refresh yourself?"

"Has my lord brother, King Richard of England, visited your island?"

"No. Yours are the first ships we have seen in many weeks."

That, I decided, was good news. He had not come and gone.

"But where are our knights?" I asked. "From the dromonds wrecked on your rocks. Why have they remained on shore? Why are they not with you, my lord?"

"They are safe in my palace at Limassol. Come with me and join them there."

I glanced at Robert de Turnham. He shook his head almost imperceptibly.

"I am too weary to go ashore today," I replied. "Send me my knights, and we will visit you in a day or so."

Isaac, his smile fading, now saw Berengaria, who had just moved closer to my side.

'The Damsel Berengaria, my lord King," I said hastily. "Soon to be King Richard's bride."

Almost before I had finished speaking the most astonishing change came over the man: his face darkened, his eyes flashed, and he began to bubble with rage, like a pot of boiling water. Apparently he still nursed a feeling of injury toward Berengaria, although she was a child when his suit was rejected and had had no say in the matter. His attitude was another reason, it seemed to me, why we should not place ourselves in his hands.

Stepping forward, Sir Robert took charge of the situation.

"Queen Joan has said she is weary," he announced firmly. "And she is anxious to interview the survivors of our lost vessels. After she has talked to them and has had time to rest, we will be happy to accept your invitation. So now, my lord King, if you will draw away from the side, we will sail out where the air is fresher."

*　　*　　*

All these adventures had taken us the better part of the month of April, and after we had anchored in a spot where we could watch the harbor in safety, Sir Robert and our sailing master had a serious discussion about our dwindling food and water supplies and the need to make some repairs. We should have reached Acre in the time it had taken us to sail to Cyprus; as a result of missing the other ports along the way, we were now caught without any possible place to obtain provisions or to work on our ships.

Added to this serious dilemma was our uncertainty as to my lord brother's whereabouts. Was he searching for us still or had he despaired of meeting us and gone on to Acre? How long should we await him here—if at all?

For three more days and nights we hovered around the same area, still undecided as to what we should do. The weather was rough during most of the time, and when it turned fair again we were in such desperate straits that we feared we must enter the harbor and throw ourselves on Isaac's mercy. We were, in fact, just about to do so when the same small vessel that had visited us before appeared again and called out that they had six of our knights on board.

We were all waiting on deck as they climbed the swaying rope ladder and clambered, one after another, over the rail. What a sorry sight they were! Thin, unshaven, garbed in an odd assortment of borrowed garments, one with a bandaged head and another limping badly, they were greeted by Sir Robert then fell on their knees before Berengaria and me.

Ordering them to rise, I asked them to tell their story. It was not a pretty one, certainly, and my heart sank as I listened. From the moment that Isaac imprisoned them they had had only a little water to drink and a few dry loaves of bread to divide among all of them.

"What he hoped to achieve by starving us, I do not know," said young Roger Malcael, who apparently had led the escape. "And he kept us in a small chamber overlooking the harbor which made it possible for us to watch his men plundering our wrecked dromonds. There we were, your Grace, hungry, thirsty, and infuriated by what we saw. All King Richard's treasures! We talked of nothing but escape, of course, and finally the opportunity came. There was one guard a little more stupid than the rest and we killed him when he unbarred the door to give us water. We overpowered several more in the guardroom below and found three bows. The six of us were able to break down the castle gates, the three bows put the fear of God into the rabble we met on our way to the beach—and we were safely in the water at last! Thank God for the English pennant on the vessel that brought us here to you, my lady, or we would still be swimming."

"It's a lucky thing that we refused to visit the island," I said. "But if you had not risked your lives and come to warn us, dear sir, we might well have been Isaac's prisoners, too, by this time tomorrow."

I then told him what our difficulties were and thanked each in turn for their bravery; after I had done that, I asked how some of our other friends had fared.

"Your good father, sir," I said, remembering that this Roger Malcael must be the son of England's Vice-Chancellor, the guardian of its Great Seal. "I hope he is being treated with more courtesy than you found in Limassol."

The young man's eyes filled. "My father, your Grace, was drowned. I saw his boat founder with all on board—and the Great Seal was around his neck."

While these courageous knights had saved us from Isaac, this did not in any way solve our problems. The whole of that evening was spent discussing them again in the hope of finding a solution, but there seemed no safe answer: if we ventured on to Tripoli, the nearest port on the African coast, we might not survive another spell of rough weather; turning back to Rhodes was out of the question —it was farther away now than Tripoli—and according to our master there was no small island nearby where we could make our repairs.

The only suggestion with any merit was that we sail to the farthest end of Cyprus—beyond Famagusta—and hope to prevent word of our landing from reaching Isaac. There, perhaps, we could procure water and provisions and make our dromond more seaworthy.

"We will sleep on it," said Robert, finally. "And as tomorrow is Sunday I think we should spend the day praying for guidance."

* * *

I could relate in my own words the wonderful answer to our prayers, but I prefer the vivid account of that happy day in Richard de Templo's *Chronicle,* an account he wrote after hearing Berengaria and me discuss it:

While the Queens [by the time Richard set this down Berengaria and Richard were safely wed], anxious with biting cares, were sadly complaining and talking to one another, an unforeseen aid arrived by the good provision of God. For that same Sunday, while they were anxiously looking out, behold—between the foaming tops of the curling billows, two ships, moving like sea-birds, appeared sailing toward them! And while the Queens and others were yet uncertain and doubting who they might be, other ships hove into sight and a great fleet following rushed swiftly toward the port. The heavier their former desolation, the greater was now their rejoicing! . . .

Ah, indeed, indeed, how great was our rejoicing! Never shall I forget our hopes and fears as we sighted those first two ships, nor the wild shouts when we saw our great fleet following them and we saw, among them, a war galley rigged with bright red sails. . . .

CHAPTER

IX

Richard's anger, when he came aboard and heard our story, was almost frightening. It was, however, more than justified, and I must confess I was a little annoyed with Berengaria for cowering like a timid mouse while he raged up and down the cabin. Not that he seemed to care, or even to notice, for he was fully occupied in questioning me, Robert de Turnham, and the six knights who had escaped from Isaac's palace, his fury increasing with each fresh evidence of the emperor's treachery.

"By God," he said, at last, "that little traitor shall hear from me this very night! I will demand instant restitution of our imprisoned soldiers and every bit of plunder, large or small. I want Isaac's personal apology for his behavior, everything we need in the way of fresh supplies, and enough gold to make me forget his barbarous treatment of our friends and his insults to my sister and my bride. If he refuses, and I must admit that I hope he will, I shall make him sorry he was ever born!"

Next morning I was awakened very early by raised voices and

running feet. Isaac's only reply to Rick's message, they told me, was an impatient "Phrut!" and the same bubbling, frothing at the mouth that I had seen him display before. He had begun assembling his troops on the shore of the harbor, and my brother's immediate response was to call our own men to arms.

Our dromond, surrounded by the fleet, had moved right into the mouth of the harbor; from its tall deck we could watch the great mass of Isaac's imperial men-at-arms, clad in gorgeous uniforms and gleaming armor, marching into battle formation on the sandy beach. Huge piles of stones, hulks of wrecked ships, dead trees, and odd bits of lumber had all been dragged into the shallow water to prevent our boats from landing. All this had been done during the night and, soon after dawn, Isaac had stationed five war galleys between our anchored fleet and his hastily constructed barricades.

Richard, coming on board again to wish us farewell before beginning his assault on the island, merely laughed at me when I expressed a few qualms. He waved a great battle-axe that he was holding in his hand and said he would make me a promise.

"This was forged for me in England," he told me, "and there are twenty pounds of our good steel in its head. After we've defeated his army, I shall challenge Isaac to meet me in single combat and bring it back to you dripping with his blood. And, if you would like it, with one of those gaudy purple banners we see over there tied to its handle."

Shuddering, I replied that I would be quite content with only the banner. "The banner, please, and a feast of fresh meat in Isaac's castle. With you, my lord brother, sitting in Isaac's chair and wearing his crown. That and a good night's sleep in the royal bed are all the Lady Berengaria and I ask of you."

Rick roared with delight, put down the grim weapon, and gave me another kiss. "You shall have them!" he said. Then, freeing me, he turned to Berengaria who was standing very quietly beside me. "Command me further, dear lady. What shall I bring *you?* Isaac's ear—or his big toe, perhaps?"

"Just come back to us unhurt, my lord." She smiled, but I could see it was an effort. "I ask nothing more than that."

* * *

It was strangely quiet on our ship after the boatloads of warriors had set out for shore, and Blondel, who had been ordered by Richard to remain with us, brought his vielle up on deck. We all listened to one song, but when he began another I shook my head, and when he suggested that we all retire to the shelter of our cabin, I said, "Anyone who wishes to is free to go, but I shall watch the battle."

"But my lord King said—"

"Whatever my lord King said, I shall watch the battle."

Berengaria said nothing. She remained close beside me, how-ever, and when we saw that our galleys were sweeping close to Isaac's I reached for her hand and held it firmly in mine. I knew that she was frightened—and so was I! I had, after all, never seen a battle before, and Richard was not called "the Lion Heart" for nothing. We had good reason to be frightened.

Then, as we saw our archers and knights clambering aboard the enemy vessels, I felt a great surge of excitement. Suddenly I wanted to be there with them, sweeping Isaac's men into the water, ripping down his banners, rowing the galleys swiftly toward the barricaded beach. We could hear Isaac's waiting army howling like dogs, there on the sands, and I wanted to howl right back at them!

"Look, look, my ladies! The King! The King!" Blondel, his silvery hair on end and his voice shaking with the same excite-ment that was gripping me, pointed to a tall figure that had just leaped into the shallow water. For just a moment he stood there, alone, his helmet glittering in the hot May sun, his huge arm brandishing his gleaming battle-axe. Then he was wading ashore, his men at his heels.

It was all noise and confusion after that, and until we saw the bright purple banners scattering and the enemy running wildly toward the town my heart was in my mouth. We were not sure even then that we had won the day but apparently all was well, for a message reached us before the sun set, inviting us to come to Isaac's castle up on the rocks that overlooked the harbor.

"You and the Lady Berengaria may sleep in the royal bed as you suggested, Jo," my lord brother told me, after we joined him there, "but I am afraid your other wishes must wait. I am too busy to dine with you this evening on that fresh meat. And I have not yet had the pleasure of meeting Isaac in single combat although I chased him myself, shouting, "Emperor, Emperor, come and joust! Come and joust!""

* * *

Exhausted, Berengaria and I slept late, rising to find the elaborately furnished castle quiet and the town around it deserted. Rick, we learned, had set out before light to make a surprise attack on Isaac's camp, which our scouts had located some five miles away in the mountains. This was Tuesday, the seventh day in the month of May, and he did not return until Friday, when he rode back into Limassol followed by so many prisoners and so much plunder that the triumphal procession took several hours.

Isaac, it seemed, had escaped to Nicosia, but Rick spread before our appreciative eyes his gold and silver plate, the richly carved bed from his tent, ells and ells of heavy silks (much of it the deep purple of his banners), and the royal standard my brother had carried back especially for me. "As for that fresh meat you wanted," he said, his blue eyes laughing at me, "you may choose from oxen and kine, fat capons, succulent lambs—even goats, if you prefer their flesh. I have not yet acquired Isaac's crown, Jo, but tomorrow I shall sit in his chair and dine with you and my lady Berengaria. On Sunday, God willing, my lady and I will become man and wife. And my wife"—he gave Berengaria, who was flushing and paling by turns, his courtliest smile and, half turning back to me, a small, wry one—"will then be crowned Queen of England and Cyprus."

"Mother of God!" I protested. "You give us very little warning,

99

Richard! Would not Acre be a more suitable place for the ceremonies?"

"With Philip of France sulking in his tent and perhaps a battle being waged nearby? Nonsense, Joan! You and my lady have had more than enough time to ready yourselves."

He was quite right. Berengaria's wedding cote had travelled with her from Pamplona, the pearled girdle had been finished long since, and Rick's cloak was embroidered, folded away, and waiting. I suspect that my unthinking response was a renewal of my secret hope that he and Berengaria would grow fonder of each other—perhaps here on this beautiful island—before their actual marriage. Well, I consoled myself, Rick was at his most affable and making a strong attempt to appear the gallant bridegroom. There was still tomorrow. Berengaria must certainly sing the songs we had learned for him, I was determined on that; my brother could never resist music.

* * *

The palace, the following day, was in such a bustle that Berengaria and I remained in our apartments, occupying ourselves with the pleasant task of choosing our cotes, jewels, headdresses, and mantles for the evening's festivities. We had finished and were chatting quietly together while our tiring-women brushed our hair when my swarthy little Lady Elizabetta scuttled in with the news that several galleys had just arrived from Acre.

"They say that King Guy de Lusignan, Count Bohemund of Tripoli, and many other great noblemen have come to confer with King Richard," she added breathlessly. "They will all be at the feast, and the kitchens are swarming like a beehive!"

King Guy de Lusignan—I knew that he had been King of Jerusalem until Saladin captured the city. And Count Bohemund, of course, had been an attentive host to William and me at Tripoli.

I looked at Berengaria, her black hair spread over her shoulders like a silken cloak, her large eyes soft and appealing, her rosebud mouth the size and shape it should be, and I felt a stab of jealousy. Her life as England's Queen was beginning; mine, as Sicily's Queen, was over. She would be a bride tomorrow as well as a queen, and her beauty, in the pleated cote of white and silver baldachin, girdled with pearls, and the lustrous samite mantle, would make our noble guests envy my lord brother.

There, on a cushioned divan, were the garments we had chosen for tonight's feast: Berengaria's a dull blue, mine apple green. Both were made in the old fashion as, of course, were all Berengaria's, including her wedding cote. Mine was one that my dear lord had commended, for he liked its color and the way its soft folds hid my body; in our boxes was another, of richer silk, that I would wear to the wedding and Berengaria's coronation, and it, too, was dignified and well suited to the part I must play—the widowed sister, remaining always a step or two in the background.

Suddenly, and I suppose I should be ashamed of this, I found myself determined that tonight, at least, I should look as young and lovely as possible. Tomorrow would be Berengaria's day; tonight must be mine.

"Take these away," I said, pointing to the green cote and mantle. "Bring me the apricot robes that my lord brother the King gave me, the ones made in the French fashion."

*   *   *

When we were all gathered in the antechamber of the dining salon I saw that besides Count Bohemund there was another familiar face among the group of noble guests. It was that of Count Raimond of St. Gilles, heir of Toulouse, and as our eyes met he gave me a glance of such startled admiration that I was glad I had taken pains with my appearance.

I was presented to King Guy first, of course, an elderly man but with a pleasant face; then the other strangers were presented to me: Guy's brother Geoffry, Count Humfrey of Toron, and Count Leo de Montaine. Count Bohemund and I greeted each other warmly, and a moment later Richard brought Count Raimond to my side.

"We may thank the Crusade, Jo, for having Raimond for a friend again," he said. "You remember him, from the old days at St. Gilles? I have been drawn into our parents' quarrels over Toulouse in recent years, I regret to say, but all that was stopped the moment I took the Cross—for me, if not for our lady mother."

Raimond smiled at him. "I suspect Queen Eleanor enjoys that old struggle as much as my father does," he said. "You and I would settle it in a moment if it were left to us."

"As it may well be, one day," Richard added. "In the meantime, it is good to welcome you here, my friend, and to know that we will be setting out to Acre together before long. And to thank you for carrying my letters to the Lady Joan and King William so many months ago."

"Count Raimond delivered them to us himself," I told him. "We had only one brief meeting in Tripoli, but it brought back very vividly those evenings long ago when we all sang at his supper table."

"We will do so again," promised Richard, giving us both an affectionate nod as he moved away to join Berengaria and lead her to the dais.

I was placed on one side of my lord brother, his promised wife on the other, and, when we were all in our chairs and beginning the lavish banquet, it seemed to me that Rick was less stiff in his manner to her and Berengaria much less shy. As a result, I settled down to enjoy the delicious food and the entertainment that would follow, part of which I had planned with Blondel.

Our chamberlain had been busy, too, it seemed, and had found some native dancers for our amusement. Their gyrations apparently pleased most of the company and I, having watched similar writhings and undulations in Sicily, Rhodes, and Crete, joined in their shouts for more. Berengaria, however, had turned a bright pink and was staring down at the table; Rick, following my eyes, first raised his brows at me in mock dismay then, clapping his hands for silence, thanked the veiled dancers and dismissed them.

While they were bowing their way out I signalled to Blondel, who was waiting with the other musicians. He came immediately to the dais and knelt before the King.

"With your permission, Sire," he said, "the gracious Lady of Navarre and I will sing for you and our guests."

Rick, obviously both surprised and pleased, assented and made room for the lad between his chair and that of Berengaria. The handsome young minstrel, his pale hair gleaming in the light of the flambeaux on the wall, fell to his knees again and struck an opening chord on his vielle.

At first he sang alone; then Berengaria, a little frightened, joined in softly, her voice sweet and true. It was one of Rick's songs, of course, and, after a few minutes he reached over and took the instrument out of Blondel's hands and played the accompaniment for them. Then, when they began the last few lines, he leaned over Blondel until his red head almost touched the fair one and added his deeper, heavier voice to theirs.

The great hall was silent, as they finished. When we saw Rick beaming at his minstrel and his bride, however, everyone broke into a roar of approval, and I sat back happily in my chair, congratulating myself on the success of my scheme. I was, in fact, so intent on my own thoughts that I did not see the Count of St. Gilles leave his seat farther down the table; but there he was, a moment later, whispering in Richard's ear.

Rick, nodding, handed him Blondel's vielle and made room for him as he had for Blondel, this time between his chair and mine.

"Our friend and kinsman, Count Raimond of St. Gilles," I now heard him announce to our guests, "and my dear sister, Queen Joan of Sicily, will sing you a song they sang together thirteen long years ago."

I gasped and protested but Raimond, laughing into my eyes refused to listen. Just as Blondel had done with Berengaria, he struck a few chords and began to sing:

"Whene'er green leaves and grass appear,
And budding flowers from branches spring—"

Even before he had finished the first line the melody caught me and carried me back to my mother's court and the old minstrel there, Bernart de Ventadour, who taught the song to me and gave me my first vielle lessons. It was one of his own, one I loved still, and, smiling back at Count Raimond I sang along with him:

"And nightingales do strong and clear
Uplift their voices and 'gin to sing—"

By the time we had finished a few lines our voices seemed to be blending together as if we had been singing partners all our lives; the magic of it was intoxicating, and I understood, suddenly, why Rick was happiest when he was with his minstrels.

He joined in toward the end of the song but he did not take the vielle from Raimond until we had finished. Then he rose and, all alone, sang "Jerusalem on Thy Green Hill."

We were on our feet almost as swiftly as he was, and long before the last beautiful note died away I could feel the tears slipping down my cheeks.

My lord brother then raised his right arm just as William had done on the deck of our carrack in Tripoli harbor. Every Crusader in the great hall raised his, and their shouts, in which the rest of us joined, broke the solemn silence.

"Help! Help for the Holy Sepulchre! Help, help for the Holy Sepulchre! Help, help for the Holy Sepulchre!"

I shall never forget that evening—for several reasons. One was
that I felt so young again and even desirable. It is true that Philip
of France had made me feel a little the same way, but his admiration was soiling, somehow, and Count Raimond's was not.

My other reason for remembering the evening was that I
awakened soon after we retired to hear Berengaria sobbing softly
on the far side of the wide bed that she and Richard would be
sharing the following night. Speaking softly, for I did not want to
disturb the ladies sleeping nearby on their pallets, I asked her what
was wrong.

"Nothing," she whispered. "Go back to sleep, Joan, please. I'm
sorry I awakened you. It's nothing. I'm—tired, that's all."

It wasn't all, and I stared into the darkness, wondering whether
there was anything I could say that would help.

"You are thinking of tomorrow night," I said at last, the dark
giving me courage. "I know you are, so don't deny it. I know because I cried, too. I don't think you will like it—I didn't and I don't

see how any woman could—but you will not mind it, after a while. Please believe me, Berengaria. You will grow quite accustomed to it, and there will be the joy of having a child. Just think, a child who may someday be the King of England! Oh, I realize that Richard is, perhaps, not the husband of your dreams"—I wondered again how any maid could fail to love him—"but you should have a wonderful life together just as William and I did. Why not? Your music is a bond, and when you hold his child in your arms he will be so proud and happy. I shall never forget my lord's face, looking at our little son."

"My dear Joan." Berengaria's voice shook, still, but she sounded much calmer. "My *very* dear Joan! How good you are to me, how understanding. More truly a sister than Blanche has ever been. And I will remember everything you have said, so do not fret about me any longer. Go to sleep, and perhaps I shall lie here for a little while and think how handsome my lord is."

* * *

Those last, gallant words of Berengaria's returned to me the next day as I stood in the Chapel of St. George and watched Richard's chaplain unite them in the bonds of holy matrimony. Never had my brother looked handsomer than he did at that moment, so handsome, in fact, that his small bride's black and white beauty paled beside him. Clad in a magnificent rose-colored satin surcoat, with the richly embroidered mantle we had made for him swinging from his broad shoulders, and with his red-gold hair and beard gleaming in the light of the many candles on the altar, he might well have been the God of the Sun. That he was born to be a king was obvious, and later, after Berengaria's coronation, when he rode beside his newly crowned bride, he was even more dazzling.

She was lovely, of course, with her silken ebony hair spread over her shoulders and her head held high under the burden of the glittering double crown. If Richard was the Sun God, I told myself, Berengaria was the Goddess of the Moon, white and silver.

As for me, I played a sister's part at the two ceremonies, loving them both with all my heart and wishing them well with every breath I drew. It was a long, long day, and finally at the close of it I helped my new sister's ladies prepare her for bed, waiting until Rick entered in his long silk bedgown and climbed in beside her before I retired with the others to drink a last toast to their happiness.

That happiness was my lord brother's responsibility now, and I found myself praying that somewhere under his affability, jocoseness, and hearty good nature was enough sensitivity and tenderness for his timid wife to guide him through the difficult hours ahead.

I have no way of knowing whether or not my prayers were answered, for Berengaria, after that, never discussed her lord with me or with anyone else. They spent the next three days together at Isaac's castle, and I must confess that they displayed such a determined gaiety during all that time that I almost wished myself back in La Ziza. It made me actually uneasy, and I was quite relieved when the celebration was over and Rick left us to subdue the rest of the island and bring Isaac to his knees.

There had been one attempt at a truce but Isaac violated it immediately, so my lord brother, aided by King Guy and the other nobles who had joined us there, felt no compunction in taking one town after another. It was not, however, until after they had captured Isaac's young daughter in a remote castle that the emperor, as he called himself, came out of hiding and surrendered.

The campaign had taken the better part of two weeks; May was almost over when Isaac, riding Fauvel, the superb horse that had made it possible for him to evade capture for so long, clattered into the courtyard of his former palace and asked to see the King of England. Word of his arrival spread over the sprawling building like a forest fire, reaching Queen Berengaria and me long before Richard summoned us to his presence chamber, so we were not surprised, when we entered, to see the fallen monarch on his knees in front of my lord brother, begging for mercy.

"Not for me, my lord King," he cried, "but for my daughter, whose life is dearer to me than my own. Allow me to see her, treat her with kindness and generosity, and I will agree to anything you ask of me."

Rick, without replying, raised him to his feet and pointed to a nearby chair. Then, after whispering an order to one of our servants, he sat in silence, apparently deep in thought. The rest of us, among whom were King Guy, Count Bohemund, Humfrey of Toron, and Count Raimond, were quiet also.

There was a bustle at the entrance to the chamber, and as we watched two men-at-arms bring forward a small, olive-skinned maiden, the elderly prisoner held out his arms and began to weep. She flew to them, kissing his wet cheeks and cradling his grizzled head on her surprisingly full bosom. It was a moving scene and I found my hatred for Isaac lessening a little, for it was obvious that the life of this sloe-eyed, plump young daughter, with her head of crisp black curls and her dainty feet, was, as he had said, dearer to him than his own.

Richard rose; Isaac, the tears still streaming down his face, led the girl to him and bowed low.

"This is my daughter, my lord King. The Lady Bourgigne."

My brother, lifting the maiden's dimpled fingers to his lips, smiled down into her oddly shaped black eyes. She smiled back, apparently unafraid. Keeping her hand in his, Richard addressed her father.

"Because of your insulting and treacherous behavior to me and mine, and your disregard of the truce to which you agreed some weeks ago, I accept your unconditional surrender and will decide, at my leisure, whether you shall live or die. I have, however, a forgiving heart and I shall listen to your plea in behalf of the Lady Bourgigne."

Turning away from his trembling prisoner, Rick stepped down from the dais, brought the girl over to where we were seated, and, when we rose, placed her hand in Berengaria's.

"A charming handmaiden for you, my dearest lady," he said. "A wedding gift from your King and husband."

Isaac's face darkened at the word "handmaiden"; he opened his mouth to protest, then closed it again. He stood, while Berengaria murmured a few soft words of welcome to his daughter, watching and listening, his eyes fixed anxiously on Bourgigne's beautiful, if strange, little face. But when two more men-at-arms entered a moment later, their arms loaded with clanking iron chains and manacles, and advanced toward him, he again prostrated himself before my lord brother.

"Not iron chains for an emperor!" he screamed. "Spare me that insult!"

Richard looked down at him as he grovelled on the floor. Spreading his hands wide, he glanced over at the assembled nobles.

"What do you say, my lords? Are they an insult?"

A few nodded, and one or two muttered a half agreement; the others did not seem to have an opinion.

Richard, smiling a bit wearily, clapped his hands for a servant. "Go to the keeper of our Royal Treasures," he told him, "and fetch the silver chains we found in Sicily."

He turned back to Isaac. "You must forgive me for not chaining you in gold, my lord Emperor, but all our gold—and yours, too, of course—is dedicated to our Holy Crusade."

* * *

Not long afterwards Rick sent for me to say that we would very soon be leaving Cyprus.

"I want you to explain to Berengaria," he said, "why I consider it necessary for us to sail on separate ships. Women are not supposed to go on Crusade with their husbands and, even if they were, the ship that carries the King of England is a dangerous vessel on which to travel. The Saracens would like nothing better than to sink it."

I nodded and agreed, although I wondered why he himself did not say all this to Berengaria.

"My reason for speeding our departure," he continued, "is that young Baldwin of Flanders has just brought me a letter from Philip in which he says he will take Acre very soon. I don't believe it, for I know that, although Philip and his men have surrounded the city, Saladin and his Saracens are encircling *them*. But on the chance that he is right I shall not delay our voyage another moment. The King of England will capture Acre, by God, not the King of France!"

"What are King Guy and Court Bohemund and the other nobles doing here at such a time?" I asked. "Why did they leave Acre and Philip?"

"To make sure that I will support Guy," Rick replied a little grimly. "He wants to be king again when we free Jerusalem, and Philip is now favoring Conrad of Montferrat."

Then my brother told me just why these two men were both claiming the throne to the Holy Land, tracing their lineage and mentioning births, deaths, and marriages in such detail that I became hopelessly confused.

"It's a very difficult question to decide," Rick agreed, "but although old Guy is a bit of a fool I have promised to give him the support he wants. First, of course, we must drive out the Saracens."

* * *

As this last leg of our journey would be short, the whole fleet set sail together, leaving Cyprus in the care of Richard de Canville and our Robert de Turnham's brother Stephen. Isaac, wearing his silver chains, was already on his way to Margat, a town between Antioch and Tripoli, where he would remain as a prisoner of the Templars until the Crusade was over.

His daughter Bourgigne accompanied us. But before we had been more than a day or so at sea both Berengaria and I realized that Richard had done us a disfavor by adding her to our household. Had she been sad, homesick, or even bitter and resentful, we would have treated her with sympathy and tried to set her at her ease, but when we discovered that all she cared about was painting her face, oiling and perfuming her voluptuous little body, and looking for amorous adventures, we lectured her on the subject of western manners and morals and gave two of our sharpest-eyed ladies the task of guarding her virtue.

What made this extremely difficult was the fact that we had many handsome young noblemen on board, on their way to a war in which they might well be killed. Who could blame them for cramming every moment full of pleasure? And several of them obviously thought that a love affair with Isaac's sensuous daughter would be very pleasant indeed.

Philip of Flanders's awkward and rather shy young kinsman Baldwin was the first to succumb, and both Geoffry de Lusignan and Count Raimond of St. Gilles soon entered into a lighthearted rivalry with him that provided our company with several extremely entertaining evenings. All three, it seemed, were determined to teach her some of our songs, this being the best excuse they could think of for taking her off alone to a dim corner of the deck with only a vielle to play propriety. When young Baldwin—who, we discovered later, was truly in love—actually threatened to fight his more frivolous rivals for the privilege, Count Raimond suggested that we set up a Court of Love to settle the matter.

"The question for the court will be a simple one," he said. "Which of the lady's knights would be the best teacher?"

As everyone agreed I should be Queen, I took my seat on a hastily improvised dais and gathered my court around me. Having watched my lady mother play the game at her castle in Poitiers when I was a small girl, I remembered enough of the rules to insist that the supplicants pretend to be anonymous and plead their cases through an advocate; a short consultation resulted in Geoffry arguing Raimond's case and Raimond appearing for Geoffry, each, while supposedly praising each other, succeeding wittily in doing just the reverse. Their efforts were rewarded with much loud applause, but poor Baldwin, an earnest lad, chose an equally earnest advocate who was not smart enough to enter into the joke and whose sober arguments almost spoiled our charming contest.

When everyone had finished speaking, I conferred with my

court before rendering my judgment. Then I called for silence.

"As the court wishes to be fair to both the lady in question and to the three supplicants," I announced, "we have decided that we must waive the rule of anonymity and order each knight to prove his case in person. I therefore command that we convene here at the same hour for the next three evenings and call on each one in turn for a song or two."

Our days, too, were now pleasant, for the weather was sunny and our fleet was moving swiftly toward its destination, first passing Margat, where we could see Isaac's prison high on a hill, then Tortosa and beautiful Tripoli, the city I had visited with William, then Beyrouth loomed into sight. Soon after we left Beyrouth behind, we saw a huge, clumsy carrack, heavily loaded.

We heard it answer a hail from my lord brother's ship, some distance ahead of ours, but we were not close enough to know what was said. While we watched, a small boat set out toward it from the *Trenchmer* and was met with a shower of arrows and bolts.

"It's a Saracen ship," said someone near me. "King Richard will take it."

We all crowded to the rail, but to our great disgust our ship kept right on its course and soon we were too far away to see the battle. The master of our vessel was obeying orders, of course, and, as a result of his obedience, we reached Acre a day before my brother and the rest of our fleet.

A great shout from the lookout took us up on deck and there, ahead of us, were the white minarets and towers of Acre, the city we had come to take; and there, as we dropped anchor and sails and set out for shore, was a great crowd on the beach, awaiting us. While I stood in the prow with Berengaria, watching the water shallow and wondering what the next few hours would hold, I heard Count Raimond of St. Gilles speak right behind us.

"Look, my lady," he said. "King Philip of France, wading out to carry you in."

I looked—and my heart sank. It was certainly Philip; he was so close that I could see his ugly face and gemmed circlet, its gold and jewels gleaming in the sun. I shuddered and, without giving myself time to realize that it must of course be the new Queen of England he was coming for and that Raimond was speaking to Berengaria, not to me, I turned to the young Count and held out my hands.

"You carried me at Tripoli, my lord. Will you do so again?"

Almost before I had finished speaking, Raimond was over the side of the galley, in the water, and I was in his arms. A moment later I saw Philip reach the little vessel and heard him greet Berengaria, asking permission to carry her the rest of the way. I suppose Raimond was watching, too, for he stumbled, and as his arms tightened suddenly around me I felt something I had never felt before. How can I describe it? All I can say is that it made me want to move even closer into Raimond's arms.

It was fortunate, I think, that another few steps took us out of the water and that when my feet touched the sand we were surrounded by a mass of noblemen shouting greetings and asking questions. In the flurry of finding old friends and being presented to new ones, I had time to quiet my wildly beating heart and to tell myself, firmly, that such a thing must never happen again.

CHAPTER

XI

The heat on the beach was so unbearable that both Berengaria and I were grateful to King Philip and the others for the celerity with which they made their formal speeches of welcome and carried us off to the encampment. It was not far, but as we entered it I was shocked and horrified by the sickening stench, the clouds of insects, and the hideous disorder that prevailed. Unlike Rick's camp outside Messina, in which straight rows of neat tents housed the men-at-arms and the knights and noblemen were in larger silken pavilions, and where all refuse was either burned or buried some distance outside the tall palisade that enclosed them, this settlement at Acre was a filthy, haphazard affair.

Ragged and dirty tents of every possible shape, size, and color sprawled here and there; packs of snarling dogs rooted in dead campfires and fly-covered piles of unspeakable matter; and we passed more than one cartload of naked corpses rattling toward a deep ditch surrounding the city walls that loomed over us.

I learned later that dead bodies of both men and horses were being thrown into the ditch every day to help fill it, and this great open grave accounted, of course, for most of the smell that permeated the camp. In the long two years of the siege—it began in August of 1189 and this was now June of 1191—many thousands of the Crusaders had been dying at the hands of the Infidels but even more from starvation and disease. Often there was nothing to eat but camel meat and cabbage, sometimes not even that, and the death toll was increasing every day.

These grim facts, as I have said, we were to learn later. Now I was glad to see that the pavilion which was to be our temporary domicile stood slightly apart and looked to be a little cleaner and more comfortable than most of the others. King Philip, who had escorted us inside its silken walls, told us that it belonged to Philip of Flanders.

"We buried him today, God rest his soul," he said sadly. "Another victim of the deadly fevers raging in the camp."

Shaken by this unexpected, tragic news, I thought first of how it would grieve my lord brother, who loved him well, and then of our young friend Baldwin. Poor lad, this would be a heavy blow! Philip, a childless man, had been extremely kind to his kinsman, treating him almost as his own son.

I waited a moment for Berengaria to speak; when she remained silent, I hastened to express our sorrow and to thank King Philip for his courteous welcome.

"We will try not to be a burden, my lord King," I said. "For we realize that our presence here cannot fail to add to your difficulties. With your permission, the Lady Berengaria and I"—and taking her hand in mine, I drew her closer to my side—"will be more than content to remain in seclusion until my lord brother arrives. In fact, we would prefer it, as your news has saddened us and we are very weary from the voyage."

I hoped that my little speech was what King Philip wanted to hear. It is true that from the moment he waded out to our landing barge he had been all politeness both to me and to Berengaria;

but whether he was merely hiding his true feelings or whether time had softened his anger over Richard's marriage, I could not tell. In either case I did not want to be a guest at his table that night, and it seemed to me that our friend's death freed us from that awkward necessity.

"The presence of two such lovely ladies could never be a burden," replied Philip with a stiff smile. "But I think that most of us here at Acre will want to spend the rest of the day mourning our lost companion and praying for his soul. In the meantime"—he glanced swiftly around the richly furnished pavilion—"I hope that you will not be too uncomfortable. Do not hesitate, I beg of you, to summon my chamberlain if your own people need any assistance. He will be most happy to serve you."

I heaved a great sigh of relief after he left us alone, and Berengaria looked at me with sudden concern. "You *are* weary, dear Joan," she said, "and it is my fault. I cannot seem to remember that I am the Queen of England and that I should have said all those polite things to King Philip, not you."

This, from anyone but Berengaria, would have implied a rebuke, and for just a moment I wondered if I had taken too much on myself. Her next words, however, set my mind at rest. "I promise to do better," she went on earnestly, her white brow wrinkled in a frown. "Truly I do. Make *me* speak next time, Joan. I'll hate it, but I'll do it!"

I laughed and dropped a kiss on top of her dark head. "It will soon be easy for you," I assured her. "You'll see. I've done it for so many years that I think nothing of it. Now let us be comfortable —I wonder where our ladies and our boxes can be?"

* * *

A cooling breeze from the hills sprang up later that evening, and when I saw that both Berengaria and Bourgigne had begun to disrobe for bed I wandered alone out of our pavilion, nodded to the guard, and stood, for a few minutes, just beyond the entrance.

The air was sweet, for the ghastly smells were blowing out to sea; the night sky was a soft black velvet, pierced by countless stars, and, scattered around on the hillside that encircled the plain on which our camp stood, were the campfires of the enemy. Saladin and his Infidels were there, so close that they could watch our every move; so close, in fact, that their scouts had been slipping down in the night and killing some of our own sleeping men in their tents.

It was a frightening thought. I shivered, hoping that Richard would soon join us. We would all feel safer then, I was sure. But what, I wondered, would *he* feel, coming into this death-ridden, filthy place? Would his heart still beat with a Crusader's high hopes and purpose, or would he have a few doubts as to whether any cause should call for the sacrifice of so many lives? His dear friend Philip buried today—who tomorrow?

It was not enough to be young and strong. The list of the dead proved that only too well. It could be any one of our companions— or Rick himself. I tortured myself with the picture of my brother, awaiting burial in his royal pavilion; I then settled the question of who would be the King of Jerusalem by placing kind, stupid Guy de Lusignan on a bier; I stood, while the breeze, shifting a little, blew my veil, and imagined Count Raimond of St. Gilles stricken, his dark eyes sunken in his head, the arms that had carried me ashore that day shrunken and useless.

I laughed at myself for a fool and made myself think of something else. The "something else" that immediately came to mind was the strange and exciting way my body had behaved when he stumbled in the waves. The memory was disturbing, puzzling, and enlightening, answering many questions I had asked myself in the past and raising others. I saw, suddenly, why even ladies of gentle birth sometimes betrayed their marriage vows, and I wondered why my dear lord's lovemaking had never stirred my senses in this way.

I had loved William—and he was a much handsomer man than Raimond. I thought of my lord's golden curls and chiselled features, his tall, slender body. Raimond was shorter, stockier; his hair was brown and straight, his nose too blunt. I liked the way his dark eyes smiled at me, when we were both amused, but that was no reason for me to turn hot and tremble in his arms. . . .

As I pondered the problem I resolved that I should, perhaps, avoid his company in the future. Certainly I must avoid his arms—and, to be on the safe side, the arms of any other young man from now on!

Having reached this sensible decision, I looked around at all the tents nearby and wondered in which one Raimond would sleep that night and if he, too, was remembering that moment in the curling waves. Again I laughed at myself for being such a fool; then, before I could be guilty of any more ridiculous nonsense, the stench from the camp drifted back, driving me toward our shelter. As I reached the entrance a hideous noise broke out, a sound half like the beating of drums, half a wild metallic clangor.

"What *is* it?" I asked the guard.

"King Philip's men again, my lady," he replied in a resigned voice. "They think that noise will drive away the sand flies and mosquitoes that swarm into his tent. It's over there, you see, right under the Accursed Tower, much too close to the trench."

* * *

I was sitting with Berengaria just before sundown on the following day when she looked up, startled, dropped her needlework, and ran to the door.

"What are they shouting?" she asked.

I joined her, although it seemed to me that we had heard nothing but shouting all afternoon. A camp, we had soon discovered, is noisier than a busy city or a castle courtyard at holiday time, and, what with the constant clamor of voices, barking of dogs, clanging and hammering around the assault towers, there had been very little quiet since long before we left our beds. Even during the hottest hours, when many of the activities were halted, enough of our men-at-arms continued to raise their voices so loudly that we could not sleep—and as we had been awakened several times the night before by King Philip's men routing insects, we really needed more rest.

The moment we stepped outside, however, I realized that Berengaria was right. Another great shout followed the one she had heard, and it was not just a soldier calling to a friend.

"The Lion Heart! The Lion Heart!" We heard it again and again, from all sides of the encampment. "The Lion Heart! The Lion Heart! The Lion Heart!"

Men rushed out of the pavilions and tents and began running toward the waterfront; others pounded by on horseback, everyone heading the same way. We stood, for a moment, wondering what to do. Bourgigne joined us there, her black eyes open for the first time that day; Isaac's indolent daughter could always sleep, and she had spent both morning and afternoon curled up like a dormouse on a pile of silken cushions.

Lady Caterina was close behind her, carrying veils and light mantles; we were donning them when Baldwin of Flanders and Count Raimond rode up, followed by Geoffry de Lusignan.

"Call for your horses, ladies," they said. "King Richard's fleet is in sight."

By the time we reached the strand it was so crowded with wildly cheering Crusaders that our escorts had to clear a path for us.

" 'Way!" they shouted. "Make way for the Queen of England. Make way for the Queen of Sicily!"

As the men around us moved aside I was struck by the jubilation on their faces. Then they began cheering for us: "The Lion Heart's lady! The Lion Heart's sister!"

It was all "the Lion Heart," and when we joined King Philip under a hastily erected canopy my heart was leaping with pride. He said little while we waited, and I did not blame him. The happy shouting never stopped, growing louder as the harbor filled with sails bellying in the breeze. The last of the sun glinted on the armor of men crowded on the decks and on hundreds of oars cutting through the dancing waves.

Count Raimond, standing behind me, laughed delightedly.

"Mother of God!" he whispered to someone. "They must think Richard has come from Heaven to deliver them!"

Just then Berengaria clutched my arm.

"Look, Joan," she said, "my lord's landing stage!"

There it was, with its bright red sails; and there, standing on the high carved and gilded prow was my huge, redheaded brother, clad in his gleaming armor, his long arm raised in greeting to the seething mass of Crusaders all around us.

If the shouting had been loud before, it was truly deafening now; the moment Richard jumped onto the sand, trumpets pealed, there was a merry sound of dozens of pipes sounding here and there, and from a group of musicians behind our dais was added a continuous beating on drums and timbrels.

Both the cheering and the music went right on while Rick kissed King Philip, Berengaria, and me, then greeted the other nobles; the noise followed us from the beach to the camp; when we sat down to supper the cheering changed to singing, and we realized that our soldiers were now celebrating my lord brother's arrival around their own campfires.

"I suspect the revels will go on till dawn," Richard said a little ruefully, as he bade us good night. "The men out there will make merry while Philip and I are working at the council table—planning how best to end this interminable siege and take them away from this pesthole."

I realized that Rick was choosing this way to tell Berengaria that he would not share her bed that night, so I murmured something about his devotion to the Holy Crusade and hurried Bourgigne away before she could distress my sister by saying what I could see she was thinking.

As we set out for our pavilion a little ahead of the others, she began to sneer at Richard's lack of ardor. I tried to explain to her that we were here at Acre on sufferance, that Crusaders were not encouraged to bring their wives or sisters with them, and that my brother had warned us that he could not allow our presence to make him neglect his duties.

"If Malek Ric was *my* lord," she replied, smiling derisively and using the Infidels' name for Richard, "he would think his duty as a husband the most important."

"Ah," I said, wishing I could slap her dark face, "but King Richard is *not* your lord—and never would be. He chose a wife to share his throne as well as his bed. A queen, not merely a concubine."

My words struck home. Bourgigne gave me a venomous glance and walked away, leaving me feeling a little sick and more than a little sorry. I had spoken in anger, which I should not have done, and I could see that I had made an enemy. Bourgigne was so much the small animal that I had begun to dislike her almost the moment she joined our household; now I had given her good reason to dislike me as well, and small animals, when they are roused, will bite and scratch.

* * *

Just as Richard expected, the men celebrated his arrival until dawn broke the following morning, and I doubt that anyone slept much that night. Despite this, however, the camp was busier and noisier than ever the next day, and it was apparent that my lord brother had brought new life and hope to the weary Crusaders. While some men-at-arms made a valiant effort to clean up the filthy place, others fetched the heavy planks of a tall wooden tower that Richard had erected in Messina, then dismantled to use here in Acre; when it was put together again it would be higher than any of King Philip's assault towers and everyone was confident that it would play a great part in subduing the beleaguered city.

In the meantime my brother sent a courier to Saladin requesting a private meeting. So many tales of Saladin's chivalry had reached his ears that he thought it possible some peaceful solution to the struggle between them might be reached if they discussed it together.

The Infidel leader's reply was brief: "I do not consider it wise for enemy kings to meet until a truce has been signed. If, however, you will agree to a three-day respite in the fighting, I shall send my brother al Adil to talk with you."

All this we heard from our young friends who continued to spend an hour or two with us from time to time when they were not needed elsewhere. As Rick, needless to say, was occupied every hour of the day and, I suppose, most of the night, we did not hope for any visit from him until after the conference with al Adil—or Saphadin, as he was more familiarly called.

Young Baldwin, more in love with Bourgigne than ever, told us when the meeting was to take place. It was from his lips, also, we learned that both my lord brother and King Philip were ill—much too ill to venture out to the plain between the two encampments. The meeting must be postponed.

The moment he finished speaking I turned to Lady Caterina and Berengaria and announced that I was going to my brother's sickbed. "Come with me if you wish," I told them, "but I shall go alone if you prefer not to expose yourselves. I must find out for myself how seriously ill he is."

Remembering my William's death, I feared that Richard might be suffering from a similar fever. I wanted to see him and I wanted to talk to his physician. I was very, very frightened, so frightened that I was glad when both Berengaria and my good Caterina accompanied me to his pavilion, and more grateful than I can say when they followed me right up to his bedside.

He looked, it seemed to me, more angry than sick.

"Well, dear ladies," he greeted us immediately, "you find me in a sorry state. What a miserable time to be chained to my bed—and Philip, too! A fine pair of Crusaders we have proved to be!"

Berengaria now surprised me by moving swiftly to his side, falling on her knees, and taking one of his hands in hers.

"What is it, my lord?" she asked him. "What ails you?"

"Arnaldia," he replied bitterly. "My mouth is a mass of sores and they tell me I shall lose some of my hair and finger nails. I don't care about that, but I'm as weak as a sick cat. I can't eat—or drink anything but the filthy warm water they have here in the camp. I took a sip of wine, and it was worse than swallowing a knife."

"We must find you some fresh milk," said Berengaria, "and eggs. I will beat them together for you with some spices. Now rest—you should not tire yourself by talking."

Rising, she made way for me. But I merely smiled down on him and bade him have a good night's sleep; now that I knew he was not seriously ill I was quite satisfied, and his physician, who followed us out of the curtained-off alcove that was his bedchamber, set our minds even more at ease.

"My lord King is miserable, of course," he told us. "Much more miserable than King Philip. If he remains quiet, however, he will soon be well."

"And if he does not?" Knowing my brother I doubted that he would lie in his bed for very long.

"Then it could be weeks before he fully recovers," he said.

Berengaria, apparently happy to have something to do, hurried us back to our quarters and sent men scurrying around for milk and eggs. Where they found them, for find them they did, we did not ask. Some money changed hands, however, and Rick's little wife filled a silver cup with a soothing and strengthening drink which she sent him late that night and again early the next morning.

She was not, we learned from his physician, the only one who was concerned about the King's health. Saladin, after hearing of his enemy's illness, despatched a messenger with a great bowl of soft, very ripe peaches embedded in snow. Someone climbed very high to find that snow, and it delighted Rick, who held it in his sore mouth until it melted and ran comfortingly down his throat.

As it turned out, I proved to be both right and wrong about my brother's behavior; he neither remained in his bed nor did he rise and walk around the camp. Instead, he was carried about in a litter and, when an attack of ague added to his misery, making him hot and cold by turns, he merely wrapped his long legs in a padded silken bedcover and set out as usual. From this conveyance he gave his orders, watched the final work on his tall assault tower, and even took part in the occasional task of routing Saladin's men who rushed down to attack our encampment whenever we endangered the city's walls.

It was not necessary for the inhabitants of Acre to send messengers asking for Saladin's help; all they had to do was make a noise —beat on metal objects, shout, blow horns—and the arrows of the Infidels would shower on our men-at-arms.

June dragged slowly away in this unpleasant fashion and we, in our separate quarters, found time hanging heavily on our useless hands. The only other women in the camp were the laundresses and the usual camp followers, and as our friends were too occupied elsewhere to visit our pavilion we were hard put to it to amuse ourselves.

Bourgigne was still content to paint her face and loll on her pillows; she would, during the evening hours, pluck at the vielle strings with languid fingers and join in our singing with her husky little voice, but we could not interest her in anything else. Blondel, who came to us when Richard could spare him, brought us a handsome board and men so that we could play merels, and although we tried to teach Bourgigne that simple game it proved to be impossible. Berengaria knew it well, I had played it all my life, and we were very well matched, wagering huge sums that never changed hands.

Blondel was the only one to bring us the true story of what was happening in the camp around us. From him we heard, although he did not say it in so many words, that King Philip and my brother were continuing in their secret rivalry, each determined to be the one to bring Acre to its knees. Rick, using his illness as an excuse, played a waiting game and rested his men, while Philip, soon fully recovered from his bout of arnaldia, made several assaults on the weakening city. Richard also bribed hundreds of Pisans to desert Philip's standard and fight under his; he loaned our mutual nephew, Henry of Champagne, four thousand pounds, horses, and food for his men, to win *his* loyalty, and, in every way he could, undermined King Philip's importance and established himself, King Richard of England, as the leader of the Crusade.

I was, I must confess, in sympathy with my brother's aims, but being a woman I was eager to see the end of the siege. Not just for our Crusaders; my heart bled, as well, for the starving inhabitants of Acre, now cut off from all supplies and hopes of succor. And my admiration went out to them, as they continued to defend their city, refusing repeatedly the unconditional surrender that was now demanded of them.

On the third day of July Philip finally breached the city walls. His men were repulsed, however, and we awakened the next morning to find that the valiant townspeople had repaired the gap in the night. But the fact that we had broken through sent a new feeling sweeping over our encampment, a confident hope that the end was now in sight, and Richard, less than a week later, although still too weak to wear his heavy armor or remain on his feet, decided at last to take over the command of the besieging Crusaders.

He had, for some little while, been observing the almost daily skirmishes from a raised shelter placed well away from danger but in a spot that afforded a good view of the part of the city walls under attack. Now he was to be carried to a large shed, just completed, within arrow's range of that same piece of wall. Previous towers, sheds, and scaling ladders had all been burned by showers of Greek fire, a mixture of quick sulphur, dregs of wine, Persian gum, baked salt, pitch, and two kinds of oil. This dreadful stuff, once it was ignited, could be extinguished by only two things—sand or vinegar —so Richard had roofed his new shelter with some material that would not burn.

When I heard of his plan I hurried to his pavilion. He scowled, as I entered, and spoke before I could even greet him.

"Go away, Joan," he said. "If you have come to scold me out of taking part in today's foray, I tell you now it is no use. Go back to your own quarters and keep your fingers out of my business."

I laughed. Instead of a lion, he looked just like a scraggly rooster, his red hair ruffled on the pillows, his nose beakish in his fever-thinned face.

"You might at least hear what I want before ordering me away," I told him. "I only came to ask if Berengaria and I might watch the attack from that other shelter of yours. Do say yes, Rick. We'll be quite safe there, as you know, and we're both very tired of being shut up day after day."

"This is why women should never be allowed on Crusade," he replied. "You *will* make trouble, even the best of you. No, Joan—some stray arrow might reach that little building, remote as it is."

Raimond of St. Gilles, who was standing behind my brother's bed, saw my disappointment. "Why not have the ladies wear haquetons and surround the shelter with a few men-at-arms?" he suggested.

I agreed to this instantly. The quilted cotton jackets would be smotheringly hot, of course, but only an arrow fired at close range could penetrate their thick folds and they would be all the protection we could possibly need.

Instead of answering me, Richard turned his head and smiled maliciously at Count Raimond. "Guard them yourself, Raimond, and I'll not raise any more objections. That wounded arm"—he pointed to a bandage around Raimond's sleeve that I had not noticed before—"will keep you out of the fighting in any case."

Flushing indignantly, Raimond insisted that it would not. "I can still wield a battle-axe!"

"Not while we have men with two good arms," said my brother. "No, no, Raimond—protect my ladies today and come into battle with me later. We are only beginning to fight, as you well know."

There being nothing else to say, Raimond undertook the task allotted him so gracefully that although I had been avoiding his company I decided to forget my good resolutions for the time being and enjoy his companionship. Bourgigne, hearing that we were to be in his care, climbed down off her divan and announced firmly that she, too, would join our little party.

I hoped that the sight of herself in the ugly, uncomfortable, padded haqueton might make her change her mind, but she merely laughed

and trotted obediently along with the rest of us when Count Raimond led us to the canvas-draped tower. We were surrounded by a
small band of men-at-arms, and, going by a route that kept us out
of sight of most of the encampment, we reached our destination
without being questioned. Once inside, we settled down on cushioned benches placed by someone for our particular use, and Raimond stationed our guards so that they could halt anyone who approached from any direction.

All we saw, at first, was what seemed to be a confused scurrying
around of men carrying all kinds of things—stones, weapons, ladders—and pushing others, battering rams and freshly constructed
assault towers of varying heights to replace those burned the previous day. Soon I realized that the men were converging on one
spot, and Raimond, who was watching closely, informed us that
Rick's great hope was to undermine the tall tower built into that
portion of the wall.

"We call it 'the Accursed Tower,'" he said, "because it is from
there that the Infidels have poured so much of their liquid fire on
our men. If you look carefully, you will see where King Philip's
men broke through—there, on that side. It has been repaired, but it
must have been weakened. . . ."

Berengaria rose and walked to the gap in the canvas curtain. "It
frightens me to think of my lord being carried near that wall, not
able to walk."

Joining her there, Raimond pointed to a covered litter moving to
where the activity was thickest. "There he goes, your Grace. And
there is his new shelter, just behind those battering rams."

We were all watching as the litter reached the shelter and was
carried inside. Between a row of men-at-arms that encircled the odd
structure, I glimpsed Richard's red head rearing up from what must
be a pallet.

The next moment, under our very eyes, the attack began. I had
thought the noise horrible before, the clattering, shouting, pounding,
thudding; now the skies suddenly echoed with the blasting of trum-

pets, beating of drums, bellowing of orders in many languages, rush of running feet, crashing of stones against the wall, and screaming of the first wounded. And, while I held my breath, we heard the answering din from the Accursed Tower, the beleaguered citizens of Acre beating out their call for help on heavy metal pots and pieces of armor.

Like a tidal wave our soldiers swept nearer the tall barrier, and those who succeeded in scrambling over the loathsome ditch began tearing away at the tower's base.

Count Raimond, taut as a vielle string beside me, gave what sounded like a groan. "Mother of God!" he muttered. "Now, men, now!"

Little Bourgigne, pushing in between him and Berengaria, asked what they were trying to do.

"There's one large stone under that tower," he said. "If we can jerk it out our men may be able to pull down the whole thing. King Richard has offered a reward so high that many are eager to try."

He suddenly fell silent. Streams of liquid fire were pouring down the sides of that accursed thing, and several of our men became human torches. Unable to bear their tortured cries and contortions, I turned away and hid my face in my hands. I heard Berengaria gasp and choke, and I realized that we had been sadly mistaken in thinking we could watch such a scene.

"Take us back to our pavilion, my lord Count," I said in what I know was a shaking voice. "It is all too horrible—too horrible—"

Before he could reply, Bourgigne gave a crow of excitement.

"That huge man up on the parapet!" she cried. "He's aiming his bow at King Richard!"

Without thinking, I clutched Raimond's hand. While we stood there, speechless, we saw, even from our distant spot, my redheaded, broad-shouldered brother rise with a bow of his own and loose an arrow. It struck the menacing Infidel in the throat, and he toppled back out of sight. It all happened so quickly that I could hardly believe my eyes, and my fingers were still in Raimond's when he smiled down at me.

"No wonder they call him the Lion Heart," he said. "No wonder his men will walk into the jaws of death for him!"

I smiled also, my pulses leaping with joy and pride in my lord brother's courage. It was apparent that Raimond loved and admired Rick, too, and that he was sharing my moment of exaltation. I reluctantly withdrew my hand from his, but, as I did so, a strangely delightful feeling spread from my hand to my heart.

I moved away, my color uncomfortably high, aware that Bourgigne was watching us with a pouncing, malicious look on her face. This, however, I forgot when I saw how Berengaria was trembling; truly concerned, now, I repeated my demand to be taken back to our pavilion.

Richard's assault on Acre took place on the sixth of July, and although neither the Accursed Tower nor the city itself fell on that day it did mark the beginning of the end, for two emirs offered conditional surrender at its close.

"Look at your shaken walls and tottering turrets," was my brother's reply. "Do you think my power so small that I cannot take by force what you now offer as a favor?"

This interchange we heard about from Richard himself. He still suffered intermittently from his fever, but he was well enough now to sit at the supper table, and his spirits, when we joined him there at his invitation, were so excellent that he teased us about our sudden retreat from his old shelter. He was glad, he said, to have proved his point so easily.

"We will settle you more comfortably when Acre is ours," he promised. "And that, I think, should be very soon."

On the eleventh day of July the Accursed Tower fell at last, with a great crash and a rumbling like thunder. On the twelfth, representatives of both sides met at the Templars' headquarters to arrange surrender terms. They were not easy: ransom money must be paid to Philip, Richard, and Conrad, all prisoners held by Saladin must be released, and the True Cross must be returned to the Christians. The Infidels were given exactly one month in which to meet the terms, during which time we would hold the garrison of Acre and their families as our hostages.

While these discussions were taking place Berengaria and I were preparing to move into the city, and when Richard's escort arrived to take us there we were more than ready. The encampment, as we rode through it to the city gates, was even noisier and wilder in its joy than it had been after Rick's arrival, and the heralds, whose task it was to proclaim to everyone in it that "No man must insult the Saracens by word or deed!" had great difficulty in making themselves heard.

My lord brother was waiting for us just inside the city walls, his gaunt face alight. After pointing out that the banners of England and France were already fluttering over the ramparts, he led us through the narrow streets to the royal palace. It was a very large white marble building, quite close to the Great Mosque, and as it had been for many years the residence of the emirs of Acre it was, of course, both beautiful and comfortable.

The long cool corridors with lacy arches through which we saw green courtyards with splashing fountains and murmuring doves, the inviting salons with their deeply cushioned divans and heavily carved tables, and the quiet after the pandemonium of the encampment were Paradise to us and our weary ladies.

When I commented particularly on the peace we would enjoy, Rick grinned and shook his red head a little ruefully. "You will, I hope," he replied. "As for me, it seems my troubles are beginning, not ending, with our entrance into the city. Philip is angry because we are moving into the palace and he must be satisfied with the Templars' headquarters. Most of the other Crusaders are quarrelling over the rest of the comfortable houses here in the city, and some fool knight of mine who saw Leopold of Austria raise his banner beside ours tore it down and threw it into that ditch beneath the walls."

"Mother of God!" I exclaimed, aghast at such stupidity.

"So now, of course, Leopold is insulted. He threatens to go home, and I, as usual, am the villain. Added to that, I have just received word of trouble at York—well, well, these problems are mine, not yours, and I should not be worrying you with them. I will expect you both to join us at our banquet tonight, and perhaps your presence will make for peace at the festive board."

Perhaps it did; there were no ripples on the surface, certainly, and we ended the evening most harmoniously with Blondel's *chanson de geste* that described the stirring events of the last few days, and Bernart de Ventadour's "Robin M'Aime," which Richard, Raimond, and I sang together.

* * *

Berengaria and I were more than content, after that, to remain quietly in our own apartments. We saw little of my lord brother, occupied now with Acre and its inhabitants, Saladin's reluctant agreement to the terms of the city's surrender, and the complicated preparations for moving on toward the Holy City. We saw so little of him, in fact, that we were dependent on servants' gossip for most of our news.

It was Lady Elizabetta, I think, who scuttled in one stifling midday to say that she had heard that the Kings of England and France were meeting to settle the dispute between Guy de Lusignan and Conrad de Montferrat. "And they say," she added, "that Count Raimond's arm is not healing as it should, so King Richard's own physician has ordered him to bed here in the palace."

"Here in the palace?" I turned to Berengaria. "Perhaps we could think of something to make him more comfortable."

As I spoke I saw, out of the corner of my eye that Bourgigne, after a malicious glance at me, was whispering something into the ear of Lady Maria de Cordoba, one of Berengaria's young maids of honor. An intimacy was growing between them which I deplored, not trusting or liking either of them. They both looked at me now and giggled; I felt my color rise and was grateful when Berengaria made the suggestion that was on the tip of my tongue.

"I thought his eyes too bright the night of the banquet," she said to me, "and his cheeks too red. Fever, I suppose. Perhaps we should pay him a visit, Joan, to make sure he has everything he needs."

I agreed, and we set out immediately, taking only Lady Caterina with us. We found Raimond tossing restlessly on a divan in a long chamber that opened into Richard's private garden. He was alone, except for a small slave waving a feather fan over his head, but as far as I could see he seemed well cared for; fruit, wine, and some vile-looking potion sat on a table and a fresh bandage was wound around his arm.

Lady Caterina, after a question or two, slipped away to make him a special remedy of her own, but when we would have followed her Raimond protested.

"Stay for a little while and make me forget that I am not at the council meeting," he said. "I should be, you know, for Guy needs every one of his friends. I've been lying here listening to the drone of their voices but not able to hear what they are saying."

As he spoke, I realized that a buzz of talk was coming from some place nearby. It rose, then fell.

"Where *is* the meeting?" asked Berengaria.

"In Richard's large salon on the other side of that far wall. It opens into the garden as this chamber does."

At that moment my brother's voice rose above the others so angrily that I walked over to the wall and, seeing a small grill there, placed my ear to it. I could hear everything, but after I had repeated a few speeches to Berengaria and Raimond I grew ashamed of myself and said so. They both, however, insisted that this was nonsense.

"What harm could there be in our knowing what they are saying?" Berengaria said, to my surprise. "It is not a secret meeting. All our nobles are there."

I was more than willing to be persuaded, I must confess, and continued to listen and report back to my friends. The arguments had been going on for some time, of course, but I was not too late to overhear Guy and Conrad state their own reasons for claiming the throne—Guy that it was his already and he had done nothing to forfeit it; Conrad that he was the husband of the rightful heiress.

Rick spoke next in behalf of Guy, then King Philip for Conrad. Other voices shouted for one or the other; then someone suggested that Guy be king for his lifetime, with the throne passing at his death to Conrad or his heir. This, after more heated argument, particularly from Conrad, was finally agreed upon, and the meeting came to an end.

"Well," said Raimond, "I compliment all of them. That seems to be a very reasonable solution of the problem. After all, we came here to fight a Crusade, not each other. Nor," he added bitterly, "did we come to lie in bed, being cosseted by ladies and weakened by physicians!"

I laughed and walked to his side. He looked for all the world like an angry small boy. I found myself wanting to smooth the dark hair back from his hot forehead and straighten the tumbled pillows under his head. Not being his wife, sister, or mother, I did not obey the impulse, strong as it was.

But our eyes met, as I bent over him, and it seemed to me that he was reading my thoughts. It was as if I were looking into a mirror and seeing my own eyes there: there was no barrier between us—we shared the same feelings and understood each other perfectly. It was such an odd sensation that I stood there, saying nothing. Then, while our eyes still clung together, he found my hand and lifted it gently to his cheek.

The sound of soft footsteps leaving the chamber broke the spell, and I turned to see the tail of Berengaria's gown disappearing around the corner. With what I suspect was a very pink face I bade Raimond a flustered good day, promised to visit him again soon, and followed her hastily back to our own apartments.

She said nothing about her abrupt departure, when I caught up with her, giving me only a twinkling smile which I returned a bit sheepishly. We talked, instead, of what we had overheard and what it would mean to us. Rick had told us long since that he would leave us at Acre when the Crusaders began their march toward Jerusalem, and now that the matter of its future king was settled, we decided we might soon be saying farewell to him and our other friends.

As it turned out, however, my lord brother had different problems on his hands, problems that we knew nothing about until he summoned us both to his privy chamber.

"I have something to tell you," he began harshly, "something I prefer you to hear from me, although everyone will know it soon. Philip of France, that cowardly traitor, is planning to turn tail and run home!"

"How can he?" I asked, appalled at the thought of what this would do to the Crusade. "How *can* he, Rick? He swore a solemn oath—the whole world knows he did!"

"It seems the poor man is ill: his life is in danger."

"He told you so himself?"

"No, no, not he! He sent the Duke of Burgundy and the Bishop of Beauvais to me with a deputation, all of them bathed in tears. I knew what they were coming for, of course. I'm neither blind nor deaf! So, before they could speak, I told them to give over their tears. 'You're here to tell me that your lord wants to go home,' I said. 'And what do you want of me, my brothers-in-arms? My consent to what I consider a breach of our contract?'

"At that they wept more copiously than ever but they admitted that I was right. They were compelled to come to me, they said, 'for our lord King will surely die if he remains in this unhealthy land.'"

"And I suppose that you were shivering with chills and fever," I broke in, my eyes on Rick's trembling hands, "as you are at this very moment?"

My brother laughed. "As you say, sister, as you say! There I was, trembling like an aspen leaf before their dripping eyes. So, because I knew I must, I gave them the answer they wanted—but not in very gentle terms."

"What did you say?" I could see he was still enjoying the thought of it.

He quoted his own words in a voice loaded with disdain. " 'If his life is in the balance, let him do as his advisers see fit—although I believe he should not go. If your King goes home without finishing the task for which he came, it will be an everlasting shame to France!' "

"And even after that he will go?" asked Berengaria.

"Even after that he will go. We met face to face, finally, and fought it out together: Philip screaming that he should have half of what we won at Cyprus, I shouting back that I wanted half of Flanders! Oh, it was a merry meeting, believe me." He shrugged his shoulders, his face grim. "Well, he leaves us most of his men under Burgundy's leadership, and I have his reluctant promise to keep his hands off all my holdings in France until I return home. Whether he will do so, I do not know; I feel he is my enemy now as he never was before. That business of Alys still rankles, and his jealousy of me has grown day by day."

I nodded, sighing. "I know. I know. I saw his face, the evening you landed here."

"I hear Leopold of Austria has gone, too," said Berengaria.

"Yes, we have lost him—and all because that knight tore down his banner. At least that was his excuse. And Conrad talks of sailing back to Tyre to see the lands we gave him when we settled it that Guy would be King of Jerusalem. Another excuse, of course, but what can we say?"

"It may be for the best, Rick," I suggested. "If all these trouble makers leave you will be free to fight the Holy War as it should be fought."

"I hope so, Joan. God knows, I think of nothing else, day and night."

* * *

Although King Philip's desertion could not help but weaken our great cause, I must confess that when he finally set sail on the last day of July we were all very glad to see him go. According to Richard, the only thing now that kept our Crusaders at Acre was Saladin's failure to carry out his part in the terms of the city's surrender. He professed to be ready and willing to pay the ransom money and return the Christians in his custody, but whenever Richard demanded the hundred Crusaders of high rank, named and listed as his prisoners, he replied so evasively that we feared them already dead. Nor had he fulfilled his promise to return the True Cross.

"I will give him until the twentieth day of August," was my brother's final decision. "He must meet his obligations by then or face the consequences."

What the consequences might be I preferred not to ask. I knew, of course, that we were holding the garrison and their wives and children as hostages and that they were as eager as we were for Saladin to live up to his part of the bargain. Richard dined with us quite often now, and we watched his impatience grow. A week passed. And another. Finally, on the fourteenth day of August he bade us farewell and moved his soldiers to a new encampment very near Saladin's hillside headquarters.

Rumors of minor skirmishes, both verbal and military, reached us from time to time, but, knowing how long men take to settle anything, Berengaria and I agreed that August 20 could come and go without the matter being brought to an end. We were, as a matter of fact, deep in a close game of merels when we were disturbed by the sound of trumpets and loud shouts, followed by rushing feet and a great babble of voices.

I looked at Berengaria and she at me. I put down the man I was about to place on the board and rose to my feet. The noise was increasing and seemed to be coming from all directions, and, as I stood there, listening, I began to hear women's and children's voices raised over the others, frightened voices and screams. I was about to send Lady Elizabetta to find out what was happening when Lady Maria ran in so out of breath she could hardly talk.

"King Richard has sent for all the hostages," she gasped. "Our men are driving them out of the city like a herd of cattle, and they are all going to be killed!"

"Nonsense!" As I spoke I thought to myself that it was the sort of irresponsible thing Maria would do, spread a wild story and throw the palace into a panic; she loved excitement and was always stirring it up. "This is the day for the exchange of prisoners and someone has stupidly frightened some of the women. King Richard would never kill them! I wish you would learn to reason things out, Maria, or at least hold your tongue!"

Turning to Berengaria, who should, I suppose, have been the one to scold Maria, I suggested that we ride out to the camp and watch the interchange of prisoners.

She hesitated. "Not without my lord's permission," she said.

"It's too late for that. I'll go and turn back if I'm not welcome."

After giving orders for horses and an armed escort, I waited only long enough to don a thin cloak and a fairly heavy veil. I followed the huge mass of men, women, and children, moving slowly from the city gates to the hot, unshaded plain that lay between Acre and Saladin's hillside stronghold. The guards, urging them on, rode up and down the columns of chained prisoners, stirring up huge clouds of dust, so thick that it penetrated my veil, coating my face and eyelashes, making it unpleasant to breathe.

Fortunately it was not a long ride, for Richard was waiting in the middle of the plain, he and the men around him a bright splotch of color on the sandy stretch. As I drew near them I saw that the guards were dividing the hostages into three groups—richly garbed men in one, those men who seemed to be young and strong in another, and the remainder in a third, which apparently included the women, the children, the aged, and the poor. There being several thousand to be sorted out, I reached my lord brother long before the task was finished.

His expression was very far from pleased. I knew instantly that I should have remained with Berengaria. Without even greeting me, he demanded the reason for my unexpected appearance.

"And whatever it is," he added harshly, "you could not have chosen a more unfortunate time to seek me out. Go back to the palace immediately. This is no place for you!"

"But, Rick," I protested, "I came to watch the exchange of prisoners. I'm sorry if you are angry—I thought it too late, when we heard the noise of the hostages leaving the city, to send to you for permission."

"There will be no exchange of prisoners!" he replied roughly. "Saladin has failed again to keep his word, and he must take the consequences. I have wasted too many precious weeks already, awaiting his convenience!"

"No exchange of prisoners? Then why are they here?"

"Because we cannot take them with us, or continue to guard and feed them in Acre! Mother of God, Joan, this is a Crusade, not a Court of Love! Use your head! Now go—go!"

"But—"

"Go!" He turned on his heel, ordered my escort to take me back to the palace, and strode away.

A dreadful thought that had come to me while Richard was speaking made me eager to obey him, so eager that I turned my palfrey and urged it back toward the white towers and minarets of the city. Before I had gone far, however, a loud scream, then another, made me rein in and look back over my shoulder. I saw one of our soldiers jerk a baby from its mother's arms and slash its head off with his sword. He butchered the mother next; then, with blood dripping from his sharp-edged weapon, he plunged into the mass of shrieking prisoners, all trying desperately, despite their chains, to force their way through the circle of guards.

While I sat numbed with horror, scores of my brother's men followed that first executioner into the terrified crowd and, without wasting a moment, slaughtered men, women, and children.

"Stop them, stop them, we must stop them!" I heard my voice shouting over and over; without even realizing that I had turned,

I found myself galloping across the plain to where Richard stood. My escort was left far behind. My heart was pounding and I felt an almost overpowering need to vomit, but somehow I controlled it as I urged my horse on, faster and faster.

Before I reached my destination I saw a group of horsemen leave my lord brother and head my way. They blocked my path, and I realized that their leader was Count Raimond, looking as ill as I felt.

"Let me pass, my lord." I think I screamed the words. "I must make Richard stop them! He cannot—he must not—"

He leaned over and snatched the reins out of my shaking fingers. "Please, my lady, please listen to me!" He swung my mount around to face Acre again and moved me gently forward. "You will only anger the King if you interfere, and nothing you could say or do can halt this—sad but necessary business."

"Sad? Necessary? Monstrous, it's monstrous!" I was suddenly crying, the tears streaming down my dusty cheeks. I dashed them away with one hand and struck out at Raimond with the other. "How can *you* allow it to go on, my lord? How can any of you? This isn't war. This isn't a Holy War, killing women and children—"

All this time the terrible screaming and the noise of frantic running feet was in our ears, a sound I shall never forget. Never. Never. Never!

It faded gradually, thank God, as we rode swiftly on, my escort out of sight and disregarded, my veil streaming out behind me. When we reached the city gates we could hear it no more, but once we were inside, and proceeding more slowly toward the palace, I thought I heard it again, nearby: the same screams, the same running feet, this time on cobbles, the same shouted orders to halt. . . .

Raimond swore a stifled oath, and I saw him looking all around the narrow street as if for another way to approach our destination. Apparently there was none, and when we made the turn that led us to the open square fronting on the palace and the neighboring mosque we found ourselves circling another scene of slaughter, much like the one on the plain. There, some distance away, sat the Duke of Burgundy on a large stallion, urging his men to kill the screaming, struggling masses of chained prisoners, who were trying to escape the ruthless swords.

A small child, breaking away from its frantic mother, ran toward me, her arms outstretched. As I reached down to pick it up a soldier overtook her and cut her head half off. A jet of blood spurted over the tail of my cote and ran thickly over the cobbles under my palfrey's hooves. . . .

I heard myself shout and shout again, and again the tears poured down my face. Again I felt the reins taken out of my hands. A moment later Raimond hurried our mounts past the palace guard and into the enclosed courtyard. Without a word, he lifted me down. Then, taking my cold fingers in his, he led me swiftly through the long, dim corridors and into the antechamber to my own apartments.

It was deserted and so, apparently, were the adjoining salons. We stood for a moment in the silence, hearing only the splashing of the fountain in my garden. This part of the palace lay far from the square, and I suppose everyone was watching, or keeping Berengaria company in her privy chamber.

I began to tremble. I felt hot, then cold. Dark mists gathered in front of my eyes.

Two arms encircled me gently, supporting me, and just before the whole world turned black I thought I heard a dim voice saying, over and over, "There, there, my sweet, there, there. . . ."

CHAPTER

XIII

It was, I think, very fortunate that I did not see Richard again for many weeks. Within a few days of what I can only call the massacre, he and what remained of the army set out toward Jerusalem, leaving us in the palace at Acre. I suppose he was forced to do what he did, but it is difficult for a woman to accept the slaughter of so many innocent people, and by a Christian leader—difficult to accept and to understand, particularly as Saladin wasted no time in following Richard's example. Our men, instead of being returned to us, were either executed or sent into slavery; the True Cross, which he had promised us, was dispatched to Damascus; and we saw no more ransom money.

I tried to forget the scenes of horror I had witnessed, hiding my distress from Berengaria as best I could, but it was a long time before I could think of my brother with any of my old love or enjoy the blessing of an untroubled night's rest. Nightmares of blood, screams, and dying faces wakened me over and over, leaving me trembling on my pillows and unable to sleep; in those restless, miserable hours, waiting for the light of day to release me from torture,

I allowed myself, too often, to remember the comfort of Raimond's arms and the words I thought he whispered.

I had not seen him again either, and this, too, was fortunate. For if I needed time to forget my lord brother's ruthlessness I needed even more to stamp out the love for Raimond that I feared was growing in my heart. The realization that he might be loving me, in return, made my task bitter-sweet. Marriage, I was sure, was out of the question; a princess of England, a dowager queen of Sicily, must look higher than the heir of Toulouse for a husband, and I was not willing to take him or any other man as a lover. I knew, of course, that many women in my situation would consider it their right, after years of virtuous compliance in the marriage bed, to accept and enjoy Raimond's embraces, but such light behavior was not for me. Why, I cannot say. Perhaps it was the fear that having been born of a father and mother who laughed at moral restraints, I might too easily follow their example.

Had we been able to fill our days I would, I am sure, have achieved peace of mind much sooner than I did. But unfortunately, life in this hot city, where women were usually kept in strict seclusion, had nothing to offer in the way of entertainment, and although the palace and its gardens were ours, Berengaria and I soon found its confines irksome and longed for some lively company or interesting occupation.

Bertrand de Verdun and Stephan de Longchamp, in whose charge my brother left Acre, his royal treasures, and us, were much too busy bringing some order into the devastated city and rebuilding its walls to do more than sup with us once in a while, and then they were so weary that they all but fell asleep in their chairs. Neither man was young; Bertrand de Verdun had already spent twenty-five years serving England and Ireland as sheriff, judge, itinerant justice, and seneschal; de Longchamp, a kinsman of Richard's dwarfish favorite, the Bishop of Ely, was considered too old for the arduous march to Jerusalem.

As usual we turned to our music and needlework, but we found little satisfaction in either. It is true that a pair of gloves for Richard, made of the softest available goatskin and elaborately embroidered and bejewelled, kept us contented for a while. We took a long time choosing the leather, drew many designs before we were satisfied, and sent Lady Caterina rummaging through all our boxes for pearls and precious stones to intersperse among the glittering gold thread. An old pair of William's leggings provided us with more pearls than we could use, and as we stripped them off and sewed them firmly into the leather I told Berengaria of my happy life with William in Sicily.

Our court there differed greatly from her father's small castle in Pamplona, an old building, I gathered, bleak and with few comforts. Certainly she sighed enviously over my descriptions of our many richly furnished palaces in and around Palermo and the close companionship between me and my dear lord.

While we busied ourselves in this fashion, young Bourgigne, who insisted that she had no skill with the needle, spent her days in her customary way, taking long hours over her dressing and undressing and falling even more deeply into the intimacy with Lady Maria de Cordoba which we had no good reason for forbidding. So it was, I think, more for her sake than for ours that we welcomed back Baldwin of Flanders. He returned to Acre in the middle of September, carrying letters and orders to Bertrand de Verdun and Stephan de Longchamp from my brother Richard. He brought, as well, the news of another great victory over Saladin and his Infidel troops.

"We were outnumbered by at least three to one," he told us jubilantly. "But we met them in open battle at a place called Arsuf and we crushed them like so many ants under our feet. What a leader King Richard is—and how magnificently our soldiers obeyed his orders! If they worshiped him before Arsuf, think what they must feel for him now. And what Saladin and *his* men must feel! After Acre, this!"

"Will you besiege Jerusalem next?" asked Berengaria.

"Not until we have established a supply base on the coast," Baldwin replied. "When I headed this way with my lord's letters, the army was moving toward Jaffa."

Then, his usually mild face alight, he pictured the battle at Arsuf, describing it so vividly that we could hear the brass drums of the Infidels and their shouts of "There is no God but Allah, and Mahomet is his Prophet!" We felt the blazing sun suffered by our warriors in their armor and choked on the dust raised by the trampling of thousands of desperate feet. We saw Rick in the thick of it all, his heavy sword flashing, slashing, leaving a trail of dead behind him; we saw Saladin, equally brave but refusing to kill with his own hand, riding around the battlefield as fearlessly as if the whizzing arrows were drops of summer rain.

Berengaria was quite white when he finished, and I, reminded of the slaughter I was endeavoring to forget, felt sick. Bourgigne, however, her dark eyes afire, plied the awkward young man with scores of questions about the fighting and, when the rest of us turned to our music to end the evening with a song or two, led him into a cushioned alcove where they apparently continued the conversation.

Whether the damsel from Cyprus was charmed by Baldwin's unexpected skill as a storyteller or merely willing to accept his advances because there was no other man available, I do not know. Whatever her reason, he came to me triumphantly, on the eve of his departure to rejoin the crusading army, and confided that his first errand there would be to ask Richard for Bourgigne's hand in marriage.

"With my lord King's permission and your gracious assistance," he said, his gentle eyes beaming with happiness, "we will wed the very next time he sends me here as his courier. My lady and I have exchanged solemn betrothal vows, and she has assured me that her father would wish her to follow her heart."

If I wondered a little about this last statement, I kept my doubts to myself. The decision, in any case, was Richard's, not Isaac's, and as far as I was concerned I would be relieved to have the hot, troublesome maid safely tied in wedlock. That Baldwin might live to regret his choice caused me some concern, but I reminded myself that it was not my problem, nor is there ever much use in arguing with a young man in love.

I did ask him if he had remembered the differences between them, and had he satisfied himself that a damsel from Cyprus could settle into the domestic life led by young Flemish wives?

He nodded, flushed, and made an awkward gesture with one of his large, bony hands. "She is so lovely," he said, "and so loving. What more could anyone ask of a wife? She is an emperor's daughter, after all, and should not be expected to change her ways. I have promised her that all will be as she wishes."

I groaned silently and said no more.

*   *   *

After young Baldwin left us we settled down again, accepting the probability that we might hear nothing more from our warriors for some time. It was, therefore, a surprise when early in the month of October King Guy de Lusignan suddenly appeared at the palace.

"My errand here is far from pleasant," he replied to our first questions. "The shameful truth is that increasing numbers of our men have been leaving the camp at Jaffa and sneaking back here to Acre to find—er—amusement. It is my distasteful task to round them up and force them to return to their duties."

"Amusement?" Berengaria looked bewildered and her soft voice sounded puzzled. "Amusement, my lord, when they are at last on their way to take the Holy City?"

King Guy nodded ruefully. "I am afraid so, your Grace. My only excuse for them is that the—er—amusements offered here are difficult for many men to resist."

There was so much hinted at in Guy's red face and hesitant speech that Berengaria merely said "Oh!" and fell silent. I, having heard rumors of orgies in which the women of Acre were teaching our soldiers many new and unusual ways to make love, had at least some understanding of his problem. I certainly did not envy him the solving of it, and as he was obviously reluctant to say much more I pressed him instead for further news of my lord brother's progress.

"We found Jaffa a ruined city," he said. "Saladin's shocking defeat at Arsuf has made him so unwilling to meet us again in open battle that his one aim is to lay waste every city he thinks we may attack. My lord King sent my brother Geoffry to Ascalon and he found it, too, in ruins—abandoned, burned to the ground, and much of it still smoking. When we have rebuilt the walls and fortifications at Jaffa we will, I believe, move to Ascalon and fortify it, also, before beginning our siege of Jerusalem.

"We are discovering," he continued, "that being a Crusader is not all fighting and glory. But we do have our adventures! With the Lion Heart there are always adventures!"

Before he could explain, I saw our chamberlain hovering in the antechamber and realized that our household must be waiting dinner for us. After we were seated and our food was before us, I turned to King Guy and asked him to tell us more.

He hesitated for a moment, looking first at me and then at Berengaria. "I do not want to frighten you, my dear ladies," he said, "but I have been thinking that, if you added your pleas to ours, King Richard might be induced to be less reckless. I must tell you that had it not been for our brave William de Préaux, your lord would, at this very moment, be Saladin's prisoner."

"Richard will always be fearless in battle," I replied. "I would not dare scold him for that."

"He was not in battle. No, no, my lady, this was at Jaffa, not Arsuf. He rode out from camp to exercise his gerfalcon, taking only a handful of knights, and when the sun grew hot he insisted that they all stretch out in a convenient grove of orange trees and sleep. Sleep! Have you ever heard anything more foolhardy? Saladin's spies were watching and sent a band of men-at-arms to the grove. Richard awakened as they approached and roused the others; they jumped on their horses, but it was too late. Then, at the last possible moment, de Préaux shouted, 'Saracens, I am Malek Ric!' While they surrounded *him,* King Richard managed to escape and rode back to camp."

"Leaving that gallant William de Préaux a prisoner?"

"And four of his knights dead under the trees."

"You are right," I said. "My lord brother should not do these mad things."

"So we all told him." King Guy sighed. "So we all told him, reminding him that the Crusade would be lost without him. A body dies when the head is severed. Write him, dear ladies, and add your protests to ours. Surely he would heed his Queen and sister!"

Berengaria and I discussed the matter after Guy retired, but we found we were both reluctant to do what he wanted. Nothing, I felt, would irritate Richard more than such a letter from us, and Berengaria agreed. In fact, when we did write, we were careful not to mention his escapade or to say anything of our own discontent here at Acre. Our one wish now was that the army move swiftly on its way to Jerusalem, take the city, and win our great Crusade.

We certainly did not think it possible that he would leave his forces at such a time, and we could hardly believe our eyes and ears, one day soon after Guy's departure, when we heard heavy footsteps in the antechamber and looked up to see him standing in the open archway.

Berengaria, jumping to her feet, scattered a lapful of loose pearls all over the marble floor. I cried out, "Rick! Good God! What brings *you* here?"

He gave Berengaria a kiss on each cheek before answering, ruffled my hair with his huge hand, and dropped down on one of our divans.

"Two errands, Jo," he said with a weary sigh. "Guy failed miserably in rounding up our deserting warriors. In fact, he proved so ineffectual that I suspect I was wrong in thinking him the better man to be King of Jerusalem. So I have come here to see what I can do myself. My other errand is to carry you two ladies back with me to Jaffa."

CHAPTER

XIV

Our voyage along the coast, for I am happy to say that my lord brother took us to Jaffa by sea, was an extremely pleasant interlude. The October sun was kind, the breezes fresh, and we sailed so close to the shore that we could see much of the old Roman road along which our Crusaders had marched some weeks earlier.

Richard, who accompanied us—and surprised me by devoting himself almost constantly to our amusement—pointed out a straggling track through the brush and across the sands, describing the army's slow and dangerous progress.

"We marched in three columns," he told us. "One on the inland side nearest those hills, our mounted knights and nobles in the middle, and here, beside the sea, the baggage trains and the sick and wounded. Those in the first column were in constant danger, fighting off sudden Infidel attacks from the mountain slopes. Because of this we allowed them to change places, every few hours, with the men proceeding safely and comfortably with our wagons. Our heavy weapons, of course, and most of our supplies were carried by the fleet, who, at my orders, sailed always within sight of the shore, as we are doing now."

While he was talking I studied the narrow, twisting shore road, disappearing in high dunes, then reappearing again, only to lose itself in what seemed to be a series of lagoons choked with papyrus reeds. How, I asked him, had thousands of men ever traversed it on foot?

"It took every ounce of strength they had," he admitted. "Many died from heat and exhaustion, those deadly tarantulas were a constant threat, and two of our knights who insisted on bathing in a murky river one very hot day were eaten alive by crocodiles. However, our magnificent victory at Arsuf has helped us to forget all that, and everyone is eager now to march right on to Jerusalem."

"And will you leave us at Jaffa, my lord?" asked Berengaria. She seemed, I thought, a little more at ease with Richard during these quiet days together.

"That depends on several questions still to be settled," was his rather evasive answer, and he looked at me in an odd way. I decided he must have something on his mind concerning me, and I would have pressed him to tell me had not someone interrupted us. As it turned out, that was the last opportunity we had to talk privately during the short voyage, and by the time we had our first glimpse of Jaffa's tall white buildings the matter had slipped my mind.

The city ran right down to the water's edge, as did Acre, but instead of spreading over a flat spit of land it climbed a steep hill. The houses, Richard said, were mere shells and, as we drew nearer, the devastation wrought by Saladin became shockingly apparent.

"So we are camping outside what is left of the city walls," he added, pointing. "In delicious, sweet-smelling groves of orange and almond trees."

Remembering only too vividly the hideous odors of our encampment at Acre I was delighted to hear this and made ready to disembark with a feeling of pleasant anticipation. The harbor was crowded with ships of all sizes, some lying at anchor, others darting here and there over the water; while our sailing master guided us carefully through the maze, my brother shook his head in disgust at several dilapidated old vessels. "It is always the same thing," he said. "The moment our army arrives at one of these cities we are pursued by shiploads of whores and panderers. 'Dancing girls' is what they call themselves."

Soon we dropped anchor and sails, and Richard's little landing craft rowed us through the mild surf. A crowd awaited us, as usual, on the sands. Several of the people began wading out to meet us, but my lord brother jumped into the shallowing water and held out his arms for Berengaria. I called a gay farewell after them and, a moment later, found myself looking down into the smiling dark eyes of a man standing knee-deep in the lacy froth.

It was Raimond of St. Gilles, and although my heart gave a great leap I knew I must be sensible and insist that he carry in one of the other ladies. Glancing back over my shoulder, I saw the Lady Bourgigne, waiting right behind me, the breeze whipping her thin cote so that it outlined every ripe curve. This, I am ashamed to say, put an end to my good resolves and I lowered myself immediately into his waiting arms. Again my body quickened at his touch. To make matters worse, he did not, this time, carry me in the proper manner; instead, he held me shockingly close and, when I struggled feebly and protested, laughed deep in his throat and tightened his arms even more.

Then, walking slowly, he began to insist on seeing me alone. "We have a moment like this," he said, "and, before I can even begin to tell you what is in my heart, we are surrounded by people again." His lips were close to my ear, his voice urgent as we neared the strand.

"No, no, my lord Count," I replied, trying to summon up some small fragment of firmness. "We must not—I must not—surely you can see—"

"We must and we shall! I will *not* see!" As he placed me on the

sand and knelt to disentangle my cote tail from my feet, he whispered, "Meet me in the orange grove behind your pavilion tonight.
Or tomorrow night. I shall stroll there every evening after dark until you do."

*   *   *

All the rest of that day, while we were settling into our large, silk-
lined tents, I argued with myself, making up my mind one way,
changing it; deciding I should simply not appear in the grove, then
telling myself it would be wiser, perhaps, to meet Raimond there
and put an end to whatever romantic scheme he was fostering.

As it happened, Richard kept us all late at the supper table, then
demanded more music, which prevented either of us from slipping
away from the company. I could feel Raimond watching me, however, and once when our eyes met he smiled ruefully, gave his
shoulders a tiny shrug, and formed the word "tomorrow" with his
lips. The blood surging up into my cheeks, I turned hastily away.
To my horror I saw that Bourgigne had apparently observed our
small exchange; she was looking at me with raised eyebrows and a
bit of a sneer on her full lips. This did not make me any more comfortable, and I retired that night calling myself a weak fool. I would
not, I promised myself firmly, either meet Raimond secretly or allow him to importune me further.

Bourgigne's attitude had reminded me only too plainly how easy
it was to set our ladies' tongues wagging. She was, I was sure, already discussing me with her favorite Maria and naming Raimond
my lover. Her own gallant, Baldwin of Flanders, was off in Tyre
trying to persuade Conrad of Montferrat to rejoin the Crusade.
Richard had consented to their betrothal, and, Baldwin's absence
leaving her with even less to do than usual, I suspected she was
amusing herself with malicious gossip.

Fully determined not to set foot in the orange grove, I thrust the
matter out of my mind and kept myself fully occupied for much of
the next day. At Richard's suggestion, we rode down to the water-

front to watch our men unloading the supplies we had brought from Acre. He was already there when we arrived and seemed to be particularly interested in the horses as they came ashore. When we all exclaimed over a curvetting, spirited stallion with a coat that was as glossy as black satin, he had him brought to where we were standing and put the handsome mount through his paces himself.

"Superb!" he said, dismounting at last. "I shall send him to Saladin's young brother, Malek al Adil. My scouts tell me he is encamped about three miles south of us, at Ibelin. Then," he added, turning to Humfrey of Toron, "I may ask you to help me with a letter to him and another to Saladin. If my gift is received in the proper spirit, of course."

While Berengaria and I were returning to the shelter of our pavilion she broke a long silence by telling me that she was puzzled. "Can you think of any reason why my lord should send Saladin's brother a horse? Or write him a letter?"

I shrugged. "No, but Saladin has sent gifts to Richard, remember. Those peaches, when he was ill, and other things. I think it's a peculiar way for deadly enemies to behave, but I'm only a woman. . . ."

We supped alone with our ladies that evening, and after the tables were cleared away I found myself oddly restless. It was stuffy in our pavilion, or so I thought, and I was glad to join Berengaria in a short stroll, resolving, however, that we should not walk in the direction of the orange grove. Bourgigne was held in her quarters by a mild attack of the flux. None of the other ladies wished to accompany us, and as we planned to remain close to the pavilion we decided there was no need to bother anyone.

Rarely have I known a more beautiful evening. It was very like some of those we had enjoyed at sea, with the same velvety dark-blue sky, even more brilliant stars, and the soft air around us sweeter because there was a drifting perfume of orange blossoms. Music reached us from many of the tents and pavilions nearby; we heard snatches of cheerful talk, bursts of laughter, and knew that we were not the only ones enjoying a pleasant, peaceful hour or two.

For our talk was cheerful, too. The pleasant voyage, the discovery that this camp was free of the horrors we had suffered at Acre, the interest of being, once again, in the center of the Crusade —all these things made us content. And although Berengaria said nothing about her accord, or lack of accord, with my brother, I thought, from her face, that they were a little more comfortable together.

What we actually talked of I do not remember. My mind, I must confess, was not on our desultory conversation; I am afraid I was picturing a certain dark-haired young man waiting for me in the orange grove just a few yards away. It was possible that he might even be watching us as we sauntered up and down, but it was also possible that Richard had kept him at his side. I did not know, and I could not seem to prevent myself from wondering.

We were joined, more than once, by various of our friends, who wandered over for a word or two and a pleasant good night; Blondel and another trouvère had just left us when Berengaria gave a little shiver and drew her thin cloak closer around her shoulders.

"The night air is growing a bit chill," she said. "I believe I'll retire."

"Sleep well, my dear," I replied, kissing her on the cheek. "Tell Caterina that I have a small headache and that I shall stay out here in the quiet a little longer." This was a lie, God forgive me, an unplanned lie that sprang swiftly to my lips.

After I had seen her disappear past the guard at the entrance to our pavilion, I turned and walked toward the orange grove, first slowly, then more and more rapidly until I was almost running. A moment later I was deep in the sweet trees, hidden from the camp, and a moment after that I was clasped in Raimond's arms and being kissed in a way that ravished all my senses. Weakling that I was, fool that I was, I gave myself up completely to the rapture of his lips on mine, and Heaven alone knows how many minutes slipped by before I pulled myself free and begged him to stop.

Without a word he snatched me back and kissed me again and again, caressing me until my whole body was on fire and my legs were shaking so that I could hardly stand. Somehow I found the strength to escape from his embrace a second time but, frightened by my own response to his lovemaking and thoroughly ashamed of myself for coming to the woods despite all my good resolutions, I now further horrified myself by suddenly bursting into tears. As I do not weep easily and have never used tears when in doubt as to what to do or say, I made a violent effort to control my sobs and fended Raimond off angrily.

"Do not touch me again!" I said. "How *could* I behave in such a fashion? You make me hate myself!"

"That's nonsense," he replied firmly. "Admit we love each other and come back into my arms where you belong!"

"Admit we love each other? But that would be arrant folly. For me, anyway, as I shall never be any man's mistress."

"Mistress? Of course not! I'm hoping to wed you, my darling. After all," he said, "you married once to please your family; surely now they will allow you to choose for yourself."

"I wish I could think you right, my lord," I said, "but I am afraid that neither my mother nor Richard would permit such a thing."

"Confess that you love me, Joan, and I will go to Richard to-night!"

"No, no, Raimond. Please."

It was now so dark in the grove that I could not see his face. Nor, obviously, could he see mine. I stood there, my body still aflame from his touch, my thoughts confused. Was it love I felt or merely desire? What should I say—or do?

As I sought for words to explain my hesitation, we suddenly heard voices not far away, the deep one of a man and the lilting tones of a woman.

"God's wounds!" Raimond swore softly. "We must not be found

here. I'll intercept them, whoever they are, while you run back to your tent. Tomorrow night, my sweet—here, tomorrow night."

A rustle in the dimness and he was gone. With a fast beating heart I turned too and hurried to the pavilion, being careful to remain in the shelter of the grove until I could no longer hear voices. Our guard bade me a quiet good night as I passed him, his face impassive, and if our ladies wondered why I had been alone out there for so long they said nothing. Grateful, of course, for their lack of curiosity, I took my hot cheeks and troubled thoughts swiftly to bed; the presence of another couple in the dark wood had made me even more aware of my shocking behavior and I was frightened to think how easily I might have lost my good name—or my virtue—or both.

I slept little that night. For the first time since William's death I asked myself whether I might marry again. Raimond's confident words had shaken my assumption that we could never be man and wife, and I realized that I could not brush his courtship aside as beneath my notice. Just how powerful *were* the Counts of Toulouse? That they had been a thorn in my mother's side for many years I knew only too well. Would she laugh in his face, if he asked for my hand, or would she think our marriage a happy solution to the rivalry over the rich holdings to the south of her lands?

Then, as I turned on my pillows, I remembered Rick's queer expression when he had looked at me during our voyage from Acre. Was he aware, perhaps, of Raimond's hopes and wondering whether such a marriage would bring enough money into his emptying coffers? The Crusade was draining us all; I suspected that most of my inheritance from William was already spent, and I remembered Richard's voice, telling me that he was wedding Berengaria for the gold she was bringing him. Might Raimond not be considered a suitable husband for me if he paid well enough for the privilege?

Telling myself finally that I must, in any case, have more time to probe my own heart, I fell asleep at last. My only definite decision was that we must not again meet secretly; from now on, Raimond should court me openly or not at all, and somehow, before nightfall, I would tell him so.

But the next morning found me a victim of the same malady that had confined Bourgigne to our quarters the day before. She was completely recovered and I was completely miserable—so miserable, in fact, that I was unable to think of any way to send a message to Raimond or even to fret very much about it. I thought of him waiting in the grove, but I did not dare send anyone to him. How could I?

Whether he visited our meeting place then or the following night, when I was still in the throes of the flux, I do not know. By that time I was sure he had heard of my illness and would understand. I had no visitors, of course, during those first two days. I was much better by the third day and extremely happy to see my brother, when he came in, unattended, to discover how I was faring.

"I would have come sooner," he told me, "but I have been very much occupied. I am sorry, Jo—I should, in any case, have sent my physician."

"I've been swallowing more than enough foul potions, I thank you," I replied. "And the disgusting business is well on the wane now, I'm glad to say. So sit down, Rick, and talk to me. Give me something fresh to think about. What is keeping you so busy? Have you been skirmishing with Saladin again?"

He nodded. "I have, but only with my pen." He sighed and was silent for a long moment, then, his face looking a little worn, spoke again. "He is no fool, you know, and I thought we might end the bloodshed by settling matters between us. I sent him a letter, saying that surely we had both had enough of this state of things. That now it is only a question of Jerusalem and the Holy Cross, both our old possessions. Jerusalem, of course, we will never renounce, not while we have a man left to fight for it. And as for the Cross, which has such value in *our* eyes, it is, as I pointed out, nothing to him but a piece of worthless wood. If he would restore these two possessions of ours I assured him that everything would come right of itself and we could all enjoy a pleasant rest after our strife."

"He did not agree, I suppose."

"Here. Read his answer for yourself." Reaching into a handsomely embroidered pouch that hung from his girdle, Rick pulled out a crumpled piece of parchment and handed it to me.

I smoothed it out and read:

As Jerusalem is more precious to us than to you, for it was the place from which our Prophet made his journey by night to heaven and is destined to be the gathering place of our nation on the last day, do not dream that we will give it up to you. The land, too, belonged first to us. *You* are the aggressors, having gained it by a surprise attack on the weak Moslems who held it. . . . And as the possession of the Cross is very profitable to us, we will part with it only if it is to the advantage of Islam.

I cannot say I was surprised, though I would have been had Saladin answered in any other way. We were, after all, still far from victory.

"Then this means that we march on Jerusalem soon and take it by force?"

Instead of replying, my lord brother fell silent again. He began to smile to himself in a pleased sort of way, the weary lines in his face smoothed out, and then, looking down, he smiled at me.

"Perhaps, but I hope not. I still hope not. I cannot tell you yet, Joan, but I have a plan, a magnificent plan! Sleep well, wake refreshed, and, God and Saladin willing, I may have glorious news for you!"

Berengaria came to my chamber the following day and found me clothed and, albeit a trifle weak, ready to resume a few of our usual activities.

"My lord has asked us to sup with him this evening," she told me, after we had settled down with our needlework. "I am hoping you will feel strong enough, Joan. I am always happier, as you know, when you keep me in countenance."

"Nonsense!" I scolded her. "You do very well without me. I shall certainly go, however, for I am deathly tired of these walls."

Actually, I was wanting a word with Raimond. He had surely heard of my illness—but I knew I must tell him that we could not again meet in the wood.

"Sleep most of the afternoon," I heard Berengaria saying, "and ride to Richard's pavilion in your litter. They say the flux leaves your legs very weak. Although Bourgigne cannot have found it so— she and Lady Maria have spent every evening since you fell ill out walking together."

If I was surprised to hear that the indolent maid had suddenly changed her ways, I thought little of it then. She was a creature of whims, and very contrary. Perhaps our ladies had asked her to remain in the pavilion; that, I thought, would make her determined to leave it.

Taking Berengaria's advice, I rested during the hot hours and climbed into my litter for the short ride to the royal pavilion. My legs *were* weak, and I knew that I was looking far from my best, but, realizing that I would have no real peace of mind until I had seen Raimond I resisted the impulse to turn back and seek my bed again.

Richard, to my surprise, was waiting outside his tent for us and lifted me down himself. His greeting was most affectionate; he led me immediately to the high table and seated me on his left side. Then, almost before I had settled into my chair, he urged me to drink a goblet of wine.

While I sipped it I found myself eyeing him with suspicion.

"What is it, Rick?" I said at last. "Surely I was not so ill that you feared for my life. You are clucking over me like a mother hen."

He laughed. "I believe I am," he admitted. "The truth of the matter, Jo," he went on, dropping his voice and leaning closer to me, "is that I need your help. I have invited al Adil, Saladin's young brother Saphadin, to sup with us tomorrow night, and I want both you and Berengaria to don your most beautiful robes and join us. We are setting up a pavilion between our two camps—we've declared a truce for the evening—and I plan to entertain him in our western fashion."

"It seems very strange to invite our enemy to supper."

"I keep telling you, Jo, that wars are not always settled on the battlefield. That plan of mine—but it is still too early to discuss it. Just do as I ask, and it is very possible that you may play a great part in winning our Crusade."

I thought he was making too much of this supper of his, but I said no more. It had often been my task to sit beside William's eastern friends and set them at their ease—men who had never before dined in public with a woman at the table, and an unveiled woman, at that. After the first awkwardness it would not, I knew, be very difficult.

As soon as Richard turned back to Berengaria, I glanced around the dais, looking for Raimond. There he was, not far away. Our eyes met; to my surprise and distress it was as if I were looking at a stranger—and an unfriendly one. I felt a chill spreading over me, and what small appetite I had after my illness disappeared. He must have waited for me, night after night, and did not know, even now, that I had been sick.

I determined to seek him out immediately after supper and set matters right, so I waited only until Blondel began to sing and then sent a page to bring Raimond to my side. I had seated myself a little away from everyone, just far enough so that we would not be overheard.

"You wished to see me, your Grace?" Raimond's voice, as he bowed before me, was so cold that I shivered.

"I have been ill, Raimond," I began hurriedly. "Too ill to venture out of my pavilion—"

"So I was informed," he replied. "We are all happy to see your Grace in good health again. But you must be more careful in the future, my lady. The night air can be dangerous, and I may not be the only fool with a mistaken idea of my own importance. Forgive me for my presumption, your Grace, and believe that I wish you very happy in your new life. With your permission—"

Another icy smile, another stiff bow, and he moved away, leaving me sitting in shocked silence. I was stunned, bewildered, and sick at heart. What did he mean by my "new life"? And why was he apologizing for his "presumption"? Had he asked Richard for my hand and been rudely repulsed? Should I summon him again and try to find out what had happened?

My face must have shown my distress, for Lady Caterina came

swiftly to my side and suggested that we return to our own quarters. "You should have remained in bed another day," she said. "There is not a bit of color in your cheeks! Come, my lady, or you will be ill again. And that will not do—I hear great tales of tomorrow's festivities."

*　*　*

As we made our way from our camp to the village of Yazour where we were to meet al Adil, the heat of the day had passed, and although I was still disturbed by Raimond's behavior on the previous evening I found the short ride enjoyable. Richard had gone on ahead to make sure all was as he wished; one of the odd things about my brother was that, although he preferred the simple life of a warrior, when he was entertaining *en prince* he fretted over every cushion, hanging, platter, and sweetmeat.

That he had been fully occupied was obvious the moment we entered the great silken pavilion, set up just that morning. There, on the dais at the far end, were the twelve golden chairs and long gold table that had belonged to my William, and on the table were the jewelled goblets and plate that we had taken from Isaac's palace at Cyprus. All these treasures remained, as a rule, in the hold of a ship that was closely guarded day and night, anchored in the center of our fleet, and I had not seen any of them since we left Limassol.

Richard, clad in the rich garments he had worn on his wedding day, was very much the King. Berengaria, in hers, looked lovelier than I had ever seen her, and I, laced into my favorite apricot cote, and with more color in my cheeks than yesterday, was reasonably satisfied with my appearance.

My lord brother was *more* than satisfied—or so he said.

While we awaited the arrival of the Infidel prince, we chatted with our friends. Nine noblemen would sup with us at the high table, the others with Saphadin's suite at the two trestles on each side. It was a goodly company gathered around us: our elderly King Guy; Humfrey of Toron, who would act as interpreter; Robert, the brave new Earl of Leicester; my nephew, Henry of Champagne; the Bishops of Salisbury and Évreux; the Count of St. Pol; the Duke of Burgundy; and, still cold and aloof, Count Raimond of St. Gilles.

The sound of horses' hooves drew us out of the pavilion to watch Saphadin's approach. At first, as we walked to the shelter of Richard's royal canopy, we saw nothing but a cloud of dust far down the narrow road, then what seemed to be dozens of men on horseback, galloping so swiftly toward us that their flowing robes billowed out behind them like the sails on our smaller ships.

As they drew nearer, however, I realized that there were not so many after all, and that a great part of the noise and dust was caused by a herd of camels, lumbering along behind al Adil and his suite.

My lord brother, his crown glittering in the last of the sun's rays, advanced to stand alone, to welcome his guest, and Berengaria and I moved to his right and left, a pace behind him, with our highest ranking nobles in a circle behind *us*, remaining in this position while Saphadin reined in his snow-white mare, dismounted, and knelt at Richard's feet.

When he rose for the exchange of courteous greetings and the presentation of the richly caparisoned camels, a gift from Saladin, I studied his swarthy face with interest. I'm not sure what I had expected—a bearded monster of some kind, or perhaps another dwarf like Tancred. I know that I was very much surprised. He had a beard, yes, but it was small and neatly trimmed, outlining rather than hiding a good chin; his nose was large, his cheekbones prominent and high, and, altogether, he was far from ugly. He was, I decided, handsome as a well-bred horse is handsome.

If he was shocked at the sight of two unveiled queens dining comfortably in a roomful of men he hid it from us. His smile was easy, and his talk, made understandable by Humfrey of Toron, was at first just what was to be expected from a stranger at one's table. After we were seated, Richard, having placed Saphadin between us, turned to Berengaria, and our young guest began to question me about such things as my life in Sicily and our voyage to Acre, avoiding mention of the Crusade and the trouble between us.

Before long we surmounted the barrier of our different tongues sufficiently to dispense with Humfrey's aid, using gestures, a word or two in each other's language, and much laughter. His understanding was quick, his response to my efforts to amuse him immediate, and I, certainly, found myself enjoying what might have been a difficult, dull evening.

Although I tried not to look down the table to where Raimond was sitting, I could not help noticing that he was unusually quiet and that he was watching us closely. Most of our friends were doing the same thing, for everyone was curious about Saladin's young brother. My brother, joining in our conversation from time to time, was at his heartiest; so hearty, in fact, that I suspected he was feeling the awkwardness Saphadin and I had overcome. That and his over-obvious approval of my attempts to entertain his guest eventually spoiled my pleasure, and it was with a strong sense of relief that I heard him telling Berengaria he was sending us back to the camp as soon as we had finished our sweets.

"My business with al Adil will occupy the remainder of the evening," he said. "I have called for your litters."

She rose, a few minutes later, and we made our adieux, Saphadin smiling into my eyes, when I turned to him, and seeming truly reluctant to see me go. Richard led us down from the dais himself, leaving all the others standing by their chairs to await his return. His usher then escorted us to our litters and we rode back through the velvety dark to Jaffa.

I tried not to think of Raimond as my curtained shelter swayed and bumped along the rough road, but I had had one disturbing glimpse of his face at the end of supper when Saphadin and I were sharing a moment's laughter. It seemed to me that his coldness had turned to angry contempt. Distress and bewilderment suddenly overwhelmed me. What could have changed him? Should I try, again, to set matters right between us?

As we saw neither Richard nor any of the other noblemen for the next few days these questions continued to worry me, and I wondered, too, whether my lord brother and Saphadin had come any closer to an amicable settlement. Bourgigne, who was behaving rather strangely, I thought, informed us that couriers were going back and forth between Richard and both Saladin and Saphadin and that Richard had been working late with Humfrey of Toron every night.

Where she gleaned her information was a puzzle to me, and where she and the Lady Maria disappeared to almost every evening was beginning to puzzle us all. We found it hard to believe that they could be out strolling, as they said, for hours at a time, with only their handmaidens in attendance. Young Baldwin was still in Tyre; was Bourgigne finding solace during his absence?

"She may be helping Lady Maria to conduct a secret liaison," Berengaria finally suggested to Lady Caterina and to me.

"Perhaps," was Caterina's reply. "But I think she's too selfish to bestir herself for anyone else's pleasure. Talk to the King when he visits us tonight, your Grace. It was he who placed the damsel in our care—and it was he who agreed to her betrothal."

"I suppose I must." I could see that Berengaria was most reluctant to do so, however, and after thinking for a few minutes she summoned the two young women and questioned them herself.

They, of course, merely looked at her with wide, innocent eyes and insisted that they sought fresher air in the groves of trees near our pavilion. "Come with us, your Grace," said Lady Bourgigne blandly. "Or send someone else to see where we go and what we do." She turned to me with her usual malicious smile. "The Lady Joan will tell you how pleasant such walks can be. Ask *her*."

This unexpected attack brought the hot blood to my face. Had she been spying on me the night I met Raimond in the grove? But that was impossible; she was ill with the flux and safe in our tent.

She walked over to me, her hips swaying. "Come, my lady," she said insolently. "Please tell us all how delightful the orange grove can be after dark!"

Before I could think of an answer, Berengaria rose to her feet. "How dare you!" She sounded angrier than I had ever heard her, and her usually gentle eyes flashed fire. "How *dare* you speak to her Grace in such a manner! Ask her pardon immediately. Immediately!"

It was as if a kitten had turned on a wildcat, and I was both surprised and touched. Bourgigne seemed to be startled, too, but she recovered instantly and responded with a jeering laugh.

"Ask her pardon? Why, pray? *I* am the one who is being insulted by your suspicions."

"What's all this, ladies? I could hear the Lady Bourgigne as we approached your pavilion." My lord brother, who had come without warning, looked slightly amused. Close behind him were King Guy, Raimond, and Blondel, all carrying their vielles.

"Something I will discuss with you in private, my lord," replied Berengaria, frowning at Bourgigne. "You and our friends have come for music, not to listen to women's quarrels."

But Bourgigne was too angry to heed either Berengaria's frown or her words.

"Oh, no!" she protested, her voice still loud and shrill. "You shall not talk about me behind my back, your Grace! Accuse me now and perhaps someone here will have the courage to defend me!"

Raising his eyebrows, Richard glanced at each of us in turn, then smiled encouragingly at his little queen. "Well, tell us all, if the damsel wants it so. What has she done, my lady? Sewn a crooked seam?"

Berengaria sighed. "We have all been concerned, my lord, by her long absences from our pavilion. She and the Lady Maria say they walk—but we miss them for hours at a time, often after dark, and I felt I must question them."

As she spoke I watched Bourgigne, expecting her to renew her attack on me. To my astonishment I saw that she was staring pointedly at Raimond and that he had turned quite pale.

"I say I have done nothing wrong," she stated firmly. "I swear that wherever I go I have a perfect right to be."

"Then tell us where that is," said Richard. "I think her Grace has good reason to question you, child. An encampment is not a place in which ladies may safely wander at will."

"Allow me, my lord King, to answer for my wife." Raimond spoke before Bourgigne could say anything more; moving swiftly to her side and taking her hand in his, he led her to Richard and they fell on their knees at his feet.

"Forgive me for stealing your fair prisoner, my lord," he said. "We wed secretly three days ago, and the Lady Maria has been merely bringing my wife to me at my own pavilion."

CHAPTER

XVI

I cannot describe in detail the scene that followed. I was too numbed and sick to listen closely as my lord brother interrogated them both, and I was only dimly aware that he threw up his hands, finally, and sent them off alone to Raimond's quarters.

When they had gone he turned to us, his face rueful.

"Now you see why women should never go on Crusade," he said. "I wish, with all my heart, that I'd left that trouble-making damsel in Cyprus. First young Baldwin was caught in her net, and now Raimond! Baldwin I can understand, poor lad, but for St. Gilles to play the fool—"

There seemed nothing to say. Berengaria was very white and I had all I could do to remain standing.

"A most distasteful business," Richard added, "and one that has spoiled our evening. I shall return to my work. Will you come with me, Guy?"

I retired immediately, but Bourgigne's triumphant face returned to my memory over and over, making it impossible for me to sleep. Raimond's, perhaps because I saw nothing of the proud bridegroom in it, puzzled and distressed me too, and I passed the long wakeful hours of the night in a futile effort to understand how this strange marriage had come about. That Bourgigne had somehow trapped him into it was the answer I liked the best, but even that held little comfort for me.

One thing I *did* know—I was forced, at last, to put all thoughts of the young Count out of my mind. The door that he had opened briefly was now shut forever: whatever his reasons might be, he had closed it firmly in my face and all I could do was to pray that my love for him, if love it was, would soon die.

Lady Caterina exclaimed over my weary face when I rose the following morning, blaming it on my recent illness.

"Return to your bed, my lady," she urged me, "and allow me to send for the King's physician."

This, however, I would not do. I did not want to be pent up with my thoughts another moment, and although I was as weary as I looked I determined to busy myself just as much as possible. I worried her even more by accepting Richard's invitation to ride with him before the day grew too hot.

Had she known how little I was to be in the saddle she would not have scolded. We were still within sight of the camp, after a brisk canter that smothered our attendants in dust, when my brother reined in his mount and pointed to a small stand of olive trees.

"Come sit over there in the shade with me," he said. "I have private business with you."

By the time I was comfortably settled on my cloak and our attendants were on guard but out of earshot, I realized that Rick was uneasy. Instead of sitting down and telling me what was on his mind, he prowled around, making sure our horses were safely tethered, which I could see they were, and then towered over me, commenting lengthily on the appearance of the countryside around us.

This, added to my sleepless night and aching heart, was more than I could stomach.

"Mother of God, Rick," I said testily. "Sit down and tell me what this private business is that you say you have with me. If you wish to send us back to Acre, say so. Or are you thinking that Berengaria and I should set sail for England? I will not argue, I promise you! I have come to agree with you that a Crusade is no place for women!"

Sitting beside me at last, he shook his head and fidgeted with his gloves. "It is not that, Jo," he said. "As a matter of fact, what I have to tell you may well mean that you will spend the rest of your life here."

Until this moment he had been avoiding my eyes. Now he faced me and let me see his mounting excitement. His color was high and his voice rang with enthusiasm.

"I am going to make you Queen of Jerusalem," he said. "You, my dear Joan, my dearest sister, the Queen of Jerusalem! Can you think of anything more glorious? Our Crusade at an end after all these long months and a daughter of England sitting on the throne in the Holy Land!"

"But—" My words came slowly. "How can you do this? Are you suggesting that I wed Guy?"

Richard laughed scornfully. "I am not. Forget Guy. He's a weak old fool. And forget Conrad, too. If I'm not mistaken he is trying to sell himself to Saladin at this very moment. No, no, Joan, if we are to come to terms with the Infidels it will be *my* plan that wins the day. This is it; these are the terms of our agreement: we will give back Acre, Jaffa, and Ascalon. Saladin will return the True Cross to us, the Templars and Hospitallers will receive all that was taken from them except some fortresses. Prisoners will be released by both sides. Christians will again have free access to the Holy Land —and you and Saphadin will rule Jerusalem together."

"How could we?" I was still bewildered.

"By marrying, of course," he replied, as if this were a perfectly natural suggestion. "Do you see *now,* Joan, what a magnificent solution it is? That is why I wanted you two to meet, and why I was so content when you enjoyed each other's company. He's a splendid fellow."

I could not believe, at first, that he was not joking. Then, when I saw that he was perfectly serious, I wondered briefly whether he was suffering from too much sun. But as he continued to describe the advantages of the match and said that both Saphadin and Saladin were ready to do what he had proposed, I felt a great flood of anger sweep over me.

"Are you mad, Rick? Are you mad? *You*—asking *me* to wed an Infidel? After risking your own life, over and over, to free the Holy Land from these people—yes, and impoverishing all of us, and all England, too, to do it? How could you possibly think that I would marry one of them?"

I must have jumped to my feet, for he pulled me down again.

"Try to understand, Joan," he said, holding my hand firmly. "Do be quiet for a moment and try to understand. I am suggesting this plan to save further bloodshed—because I dare not think what our Crusade has cost us in lives and gold, and because the prospect of continuing our march on Jerusalem with so few men and so little arms, and with the winter months ahead, appalls and frightens me."

I knew this was true. I knew that famine and disease had added so many deaths to the toll of those slain in battle that we had lost two thirds of our warriors already. But I also knew that my lord brother was wrong: for a daughter of England to wed an Infidel prince and share with him the throne of the Holy City was a denial of everything for which our men had been fighting and dying. And for me, it was impossible.

He must have read all this in my face.

"Say nothing more now," he said quickly. "Think over what I have told you and you will soon see that this is the only answer."

A swift gallop back to camp did nothing to dispel my anger, an anger so mixed with horror and distress that I do not know which emotion I was feeling most strongly. In later years, when I was able to look back at these troubled months and understand more clearly the varied problems besetting my brother, both in his personal life and in the waging of the Crusade, I was more tolerant of his shocking suggestion. At the time it aroused, again, those heart-rending doubts as to his wisdom that I had suffered during and after the slaughter of the prisoners at Acre.

There, of course, I could do nothing. But here at Jaffa, facing the sacrifice of my own body and soul to carry out an arrangement that I knew to be a hideous mistake, I determined to fight with every weapon that came to hand. My first step was to calm my outraged feelings and consider more coolly what should be done.

Although I did not think Richard would use force to make me marry Saphadin, I could see that if I merely continued to refuse to do what he wanted he would bring more and more pressure to bear, damaging, perhaps forever, the love between us and hurting our great cause at the same time. I was sure, as my immediate response to his plan had been so violent, that I would not be alone in thinking it an impossible solution. The clergy, I told myself, could not countenance such a marriage and must stand with me. What the nobles might say I could not tell. Some of them, surely, would agree that for the sister of the King of England—and the widow of King William the Good of Sicily—to wed the brother of Saladin would make a mockery of this Crusade and all the Holy Wars fought in the past.

After an hour's quiet thought and prayer in what small privacy I could command in our pavilion, I sent a page to Rick's closest adviser, Hubert Walter, Bishop of Salisbury, asking him to come to me. The mere sight of his face was comforting, and from the moment I asked my first question I knew that he thought as I did.

"Yes, your Grace," he said, his voice deeply concerned, "I know, and I have shared in these distasteful negotiations with Saladin. And when the King told me his plan, some weeks ago, I made it clear that I was violently opposed—opposed both as a man of God and as a fellow Crusader. But you and I know, my lady, that opposition often stiffens my lord's back, and I fear my words did more harm than good."

"To oppose him is not enough," I replied. "Our task is to convince him that he is wrong. Surely he will listen if most of his friends add their voices to ours."

"A few have already had the courage to express their doubts, and I have reason to know that many of the others agree with us although they have not said so to his face."

"Then you have shown me what I must do," I told him. "With your help, my lord Bishop, I shall summon all the clergy and our nobles and urge them to add their protests to mine."

* * *

Hubert Walter, I am happy to say, was successful in calling everyone together for me. He chose his time well—a Sunday, so late in the day that all were in the camp but not yet at the supper table—and he had aroused their interest and curiosity by not telling them the purpose of our gathering.

Most of them were already in the large pavilion when I entered; others joined us while I was seating myself in one of the chairs on the dais. The Bishop, stepping to my side, raised a hand for silence.

"If you please, my lords," he said. "I may tell you now that I summoned you here at her Grace's request. Her business with you is of great import to us all, and although I would be happy to speak on my dear daughter's behalf she wishes to address you herself."

Turning to me he took me by the hand, raised me to my feet, and led me to the front of the dais. I had spent most of the day repeating over and over just what I should say, but now that the moment was upon me the words stuck in my throat. A sea of faces blurred in front of me and I felt my legs begin to tremble; suddenly, far off to one side, I saw Raimond standing alone, and this, for some reason, steadied me.

Richard's plan to wed me to Saphadin had not made me forget

Raimond's secret marriage, of course, or softened the blow, but it had forced me to think of something else. The sight of him now roused my pride, making me doubly determined to acquit myself with dignity, if nothing else.

"Before I tell you just what is in my heart, my lords," I began, keeping my voice reasonably steady, "I wish to thank you all for coming here and to say that I hope you will not have reason to regret it. Most of you, I think, are well aware of the close bond between my lord brother and me and will surely understand my great reluctance in discussing openly a matter that he may think concerns us alone. I do not think so, my lords, and my lord Bishop agrees with me. It concerns each one of you and, indeed, every man who plays a part, however large or small, in waging our Holy War. Some of you here before me know that my lord brother has proposed a plan to end that war, and that Saladin has already agreed."

A rustle ended my speech and drew my eyes to the entrance to the pavilion. There, his face flaming, stood Richard, looking seven feet tall and double his usual width. For a long moment we faced each other in silence. I need hardly say that everyone else was quiet also; no one moved or even coughed.

"May I join you, your Grace?" Richard spoke first, his voice deceptively gentle as he made his way through the now kneeling company. But while he strode toward the dais I saw that not all the men were remaining on their knees. Hubert Walter drew closer to my side and the Bishop of Évreux and the other members of the clergy present rose and made a circle behind me. My courage rose with them. I drew a deep breath and addressed my lord brother in a manner that included the assembled Crusaders.

"You have asked me to bring our Crusade to a close by wedding Saladin's brother Saphadin and then to rule Jerusalem jointly with him thereafter," I said. "I refused your request when you first made it, and I have called all our friends here today to seek their support in refusing it again. With your permission, my lord King, I will declare in their presence and yours what will always be my answer to such a suggestion: I, Joan of England and Sicily, born and bred a Christian, will never marry an Infidel! Never! Request anything else of me to aid our Holy cause—my private fortune is already at your disposal—but I cannot and will not share the throne and bed of an Infidel prince!"

I turned now to Hubert Walter and knelt before him.

"Speak for me, my lord Bishop," I begged.

"You made me the spiritual leader of this Crusade, my dear son," he said instantly to Richard, his voice ringing out so fearlessly that there could be no doubt of his sincerity. "As such I must protest against this marriage. To wed a Christian lady to an Infidel would be sacrilege, no matter how pure your motive. I, Hubert Walter, Archbishop of Salisbury, will never countenance such a union."

As one man the clergy around me echoed, "Never!"

I rose and held out my arms to the noblemen still standing below the dais.

"And you, my lords?"

They surged toward me like a wave on the shore, shouting their agreement. The first to reach me, however, was Raimond of St. Gilles, his face white and set. He laid his sword at my feet and his dark eyes, as he knelt before me and then raised his head, seemed to be pleading with me, asking me to understand something.

While his eyes spoke just to me, his lips were uttering words for everyone present to hear. "I honor your Grace for your decision, and I place myself and my sword at your service." He spoke then to Richard. "To wed your lady sister to an Infidel would betray us all. No, no, my lord King, this is not the way to win our Holy War!"

As the other nobles, in turn, added their protests to his, I listened with a strangely heavy heart. I should have been exulting in their support; instead I struggled with a sense of desolation. In that bitter-sweet moment when Raimond placed his sword at my feet I saw, with cruel clarity, just what I had lost, what Bourgigne

175

had somehow stolen from me—the one man in the world I wanted beside me, to love and cherish me, with the right to fight my battles and protect me, as long as we both should live.

With an effort I thrust all this away and waited for Richard's reply. I could tell by the stubborn line of his jaw that he was still not convinced. He did not say a word, however, until the last of our nobles had spoken and the pavilion was silent. Finally he spread his hands wide and shrugged.

"I cannot quarrel with so many of you, my lords. I shall, instead, consider this matter further. If there is a way to arrange it, and satisfy us all, it shall be found."

I was very concerned, after I returned to my own quarters, with the possibility that Richard might be seriously angry with me. William and I had lived together in such harmony that I was not as accustomed to quarrelling as were most of the Plantagenets, and the threat of my brother's displeasure was, for me, a chilling one.

To my great relief he joined us for supper that evening in what seemed to be an amiable mood, not mentioning the meeting earlier or the matter that lay between us. He brought young Baldwin with him, which helped, for we were all so occupied in trying to raise the boy's spirits that we thought of little else. The poor lad had just returned to Jaffa and only that day had learned of Bourgigne's marriage to Raimond. The newly wedded couple were not present, nor had they been since the evening their secret was revealed. We had, out of courtesy, invited them to join us once or twice, but they made various excuses and remained in the seclusion of their own pavilion.

Their absence made it a little easier for Baldwin, as did the fact that we held our tongues when he persisted in excusing Bourgigne and in blaming Raimond entirely for the whole affair. Berengaria and I exchanged patient glances as he said over and over that Bourgigne was an innocent child, led astray by a vile libertine, but we said nothing. If it comforted him to defend his lost love he should have that comfort; and, we agreed later, it was possible that he was right. Possible, but not very probable; we knew Bourgigne too well.

I, certainly, believed in my heart that she had somehow made mischief between Raimond and me and that their marriage had come about as a result. His swift response to my appeal for help, the look in his eyes, had led me to think that he was regretting his hasty union. Perhaps we would be friends again. Perhaps one day he would tell me what had gone wrong between us, one day in the dim future when we might even laugh about it. Now, I told myself, I must stop thinking about him. I *must*. . . .

I slept little that night and Berengaria, when she joined me late the following morning, was so heavy-eyed and quiet that I could not refrain from commenting on it. Richard, I knew, had spent one of his rare nights with her, and I was afraid they might have quarrelled about me.

"I suppose I should not ask you this," I said, "but I must know. Did Rick say anything more about my wedding Saphadin?"

Her color rose and she looked distressed.

"Please, Berengaria! Tell me!"

Still she hesitated.

"He paced up and down my chamber until nearly dawn," she confessed, at last. "Then, just before he returned to his own pavilion he told me he had thought of a way to surmount the obstacles you had raised. He is going to ask Saphadin to renounce his faith and become a Christian, and he will send an envoy to the Pope requesting a special dispensation. He is confident that you will then agree and that the clergy will, too."

"Saphadin can turn Christian a hundred times but he will still be an Infidel to me," I replied, "and I don't care what the Pope does about it, either. Such a union, even with his sanction, would

178

shock the entire Christian world. Surely we proved that to Richard yesterday!"

"Apparently not. He thinks this plan of his is magnificent and that you will soon see it his way."

"Well," I said grimly, "he has rarely been more mistaken. I love Richard dearly, as you know, but nothing that he can say or do will change my mind."

*   *   *

For the next few days we heard nothing more about my brother's peace efforts. The only one of the men who visited our pavilion was young Baldwin, and it was from him that we learned, finally, that Saphadin had refused to embrace the Christian faith.

"As our negotiations with Saladin have come to nothing," he told us, "we are preparing to leave here very soon and continue our march on Jerusalem."

When we were alone, a little later, Berengaria and I discussed this latest move, wondering what arrangements would be made for us.

"I should think my lord would send us back to Acre," said Berengaria. "I hope so, Joan. I have no desire to remain here."

I admitted that I hoped so, too. Although I did not give my reasons, I had several. One was that it would probably mean that Richard had given up all thought of marrying me to Saphadin, another that the farther I could be from Raimond the better for me, and a third that I had not been happy here at Jaffa.

I was, in fact, thinking of just how miserable I had been when a familiar voice in our antechamber interrupted our conversation.

"Bourgigne!" Berengaria said grimly. "I suppose we'll be burdened with *her* again!"

As she finished speaking, Lady Caterina entered with Bourgigne and her tiring-women. I need hardly say that we greeted her coolly; the sight of Raimond's plump wife, wearing a self-satisfied smile on her catlike face, was almost more than I could bear. My hand itched to slap her—hard. Instead, I sat in my chair and kept my own face impassive while she told us what we did not know.

"I'm so glad we're remaining here at Jaffa!" she said. "My dear lord has promised to ride back to me whenever possible, and he says King Richard will send for all of us the moment it is safe to do so."

Berengaria merely nodded and, as soon as she could, sent her and the others off to settle her into her old quarters. Then my dear sister turned to me, her face flushed and angry.

"I hate her! I hate her, Joan!" She stamped her foot and, moving swiftly to my side, bent down and gave me a loving kiss. "She trapped him—I know she did! And he will hate her, too, before long." Then, with a sob and another kiss, she turned and ran out of the chamber, leaving me sitting there, staring at the striped silken walls.

* * *

The encampment had been mercifully quiet all during our stay, as most of the men were off repairing the ravaged city of Jaffa and its walls, but now, with their departure imminent, they bustled so noisily around us that we were reminded of our siege at Acre. Just after dawn one morning, when Saladin sent a large body of his men from Ramleh to attack us, it seemed even more like those perilous days.

We were awakened first by shouting and the sound of feet running past our pavilion; then, while we threw on our clothes, we heard the clashing of steel on steel and all the other hideous noises of battle. To our great relief it was all over in a remarkably short time, and we learned from the guard standing at our entrance that our men-at-arms had repulsed the surprise attack without any loss of life on our side.

"The Infidels were not so fortunate," he added, grinning. "I saw several of our men carrying bloody heads to their tents."

We shuddered and asked no more questions, but two days later —I think it was the last day of October—when our army set out for Yazour, we were all a little bit frightened. I know that I had no interest in walking more than a few yards from our pavilion, and none of the other ladies ventured even that far.

As the result of our fears, we spent a miserable week. Bourgigne's return added to our discontent, of course, and our patience was badly strained by the time an armed escort rode back from Yazour to take us to my lord brother's new encampment.

I cannot describe how glorious it was to be on the road again. Although the rainy season had not yet begun, a few short showers had laid the worst of the dust, and the sun, in a deep blue sky, was beneficent instead of scorching. Yazour being less than three miles from Jaffa, Berengaria and I chose to ride side by side on our favorite mounts, leaving Bourgigne behind in the stuffy shelter of a litter.

Shortly before we reached our destination, the road grew much rougher; glancing back over my shoulder, I saw that the litter was halted beside a clump of bushes and that Bourgigne was bent over them, vomiting violently.

A malicious laugh informed me that Berengaria was watching her, too.

"I hope she stains her veil," she said, delightedly, "and that her lord is waiting to take his fragrant little wife in his arms!"

Her suggestion took us merrily on to the Casal of the Plains, a castle built by earlier Crusaders. The sight of it sobered us quickly, however, for it had been almost demolished by Saladin and his ruthless men, and we rode along in silence until we saw a group of horsemen galloping swiftly to meet us.

My lord brother reached us first; after greeting us warmly he swung his mount around and we proceeded together, talking of the ruined castle we had just passed.

"The Templars are repairing it," Richard said. "When it is habitable again I may ask them to take you ladies in. The heavy rains will begin before long, and our encampment will, I'm afraid, be even less inviting than it is now."

Breaking off suddenly, he stared at the road ahead of us. All of his party had left it and were riding swiftly toward a grassy hillside where some sort of skirmish seemed to be taking place. I could see some pack mules huddled together in one spot and, a few feet away, a band of Crusaders and Templars, standing back to back, encircled by a large group of Infidel horsemen.

"God's wounds!" swore Richard, his face as red as his beard. "They're attacking our foraging party!" He shouted to Stephen de Turnham, who was close behind us. "To me, de Turnham—guard the ladies! Take them back to the Casal. I must go to the rescue!"

But Stephen had leaped to the ground and seized my brother's reins. "Wait, my lord King," he said urgently. "Wait! See, de Chauveny, Leicester, and St. Pol have reached them already. Remain here."

We watched for a long, terrifying moment while our noblemen and their soldiers slashed their way through the circle of white-robed and turbaned Moslems. Then, to our horror, we saw a second band of Infidels charging down from the hills.

With another oath Richard tore his reins free.

"Obey my orders, de Turnham!" he said. "They need me!"

"No, no—come to the Casal with us, my lord! Do not risk your precious life!"

All the color had drained out of my brother's face. "I sent those men there," he replied savagely. "If I allow them to die without me I have no right to be called a king!"

And he thundered off, spurring his horse on until he reached the melee. Many of our suite followed him, shouting wildly and waving their swords and axes in the air.

"Back, ladies, back!" ordered Stephen desperately, obviously torn between anxiety for our safety and the desire to ride after his royal master. We moved a little, but I was too frantic with fear for my brother to go far, and Berengaria stayed close beside me. What the others did I do not know. My eyes were fixed on the battle.

Richard was in the thick of it, his flaming head easy to see and his huge sword flashing. Blood spurted as he severed hands and arms; screams of pain rang out from men and horses alike, and, almost before it seemed possible, the enemy broke formation and fled, their white garments flowing out behind them as they galloped away.

For a little while we remained where we were, watching Richard and our friends pursue the escaping marauders. I think we were shouting, too; I know I must have been, for when we reached the encampment at Yazour I discovered that my throat was sore and my voice thick.

When we looked around our new home, my glow faded and I began to wonder just why my lionhearted brother had brought us from the comparative comfort and security of Jaffa, exposing us to the dangers along the way, to the bleakness of this new resting place. At Acre and Jaffa we were close to city walls when we were not inside them; here the tents and pavilions were set up in the middle of a flat plain lying between two Crusader castles, with the sea some distance off on one side and the enemy-infested hills on the other.

There were no sweet orange groves, and our ladies, already frightened by the skirmish, heard that Saladin often made surprise attacks on the camp, more often than he had before. These fears were what they talked of most, and there seemed no way to allay them.

My private fear was that Richard wanted us with him because he still thought to bring about my marriage to Saphadin. Why else would he add us to his problems in this dangerous place? I determined to ask him that night and to tell him again that he was wasting his time, but he neither invited us to his supper table nor joined us at ours. Count Raimond, who sang with us for an hour or so before retiring with Bourgigne to their quarters, which, in this more perilous situation, adjoined ours, said that my brother was suffering from another of his intermittent attacks of fever.

"They do not last long," he told us, "and by this time tomorrow he should feel well again. They strike without warning—many of us have them. First you burn up; then you turn so cold your teeth chatter; after that you sleep heavily."

Raimond's visit further disturbed my peace of mind. His gaiety sounded forced, we avoided each other's eyes, and, after he and his bride left us, the fact that they were so near somehow made it impossible for me to forget that they were together. As a result, the night was far from restful and I was glad to rise early.

A summons from Richard took me to his pavilion later that morning. I found him lying in bed, his face whiter than I have ever seen it, and a servant just carrying away a basin of blood.

"They have been bleeding me," my brother said, holding out a trembling hand. "Why, I do not know. The fever has gone and I have had a few hours' rest. But there's no arguing with physicians."

His eyes were so clear and his brow, when I touched it, so cool that I wondered, too, why the doctor had chosen to weaken him.

"And now I am unable to leave my bed," he complained. "Young Saphadin is here and I should be with him, discussing these forays of Saladin's that continue while we are again carrying on negotiations. I've asked de Turnham to give him breakfast. If you wish to please me, Joan, you will join them and bid him welcome."

I was about to refuse, angrily, when Stephen de Turnham hurried in to tell Richard that Saphadin was leaving. "He would like you and the ladies to dine with him at Lydda tomorrow."

"Thank him for his courtesy," I replied swiftly, "but say that the ladies have not yet recovered from yesterday's alarms and prefer not to venture away from their pavilion."

"Say nothing of the sort!" Richard was obviously irritated. "Tell him that I will be delighted. The ladies will not accompany me this time, however. Later, perhaps, when some of the problems between us have been solved."

I waited until Stephen had disappeared before speaking again.

"If you are still hoping to solve those problems by marrying me to Saphadin, Richard," I said, "I warn you that you are wasting your time. No matter what you say or do I shall never change my mind!" Then, without even asking permission to retire, I turned and ran out of his bedchamber.

* * *

My lord brother must have recovered his full strength very quickly, for we heard him riding out of the camp early the next morning and were awakened very late that night by the noise of his return. I did not dare question him about his long day with Saphadin, so after containing myself for a while I sought out Hubert Walter and begged him to tell me what he could.

"I must confess that it was a most enjoyable visit," he admitted. "Saphadin entertained us sumptuously in a large silken tent set up for the occasion and furnished with every comfort. The food was lavish, the dancing girls beautiful, and he gave the King many valuable gifts."

"Richard must have been very pleased," I said bitterly.

"So pleased that he knighted the young prince just before we finally said farewell."

"Knighted an Infidel? That frightens me. He would not do that unless—" I leaned toward the Bishop and put my hand in his. "Tell me, dear lord, does Saladin want his brother to wed me? Does he agree with Richard that Saphadin and I should share the throne of Jerusalem?"

"I don't know, my dear child. I know of one exchange of letters between them recently, and that is all." He looked so unhappy that my heart sank. "Who can guess what an Infidel thinks or means?"

"Tell me what was in the letters," I pleaded. "I *must* know, my lord!"

"My lord King wrote that he is sending to Rome for the Pope's consent to the marriage. If the Pope refuses he offers Saphadin your brother Geoffrey's daughter instead of you."

"And what was Saladin's reply?"

"He will keep his promise only if the alliance is arranged on the original terms. If the marriage with you fails, he wants no other."

CHAPTER

XVIII

Richard sent us back to Jaffa a day or so later, and we spent the next few weeks wondering whether he would leave us there for the winter or move us to Acre. We had Guy de Lusignan with us —"to dispatch supplies to the army and to keep us amused"—and I am afraid we made his second task rather difficult. None of us was in good spirits. I had my own reasons for being unhappy, and Berengaria, after her brief reunion with my brother (if reunion it was), crawled farther into her shell. As for Bourgigne, it seemed to us that she was even sulkier and more disagreeable than usual.

At least we were not now crammed into a pavilion together. Enough repairs had been made so that we could move into a tall tower inside the city walls overlooking our old camp. The rest of the building lay in ruins at its base, but three floors had escaped Saladin's men and these we made reasonably comfortable by hanging curtains on the rough stone walls and bringing in the usual cushioned divans and low tables.

Showers kept us indoors much of November; then December

brought constant heavy rains and we became prisoners. Our spirits, low enough before, God knows, sank lower and lower every wet, clammy day. I was so miserable that I found myself blaming poor Guy for it all.

Poor Guy! At sixty-four years of age he was no longer the handsome man who had courted and won the widowed Sybella, heiress to the throne of Jerusalem, but unfortunately he was still the same weakling who had, after her death and the death of her son, lost Jerusalem to Saladin and so brought us all here to moulder in our gloomy tower.

I remember looking over at him one evening and wondering in futile exasperation what would have happened if Sybella had wed a stronger if less handsome suitor. I decided it was more what would *not* have happened: my good William would *not* have sailed to Tripoli and caught the fever that led to his death; my lord brother would have remained in his own kingdom and might well *not* have wed Berengaria; Bourgigne and her father would still be in Cyprus—and Raimond would *not* be her husband.

Instead, here we three women were, mewed up in a ruined tower near Jerusalem, with the rain beating, beating, beating on its walls and our lives forever changed and entangled.

* * *

We dragged out our dreary existence as best we could until Stephen de Turnham appeared, one day after the middle of December, with news of our friends and most welcome messages from Richard. After our departure, he told us, the army had moved first to a spot between Lydda and Ramleh; then, three weeks later, when Saladin abandoned Ramleh and retreated to Latrun, they had marched to Ramleh and set up their tents among the soaking ruins left by the enemy.

"We are still encamped there," he said, "enduring a most miserable situation. We can do nothing until we receive more men and supplies, so I am here to speed them on their way. Guy should have dispatched them long since, but I suppose he has had his problems, too."

This was generous of Stephen. Our supply ships had been arriving regularly from Acre, and I suspected Guy of negligence.

"And my lord?" asked Berengaria. "He is well?"

"Well, and looking forward to having you by his side at Christmastime," was the smiling reply. "I have orders to bring you ladies back with the reinforcements and supplies."

After he went off to confer with Guy, we called our attendants together and told them what we had heard. Some were pleased, others frightened.

"I hear Saladin's scouts are watching the roads day and night and are attacking every convoy of any size," objected Lady Maria. "And the rain, of course, makes travel almost impossible."

Bourgigne, who had come trailing in after her, instantly announced that she preferred to remain in Jaffa. "With your permission, my lady," she added to Berengaria, in a tone of mock humility.

My sister caught my eye questioningly; I shrugged. Hating the very sight of her as I did, I would be only too happy to leave her behind.

"As you wish," Berengaria replied. "My lord King did not order me to bring you, and you may make your own decision. If Count Raimond is not urging you to come to him, he must prefer your safety to your company."

Smiling to myself I watched Bourgigne stiffen under the Queen's deft attack. What could she say? Admit that Raimond had not written her to come, or say that he had and appear to be too cowardly to comply with his wishes?

"My lord is much concerned for my well-being," was her answer. "He does not want me jolting over rough roads again at this particular time."

Much as I disliked the girl, I admired her quick thinking. I happened to know that she was not with child—her tiring-woman had deplored the fact to mine only yesterday—but had it been true it would have more than justified her reluctance to leave Jaffa. As it was, Berengaria and I, when we discussed it privately later, decided that her words were excuse enough for us to leave her behind.

I was actually a little reluctant myself, knowing that it would be better for my peace of mind not to see Raimond again. But Berengaria cried out against my suggestion that I, too, stay in Jaffa, and after a little persuasion I agreed to accompany her.

How shall I describe the discomforts that we endured on that journey from Jaffa to Ramleh and—after we reached Ramleh at last—on the ride to Latrun, where my brother had moved his head-quarters while we were on the way? We rode in litters that swayed, jolted, and dipped along the narrow winding road, in sheets of blinding rain, slightly more fortunate, perhaps, than Guy and Stephen, trotting along beside us with water running down inside and outside their heavy armor, which rusted on them as they rode. And we were *much* more fortunate, of course, than the men driving the heavily laden supply wagons in the rear, wagons that sank deep in the liquid mud every little while, to be dragged out by teams of mules before any of us could move ahead.

We, at least, had a canvas top and curtains to keep out most of the rain, but after a few hours they became soaked through and we were then encased in a damp box that dripped constantly. The horses, blinded by the downpour and, even when it lightened, un-able to tell which were shallow puddles and which were water-filled pitholes, stumbled along in a most frightening fashion, often almost pitching us out of our horrid shelters.

Every time that happened, with the cushions sliding here and there around me, I would clutch at the wooden frame supporting the canvas and hang on desperately until the poor animals regained their footing. Why they did not break their legs I will never know, but that, at least, we were spared.

To make matters worse, after we had left the coastal plain behind us, our road turned into a trail that ran up and over the bare, bleak, rolling hillside leading to Ramleh. Now our horses and wagons slipped on the wet, moorland surface and we were forced to travel even more slowly than before, so that it was long after nightfall before we reached the ruined city where our army was now encamped.

Instead of my lord brother it was young Baldwin who greeted us, lifting us rather awkwardly from our litters as he explained that Richard and some of the other leaders of the Crusade had moved on to Latrun, the "Post of Observation." The pavilion to which he took us was depressingly like the horse-drawn shelter we had just left, for the walls were streaked with damp, water dripped down the poles, and a servant was kept busy wiping dry the wooden flooring. The supper soon set before us was wretched, too—nothing but strong-tasting cold salt meat and soggy biscuit.

"The fires won't stay lighted in this heavy rain," Baldwin told us, "and much of our meat is too rotten to cook or eat. Saladin, as usual, has swept the countryside clean of all livestock, so we have been existing on our almost depleted stores. Thank God, my lady, for the wagon train you brought with you! And we must see that some of the fresh food goes on with you to King Richard, for Saladin devastated Latrun, also, before he crossed the Judean hills to Jerusalem."

We retired early and slept between heavy cloaks that were dry only because they had been packed away in watertight chests. These also were damp by morning so we left them behind, wrapping ourselves in fresh ones for the journey. Latrun, situated on the edge of the Judean hills, was only about ten miles from Ramleh as the crow flies, but not being crows we again had to wind slowly along a slippery trail to our destination, taking most of the day to do so.

This time it *was* Richard who parted the wet litter curtains and held out his arms to me, and I must confess that I was so happy to see his red-bearded face that I clasped him warmly around the neck and kissed him repeatedly on both cheeks. For the moment at least I forgave him his wild plan to wed me to Saphadin and realized that I still loved him dearly—and probably always would, no matter what differences we had between us.

Apparently he felt the same. "By our Lady, Joan!" he said, returning my embrace with one that threatened to crack my ribs. "Even your red nose and blue lips look beautiful to me! Now I can face the thought of Christmas in this hell hole with the hope that it will be bearable. Not merry, certainly—but bearable!"

Never did Richard speak a truer word. Christmas was just that—bearable. In that place, forsaken by both God and Infidel, we had nothing with which to celebrate the Yuletide but our music and the slightly more appetizing food that we had brought with us. Guy, Robert of Leicester, and our young nephew Henry of Champagne were our guests at my brother's small headquarters; all the other nobles, including Count Raimond, spent the holidays with the army back at Ramleh.

I, in the ridiculous way of a woman in love, was both sorry and glad not to encounter Raimond, but although I told myself firmly that I hoped never to see him again the sound of a horse's hooves approaching our camp invariably set my heart pounding and drew my eyes to the entrance to our chamber. Berengaria never once mentioned his name to me or commented on his absence, and when Richard and Blondel asked what songs they should sing for us I noticed that she was careful to avoid the ones I had sung with Raimond on happier occasions.

Dear Berengaria! What would I have done without her unspoken understanding and quiet companionship? I have often thought that she and I might well not have grown so close together had there been more love between her and Richard. This may not be so, of course; I do know that I, the stronger of the two of us in some ways, found myself, during this particular interval, leaning heavily on my gentle little sister.

I tried, too, to forget my aching heart by thinking of our poor soldiers—our poor, poor soldiers! We had assumed that the worst of their sufferings were over when Acre fell and that pestilential, disease-ridden camp was abandoned. How wrong we were! But how could we picture, during those blazing hot days, the unbelievable miseries of this winter that lay ahead?

Our own night at Ramleh had given us a taste of what they were undergoing, but those discomforts were, we were told, nothing compared to the horrors of Beit Nuba, where they moved soon after Christmas. We were still at Latrun when the army reached the bleak tableland that was to be their new home, and we were with Richard when Hubert Walter rode back to report on the dreadful conditions.

"We cannot remain there, my lord King," he said. "Our men are dying every day from the cold, the rain, and the rotten food—and so are our horses. There is no shelter of any kind on that tableland: the winds sweep over it with so much force that our tent poles snap faster than we can make new ones and the heavy rains soak everything; we cannot keep the meat or biscuit dry, our arms and armor rust no matter how often we polish them, and no one has a dry garment or blanket. And the heartbreaking thing is that our men were so happy to reach it—to be so close to the Holy City! If you could have seen them, my lord, shouting with joy, throwing their helmets in the air, the sick ones, too, adding their weak voices to the rest!"

"Now, I suppose, they are all begging to be allowed to return to Jaffa or Acre."

"No, despite everything, their one wish is to march over the hills and liberate Jerusalem. Their spirits are high, my lord, and they await your command with an eagerness that must be seen to be believed."

Richard groaned and dropped his head into his hands. After a long moment he looked up.

"And I sit here not daring to give that command! Our provisions take days—weeks—to reach us in this weather, and I have not yet learned enough of Jerusalem's defenses. I must meet with our other leaders and we will try to settle the matter without further delay. Bring them here to me, dear sir; summon them in my name, if you will."

After Hubert Walter retired, Berengaria surprised me by reaching out and touching my lord brother's hand.

"I would like to be present when you hold this meeting, dear lord," she said, "and I think the Lady Joan would, also. The Holy Cause is very dear to our hearts, you know. It is *our* Crusade, too—"

"It is very much our Crusade." I interrupted her a little grimly. "Its coffers have been filled with my twenty thousand ounces of gold and your dowry. I think we have the right to be present!"

Richard suddenly grinned at me. "Hold your fire, Joan," he replied. "You have both contributed greatly and will be more than welcome. I have been accused of many things, dear ladies, but not of ingratitude."

I believe Richard would have seated us at the council table, had we been willing. All that Berengaria and I wanted, however, was to hear what was said and decided, and after talking it over with his chamberlain we chose to sit in the curtained alcove that held my brother's camp bed. There we could listen and not hamper the discussion by our presence; as the alcove had its own exit, we could, if the meeting wearied us, slip away unobserved.

We were already in our chairs when Richard welcomed the other nobles, and we did not stir from them until the last word was spoken. Disheartening as it all was, we never had the slightest desire to leave, nor were we aware of any weariness.

Actually, they wasted very little time, and the greater part of the talking was done by the two men who knew most about the problem facing them all—the Grand Master of the Templars and the Grand Master of the Hospitallers, the two orders that had always sheltered and aided Crusaders.

"Jerusalem cannot be taken by siege," said the Templar. "Saladin has followers hidden in the caves and hillsides that overlook the great valley surrounding the city. No, *we* would starve long before they began to suffer in the city."

"Then we must attack," replied Richard. "That is what our men desire. They pray every day for the order to march on and take the Holy City."

"Suppose we succeed," said someone else. "How do we hold it? Our men will want to go home—and as long as Saladin's caravans come in safely from Cairo he can continue to harass us. I'm afraid, my lord King, we must retreat to Ascalon, cut off his supplies, wait for spring, then try again."

This speech was followed by such a babble of voices that Richard had to pound on the table to restore order.

"Before we argue the matter," he said as the noise died down, "draw me a plan, if you will, of Jerusalem and the country around it. Show me what you mean, my friends."

We were able to see the table from our alcove, so we watched a Templar step up to it and bend over a large sheet of paper that my lord brother pushed toward him. While he was busy with his task the chamber began to buzz again, falling silent the moment he laid down his pen.

No one spoke while Richard studied the hasty drawing, his face growing grimmer and his eyes bleak. Finally he sighed and placed a finger on the plan.

"This one spot to the north, where the valley is narrowest," he said. "How deep it is? Could it be crossed?"

The questions and answers went on and on. Although they meant little to Berengaria and me, we could see that everyone was becoming discouraged.

"The Grand Master is right. We must retire to Ascalon." The Duke of Burgundy, seated beside Richard at the table, spoke directly to him. "On behalf of all my forces, my lord King, and for my own King, Philip of France, I ask you to agree to his suggestion."

From other parts of the chamber came many other assenting

voices, so many that I knew Richard must do as they asked.

"So be it, my lords. Reluctantly, and sadly, I will do so."

Rising to his feet, my brother strode to where a curtain hung. He pushed it aside and turned back to the others.

"Up there on that windswept plateau await our loyal men," he announced. "The sick and the well, all eager to push on to Jerusalem, even in this wet and cold. And now we must tell them to take down their tents and retreat—retreat! After suffering from every imaginable extreme of weather, from disease, and from pestilence; after watching their comrades die beside them; after being so close to the Holy City that they can almost see it from their camp— what, after all this, will they feel when I order them to turn their backs on our goal and begin another wearying, death-dealing march?"

He looked around at all the men, but there was no answer.

"Well, my lords"—he spoke again, dropping the curtain—"I cannot do it. You must issue this command, not I. I have heard our men—and our enemies—calling me 'Lion Heart' when we faced death together. Suddenly I find myself a craven, an arrant coward. Death I can face, but not this! I am not brave enough, my lords, to stand before our armies and order them to retreat."

CHAPTER

XIX

My brother strode into our privy chamber looking extremely unhappy. "How many litters will you need for the journey?" he asked us abruptly.

Both Berengaria and I were so startled that it was a moment before we could reply, and Richard repeated his question, his voice full of impatience.

"Four, five, six?"

"It depends on the weather," I said. "If it is not too miserable I would rather ride."

"It's snowing at this moment and may well continue for some days. Come, answer my question, please. I must have all the litters we can spare!"

While I began to count our ladies, Berengaria rose and went to his side.

"What is it, my lord? What is wrong?"

"It's our men; they won't retreat from Beit Nuba. Scores of them are lying down in the snow and waiting to die, and they will, if I don't do something immediately. I'm sending over every horse and litter we can spare and ordering those in charge to use as many provision wagons as they need—we must abandon some of our provisions, precious as they are, anything, to save our men. I will not have one left behind, not one!"

"No, no," said Berengaria. "That would be dreadful! Take all the litters. We are strong and well. We'll wrap up warmly."

"Where are those camels Saladin gave you?" I asked, struck by a thought.

"Some here, some at Ramleh. We're using them as pack animals."

"Then send us down on them and use our horses for the soldiers. I've never ridden on a camel and I've always wanted to."

Rick's face lightened for the first time and he actually laughed.

"Why not? If you really mean it, Joan. They say the motion is quite pleasant once you grow accustomed to it. But what about you, my lady? Will you ride with me while this madwoman goes on her way with the camels?"

Berengaria looked over at me and smiled. "I think I'll take a camel too, my lord. This is no time for you to be hampered with me or anyone else—and if Joan can ride a camel, so can I!"

We laughed about it afterwards, but I think there were many moments during our perilous journey down to Ramleh when both Berengaria and I wondered why we had been so adventurous. The snow, instead of abating, turned to sleet, and our mounts alternated between stumbling and slipping. This would have been frightening enough on horseback; on a camel it was much worse—there was a horrid feeling of insecurity in being perched up so high, dipping and swaying without the least warning of what would come next.

On the other hand, we were warm and dry, for camels are such strong beasts that we were able to encase ourselves in layers and layers of heavy garments and, as we did not have the task of guiding the animals ourselves, we covered our faces with so many thick veils that even our noses did not get cold. Nevertheless, we were very relieved when we finally came to a jolting halt and our attendants pulled our camels to their knees and lifted us to the ground.

I parted my veils and saw that we were safely at Ramleh, where we would spend the night before going on to Jaffa.

Richard, who joined us for supper, grinned delightedly at the account of our day, of which I admit we made the most—or the worst.

"Must I send you to Jaffa in the same way, dear ladies?" he asked. "Or will you let me supply you with litters now?"

"If you can spare them, please!"

*   *   *

We remained at Jaffa only long enough to collect the ladies who had not accompanied us to Latrun and then set sail for Acre again. Guy sailed with us, for he, too, was to spend the rest of the winter at Acre. Supplies must be sent from there to Ascalon, Saladin having left that city deserted and in ruins, as was his custom. While our Crusaders rebuilt it—and intercepted Saladin's caravans from Egypt—our men at Acre would gather and dispatch food, clothing, implements, and arms.

These tasks kept Guy reasonably busy, but once we were back in the quiet seclusion of the palace we had so little to do that we welcomed his frequent invitations to dine in his part of the rambling building. He had his own state apartments, as we had ours, and he, with his friends the Pisans, reigned there as "King Guy of Jerusalem." I suspect that he wanted us at his table more for our titles than for our company; I think that the presence of two queens was proof to him and his sometimes faltering followers that he still had the Lion Heart's support.

However that may be, it was there that we gathered most of our scanty news. This, at first, consisted mostly of tales of the disgraceful behavior of many of our Crusaders who, angered by the order to retreat from Beit Nuba, had deserted the army when it reached Ramleh and were spending the winter months in Jaffa, Tyre, and here at Acre. To my bewilderment most of these men were French —and it was, as I knew, *their* leaders who had insisted on that plan

198

to retreat. But by then I had given up trying to understand the French, even though I am half French myself!

The stories of their orgies certainly shocked us all. Their drunkenness and licentiousness were bad enough in the city around the palace; in Tyre, we heard, it was much worse. As our Richard de Templo described it later, "They abandoned themselves to wantonness, women's songs, and banqueting with harlots. They applauded bands of dancing women, and the very luxury of their costume bespoke their effeminacy—round their necks were jewelled collars and, on their heads, garlands wrought with every kind of flower. Goblets they brandished in their hands, not swords, and their nights were spent in potations and profligacy!"

Meanwhile, their comrades lived in the bitter cold at Ascalon, rebuilding its ruined walls with numbed and bleeding hands! And, as there was no harbor at Ascalon for our supply ships, more often hungry than not. . . .

Then, as the winter dragged away and Easter lay just ahead, we heard from Guy that his old rivalry with Conrad of Montferrat was boiling up again.

"He still thinks he should be King of Jerusalem, not me," he told us, "and he is making trouble for King Richard by remaining stubbornly at Tyre."

A letter from Richard to us confirmed this. He was setting out to meet Conrad at Casal Imbert, which lay between Acre and Tyre, to try to settle their differences once and for all. He would, he wrote, visit us either on his way or on his return.

While we were waiting quietly for his arrival, Guy rushed into our apartments with more news of his own, news that had disturbed and shaken him. "The Duke of Burgundy and all the French forces are nearing the city." He was almost shouting in his fear and excitement. "What should we do? What should we do? What would King Richard want us to do?"

"The French are coming *here*, to Acre?" I found this hard to believe.

"Yes, yes, here! A messenger just rode in to warn me. They are only a few miles away!"

"But why? Why have they left Ascalon?"

"Oh, money, money! The soldiers refused to work or fight until they were paid, and your lord brother would not lend Burgundy anything more. I don't blame him, but what am I supposed to do?"

I had no way of knowing, of course, but I did what I could to quiet him. I had partly succeeded when another of Guy's messengers was ushered into the chamber by one of my own servants.

"I have just come from Tyre, your Grace," he told Guy. "Conrad of Montferrat has set sail for Acre. We think he plans to join the Duke of Burgundy and the French forces when they arrive here."

Well, that was the end of our dull but peaceful existence. From that moment the whole of Acre was thrown into a state of violent and noisy confusion, while Guy, having made up his mind not to allow either Conrad or the French into the city, prepared to defend it.

The gates were barricaded and mangonels set up on the walls, and both the harbor and the road from Ascalon watched day and night. We were asked to remain in our apartments and, indeed, had no desire to venture out. The constant din in the streets around us as men and horses dashed from one place to another, dragging heavy mangonels over the cobbles, was more than enough to keep us within the palace walls, and Guy's uncertainties and fears upset us all.

Berengaria and I did our best to keep our ladies calm but this was not easy, for Guy continued to hurry to us with bad news; when he ran in, late one afternoon, and shouted that the French were at the gates and one of our guards had shot the Duke of Burgundy's horse out from under him, both Bourgigne and Lady Maria fell into screaming fits. Why, I asked myself for about the thousandth time, oh, why, had Richard not left Isaac's daughter in Cyprus, where she belonged?

We had had no time to calm ourselves before the mangonels began to rumble and Guy appeared again, his face flushed and his voice unsteady.

"Conrad has sailed into the harbor," he said, "and is attempting to land. We will stand firm—we will do our best—but Richard should be here, not I! How can I be sure we are doing what he would want us to do?"

He was shaking and I could not but agree. Richard *should* be here; Guy was not man enough to weather this double storm.

"Send someone to find him," I suggested. "He must be somewhere on the road from Ascalon."

"I have!" his voice rose shrilly. "Three of my best scouts. But they may not succeed in slipping around the French."

There was nothing for us to do but wait. Whenever Conrad's ship tried to move toward shore, Guy's men bombarded it with their mangonels, and although they never hit their target their fire kept him in check for three long days. They were, for us all, three anxiety-ridden and frightening days. Certainly they were for me, for I more than shared Guy's fears and uncertainties, doubting very much that my lord brother would approve of his making open enemies of Conrad and the Duke of Burgundy.

It was not until late in the third evening that a great shout of "the Lion Heart! the Lion Heart!" rang out in the streets below our windows and we heard the sound of many feet rushing out of the courtyard. Should we set out to meet him, too, we asked each other, or should we remain in the palace? While we were still undecided, Richard himself strode through the archway into our salon and kissed first Berengaria and then me.

It was obvious that he was in a hurry, and his greeting made this more than clear.

"You are well, my lady? Joan?" he asked. "Then you will forgive me if I leave you and return later? You have heard, I am sure, that my supposed friends are causing me more trouble than my enemies. I must hold my temper and somehow make all smooth again, but I would give what little gold I have left for the privilege of knocking their fat heads together! Guy's courier reached me at Caesarea this very morning and I've been in the saddle all day; pray that I find patience and strength—"

With that he was gone, and we did not see him again until another day and night had passed, but as we were accustomed by now to his sudden comings and goings, and to the fact that he rarely seemed to have time to share Berengaria's bed, we thought little of it, and even Bourgigne made no comment—perhaps because her own husband, a newer bridegroom than Richard, had not appeared all winter. There may, of course, have been some reasonable explanation for this, but it did seem to me that Raimond, if he had wanted to, could very well have acted as courier at some time during those long weeks or might have accompanied Richard now, when a visit to Acre was known to be part of his itinerary.

I would have been less than human had I not been secretly pleased by his neglect; I had no reason, certainly, to be sorry for Bourgigne. I was confident that this marriage was her doing, and if she was not happy in it I suspected that that, too, would be mostly her doing. Nor could I be sorry for Raimond—but I must not think of him.

I *did* pity young Baldwin. My lord brother, when we finally had a moment alone just before he set out for Ascalon again, told me that the lad was still eating out his heart over her.

"Had he spent the winter here with us he would be grateful to be free of her," I said bitterly. "What we have endured, Rick, in the way of ill temper and complete disregard for the peace and comfort of everyone but herself you would not believe. I may say that it will be a happy day for Berengaria and for me when we finally see the last of her!"

Richard sighed heavily. "I am beginning to fear that day may not be far off," he said. "Between you and me, Joan, I am losing heart. As you know, I have done my very best to patch up the quarrels that brought me here, but nothing has gone right. Nothing. Conrad openly refuses to return to Ascalon and play his part in the Crusade. As a result, I was forced to announce to our other leaders that he must forfeit his revenues from Tyre. His response to that was to summon Burgundy and all the French to Tyre, both the men who had run here to Acre and the few loyal ones who had remained with us at Ascalon. How can we finish our work there and go on to take Jerusalem without them? And how can we fight a Crusade while our friends are fighting among themselves and with me?"

"What shall you do?"

Shaking his red head wearily, he sighed again. "God knows, Joan. God knows. Oh, I shall try to make peace with them when I reach Ascalon—if they haven't all deserted! And in the meantime, I am still working with Saladin to find an agreement that will suit both sides."

My heart sank at this, but as he said nothing more I assumed his scheme to wed me to Saphadin must have been forgotten, and we parted lovingly.

* * *

From that moment on I think I lost all hope that we would ever march into Jerusalem and fulfill our Holy vows, and everything that happened during the horrible spring and summer that followed made it sadly evident that I was right.

It was a few days before Easter when Richard bade us farewell; then, soon after the first of April, he wrote Guy that he had failed in his attempt to hold the rest of the French army at Ascalon and that Guy must continue to keep them out of Acre. "Seven hundred of our best knights gone!" he said in his letter. "Saladin has heard of their defection, of course, and is reassembling his forces. But despite all this trouble we work here day and night. In fact, I am helping the masons with my own hands."

We were still worrying about this seven or eight days later, when Robert, the Prior of Hereford, sailed into the harbor with news that disturbed us further. It came to us in letters from my lady mother, one for me and several for Richard, all of which the Prior delivered in person.

"You must urge your brother to come home," she wrote to me.

"If he does not, I cannot promise to save his kingdom for him. As I have written my lord son, his brother John is doing everything in his power to usurp the throne—he is even scheming with Philip of France to set aside his wife and wed the Lady Alys. And, to make matters worse, there is nothing left in our treasury. Tell him he must return to England, my daughter, and ask the Lady Berengaria, if she has any influence with him, to add her voice to yours."

My little brother John turned traitor! The dark-haired, odd one of our brood, just a year younger than I, with whom I had played and quarrelled. He had been sly and tricksy even then, I remembered, and not to be trusted with our playthings. He was our father's favorite, as Rick was our mother's, but this had not mattered too much to any of us children for our lord father was rarely at home.

I was so shocked by what I had read that I passed the next day and night in miserable indecision. Should I show the letter to Berengaria or tell her what it contained? I was reluctant, both because I was ashamed and because I doubted the wisdom of carrying out my mother's wishes. Finally, however, I did reveal its contents to her, and we were pondering over it together when my young nephew, Henry of Champagne, arrived at the palace with a group of our other nobles.

"Does King Guy know you are here?" I asked, after we had embraced.

"Alas, yes," Henry replied. "We have just had a most uncomfortable talk with his Grace."

I looked at him in bewilderment. He and Guy had always seemed friendly.

"I was given the thankless task of telling poor Guy that he is not to be the King of Jerusalem after all, a dreadful blow for him, as you can imagine. This is not King Richard's doing, but it came about when my lord uncle informed us that he had been called home to England and would leave three hundred knights and two thousand men-at-arms to continue the Crusade at his expense. The matter of a new leader was brought up immediately, and everyone agreed that Guy was not the man; he is not wise enough, your Grace, nor is he a seasoned warrior."

This was certainly true. "Then who *will* take my brother's place?"

"Conrad of Montferrat. There was not one dissenting voice. Our friends even went down on their knees and begged my uncle to name him as their new leader and as the future King of Jerusalem. He had to agree—he has learned, we have all learned, that Conrad is the stronger of the two."

I nodded. "And you will travel on to Tyre to tell Conrad?"

"I have already done so. He is jubilant—and the city went wild. He plans to be crowned here at Acre in a very few days and will then join the others at Ascalon. Now that he has what he considers his rights, he is prepared to devote himself wholly to the Crusade; in fact, he knelt before us all and prayed to God that if he were not worthy of the Crown it should not be given to him."

Berengaria now spoke for the first time, her face showing some concern. "Does this mean that my lord will be sailing for England immediately?"

"Not until Conrad arrives to take his place—and brings the French army with him. King Richard's men still hope to keep him, of course. It was a most affecting scene: they swarmed to him, clung to his feet, begged him to remain until the Holy City is ours. He had tears in his own eyes as he refused. 'My kingdom needs me,' he told them. 'But when I go I will leave my heart here with the Crusade. To raise the standard of the Cross on the towers of Jerusalem and to drive the Infidels from the Holy Sepulchre has been the dream of my boyhood and the hope of my manhood! It will be agony to abandon you now—agony!'"

There were tears in our eyes, too. My own heart ached for Richard—and for our loyal soldiers. Would Rick come to Acre for Conrad's coronation, I asked? Henry did not know. Messengers were riding swiftly to Ascalon bearing Conrad's happy acceptance, but there had not yet been time for any reply. We would probably hear in due course.

This had to satisfy us for the moment. Poor Guy did not come near us, a blessing in the circumstances, and we thought it best to remain discreetly in our own quarters, retiring later that night with our thoughts in turmoil, wondering what our future held.

All our ladies, of course, were as disturbed as we were, and to set them thinking of something more pleasant, we began next morning to plan our costumes for Conrad's coronation. Berengaria was standing in the cote she had worn as a bride and we were trying the effect of a new girdle, worn lower than usual on her slim hips, when Henry entered without being announced.

I swung Berengaria around to face him. "This is her Grace's wedding robe," I said. "We are urging her to wear it for Conrad's crowning."

"There will be no crowning," he replied, his face ashen. "Conrad has just been assassinated and I must return to Tyre. The Bishop of Beauvais has accused King Richard of being responsible for the crime."

CHAPTER

XX

Henry caught Berengaria as she crumpled to the floor, and as we helped him carry her to the nearest divan I gave him an impatient glance.

"Well," I remarked a bit tartly, "I could wish you had a gentler way of telling us frightening news!"

"Forgive me, dear Aunt." Henry sounded rueful. "But it is such a terrible business that I did not stop to think how it might upset her Grace."

Actually, Berengaria so seldom showed any emotion that I could understand his lack of consideration for her, and, despite my rebuke, I myself was a little surprised at her reaction. Our ladies, surprised too, I think, bustled about with a bunch of burnt feathers, waving them under the Queen's small nose until she suddenly opened her eyes and smiled apologetically at our anxious faces.

"What? Oh, yes—oh, dear! Conrad and my lord—"

"I should not have distressed you so, my lady." Henry knelt by the divan and took her hand in his. "My lord uncle is innocent, of course. I doubt if he even knows of this hideous murder. Conrad had many enemies, and one of the two dastards who stabbed him to death—the other was killed on the spot—has confessed that they belong to the secret cult of 'Assassins' and have been living in Tyre, disguised as Christians, while they waited for a good opportunity to perform their grim task. You may be sure that I will sift the whole business carefully and defend King Richard's name in every possible way. That is why I am leaving immediately for Tyre."

We had all heard of this band of cruel Assassins. They were ruled by a madman called the Old Man of the Mountain and killed anyone he thought unworthy of life; if they had perpetrated this crime I could not see how my brother could be implicated—or even suspected. I said as much and told Henry that I would accompany him to Tyre.

"We must put an end to these ugly rumors at *once,*" I said firmly. "I will talk to the Bishop of Beauvais myself and to everyone concerned, and you and I, Henry, shall act together until the truth is known and believed by all, and perhaps I might be of some comfort to Conrad's widow, the Lady Isabella."

When I said this I was wondering whether she needed comforting. Perhaps she was as happy to lose Conrad as she had been to be freed from her first husband, our friend Humfrey of Toron. That marriage had been annulled when the Bishop of Beauvais found some convenient consanguinity between them; dissolving an eastern marriage was, I had heard, a comparatively simple matter.

In any case, Conrad's twenty-one-year-old widow was still the hereditary heiress to the throne of Jerusalem. It was through her that Conrad had insisted on his right to the crown, just as it was through Guy's marriage to her older half-sister Sybella that he had become king and, after her death, continued to advance *his* claim. Now, with Conrad killed, the whole question would be re-opened.

* * *

Henry and I were soon on our way to Tyre. It was an easy day's journey and, by riding swiftly, we reached the city that night. We were accompanied by the two envoys who had brought us the news of the murder and the messages urging Henry to return, so we were expected at the gates and made our way without a moment's delay through the quiet streets.

Henry pointed to the black-draped houses all around us. "It's a different city from the one I visited only a few days ago," he said. "All these houses were decorated with garlands of flowers and bright silken banners in honor of Conrad's imminent coronation, and all these streets were crowded with singing and dancing people." He hesitated, then spoke again in a lower voice. "The envoys have been hinting to me that I might be acceptable to everyone in his place, because I am a nephew of France and of England. . . . Well, we shall see."

This, I must confess, had occurred to me also. It seemed to me that my kinsman would be a perfect choice, an ideal man both to lead the Crusade in Richard's absence, for he had proven his bravery more than once on the field of battle, and to rule Jerusalem when and if the city became ours again. He was young, strong, and handsome; and, having grown up at his mother's gracious and delightful court, his manners were so charming that he was everyone's favorite. His mother was my half-sister Marie, born to my lady mother and her first husband, King Louis of France, and Henry appeared to have inherited all the best traits of his royal grandparents.

I turned to him and told him how much I hoped that he would be chosen and would accept. "What a happy coronation *that* would be," I said. "I would want to dance and sing in the streets myself!"

The great marble palace now loomed up in front of us, and we fell silent. They were expecting Henry, and after admitting us and bidding us welcome one usher took him off to the council chamber and another led me through a long arcaded corridor to the apartments of the young widow.

I suppose, because I knew that Isabella's father, King Amalric of Jerusalem, had been King of Cyprus before Isaac pre-empted the throne, I was expecting her to be another Bourgigne. I could not have been more mistaken: the slender woman who rose from a cushioned divan to greet me was delicately beautiful, her features small and well-modelled, her skin a soft, luminous, pearly white. I was told later that she resembled her mother, a Greek princess, whose loveliness was well-known.

I could see that she was surprised by my unheralded arrival, and after asking her to send our ladies away, which she did, I hastened to explain why I had intruded on her grief.

"I am here to beg you with my own lips not to believe the base and slanderous rumors concerning my lord brother, King Richard of England. He would never be guilty of such a foul crime—never!"

"I don't believe them," she said, raising a pair of deeply set dark eyes to mine. "If the Lion Heart could stoop to such a thing there would be no honor left in this world. No, no, your Grace, I am quite convinced that my lord husband brought about his own death by angering the Old Man of the Mountain. He seized a shipload of their goods, you see, and drowned the crew. This was the reason the assassin gave after he was captured, and I am sure it is the only one. My lord could be very cruel."

She shivered as she spoke and I wondered, again, whether Conrad's murder had not freed her from an unhappy union. Her next words gave me more reason to think so.

"If I must wed again to settle the question of who wears Jerusalem's crown, this time I shall have a hand in choosing the man!"

I wanted to bring Henry's name into our talk but held my tongue. Later, however, when he entered the chamber to express his sorrow over Conrad's death and to take me to my ladies, I watched them both, and as Henry and I strolled down the corridor toward my quarters he commented on her beauty.

I lay awake that night thinking about the two of them, and of Isabella's words about choosing another husband. They reminded me, only too strongly, of Raimond's words to me. He had said that after my dutiful first marriage I would certainly be allowed to have a hand in choosing a second husband. Why, I now asked myself, had I not listened to him that night and gone with him to my brother? Perhaps if I had not fallen ill—

I turned my pillow over and scolded myself for these foolish, use-less questions. Raimond was wed to Bourgigne, and a thousand whys and ifs could not change that.

I was with Isabella again the following morning when the Bishop of Beauvais and the Duke of Burgundy came to inform her that Henry had been selected to take Conrad's place on the throne of Jerusalem. "Everyone agreed," they told us. "There was not one dissenting voice. His noble birth, his valor, his wisdom at the council table, his more than pleasing person, his gift for winning and holding friends—all these qualities make him the man to wear the crown and to unite our forces again as no one else could."

"I think you have chosen wisely, my lords," said Isabella in reply. "Leave me now, if you will, and bring Count Henry to me at this same time tomorrow. I would like to spend the remainder of this day praying for guidance on a problem of my own."

At the appointed time, I returned to Isabella's apartments and stood off in a corner as Henry and the others entered, watching while the Duke of Burgundy led him to Isabella and presented him as Jerusalem's new King.

Henry fell on one knee before her and smiled up into her face.

"Whatever my title, your Grace, now or in the future, I will always be your humble and faithful servant."

"Not my servant, dear lord, never that! It would not please me. Nor would it please me to be *your* humble and faithful servant. Surely we may do better than that! I think we may—in fact, I sent for you today to offer you two things."

Pausing, she drew her left hand from the folds of her softly pleated cote and held out some keys.

"First, my lord, the keys of Tyre, my own beloved city." Then, before he could take them or reply, she held out her other hand to him and gave him a trembling little smile. "With my city, dear lord, I offer myself. I think Tyre and Jerusalem need us both—and together."

There was a moment of stunned silence; then everyone seemed to speak at once. Henry was at her side in a flash, his arm around her waist and his eyes shining down into hers. The keys had fallen on the tiled floor, but no one cared for that. The nobles crowded around the young couple, shouting their approval of Isabella's daring speech and suggesting that the wedding take place without delay.

*　　*　　*

When I started back to Acre, a few days later, I could not help thinking of poor Conrad. The lengths of sable cloth were already mostly gone, the people of Tyre having replaced them with richly colored tapestries and window censers filled with incense to celebrate Henry's accession to the throne and his imminent wedding. Then I reminded myself that Conrad had abandoned two other wives to marry Isabella; perhaps she could hardly be blamed for not mourning him longer.

Such unseemly haste, however, seemed wrong to me—certainly for a royal couple. And for this reason, I thought it best for me to leave Tyre before the day of the wedding. Richard, I believe, felt the same way, for he wrote immediately that he favored Henry as King but could not approve his hasty union with Conrad's widow. Neither Henry nor Isabella discussed this with me—I heard from Richard later that he had protested—nor did they allow it to change the plans which would make them man and wife within a week of Conrad's assassination.

In the meantime I had not forgotten my purpose in coming to Tyre, and just before leaving the city I had a most unpleasant interview with the Bishop of Beauvais, in which I accused him to his face of maligning my brother. His only answer was an evasion, and I discovered not long afterwards that both he and King Philip were, at that very moment, spreading the story of Richard's supposed guilt all over Europe. Despite my failure with him, I was able to return to Berengaria partially reassured: I knew that Isabella was convinced of Richard's innocence, and I had her promise to deny any fresh rumors that might spring up in Tyre.

There being nothing else to do we settled down again into our quiet life at Acre and spent the rest of the spring and the hot summer that followed it praying for good news from the Crusaders. Henry's accession had restored harmony between the French and English forces, Guy was made reasonably content by being awarded the crown of Cyprus, and my lord brother was persuaded to remain with the crusading army a little longer.

Early in June, after many ups and downs, our forces set out for Jerusalem again, determined this time to take the city by assault. We hoped as each day drew to a close that the next would bring us word that the Holy City was back in Christian hands. A week passed, two, three, four—then, on the tenth day of July, a messenger rode into the palace with letters.

The expedition had failed. Richard was leaving the sick at Jaffa and bringing what was left of our army and our fleet back to Acre.

It is difficult to describe our emotions. Although I had hoped for good news, of course, I must confess that I feared we could not succeed. Reports of Saladin's increasing strength and the great stores of provisions that he had moved into Jerusalem had made me wonder how our Crusaders could ever bring him to his knees.

Berengaria, as usual, said little. We did ask each other just what the failure of our Crusade would mean for us—where we would go, and when.

Bourgigne was strangely silent, also. But she had been behaving oddly all winter and spring, making excuses to remain in her own chamber much of the time and, when she did join us, sitting quietly by herself in a corner. I watched her impassive face as we discussed the probable date of the fleet's arrival in our harbor and tried not to wonder what was wrong with the wench. She should have been boasting about the wonderful days ahead and the great household awaiting her in Toulouse.

As for me, the prospect of seeing Raimond again and watching him set out for home with his wife was a dull, constant heartache. And the thought of greeting my dear brother, saddened by defeat, made the pain worse. In fact, I finally admitted to myself that I was actually dreading the moment when someone would rush into our palace shouting that our ships were in sight.

On the twenty-sixth day of July the word finally came and we made our way to the waterfront. Fortunately, the sun was going down and the breeze from the sea that was bringing our fleet swiftly into the harbor made it cool enough for us to climb down from our stuffy double litter and wait on the sand for Richard to step ashore.

Long before he reached us, however, both Berengaria and I were shocked by the sight of his face—gaunt, deeply lined, and grim. And his great arms, as he embraced us, felt all bone. Robert of Leicester looked thin, also, but not like Richard, and Raimond, whom I saw kissing Bourgigne on the cheek, appeared much as usual.

There seemed little to say, and after an awkward moment we all turned and walked to where our litter and the horses were waiting. My lord brother helped us in, then stood and stared around him. There were a few groups of townspeople watching the boats pull into shore, and some of our own men who were stationed at Acre were standing nearer the water's edge, greeting their comrades in the heavily loaded galleys.

"Mother of God!" I heard Richard say bitterly, almost savagely. "How quiet it is! Nothing but the dipping of the oars and a few subdued voices. Do you remember, Robert, the evening I first landed here? The wild shouts of 'Lion Heart! Lion Heart! Lion Heart!'? The happy music; the singing and dancing that kept us all awake till dawn? I was the great hero. The Lion Heart had come and we would march right to Jerusalem and take it from the Infidel. Nothing could stop the Lion Heart; he was invincible! Invincible—ha!"

I felt Berengaria shiver. I heard her stifle a sob, but my own eyes were dry, dry and hot. A wave of misery, of desolation, swept over me. I wanted only to run away, to forget my brother's tortured face and voice. I wanted to forget the entire Crusade and what it had done to those I loved—and to me. I wanted to be back in Palermo, living my placid life with William, my senses unawakened and my heart untouched.

"Will you come to us at the palace, Richard?" I forced myself to speak.

"Yes, yes. For an hour or two, perhaps. I know you want to hear the whole damnable tale!"

I didn't, but I was sure he would feel better once it was told.

* * *

Berengaria and I awaited my lord brother's visit alone. Bourgigne was with Raimond, and we sent our other ladies to bed.

"Have you been ill again, Rick?" I asked, when he joined us. "I have never seen you so thin."

"No, more bouts of that fever; nothing, really. Most of us have them. Forget it. We have more important matters to discuss and very little time."

Berengaria and I exchanged glances. Did he mean we were all setting sail for England?

"I have given up all hope of taking Jerusalem," he said abruptly, "and matters are growing worse and worse at home. John is plotting openly against me with Philip, and if I remain away much longer I will have no kingdom to return to. But before I set sail for England I must try to free Beyrouth from the Infidels—one last task—and for that reason I should, tonight, rejoin the others at our encampment here just as soon as possible. We plan to send ahead galleys loaded with men and siege engines. It will take time to load them and gather supplies."

He was pacing up and down as he spoke, and it was obvious that he was eager to be with the army, making preparations for this final siege. I could not see that freeing Beyrouth would settle anything, but if he had given his word he would, of course, try.

"Tell us why you were forced to retreat from the Holy City, dear lord, and save the rest of the story for another time." While Berengaria was speaking she moved to a table and poured Richard a goblet of wine. He took it with a half smile.

"Yes—we will have many evenings in the years to come to discuss this heartbreaking summer. You will hear then how we took Darum and many of Saladin's convoys, of all our defeats and victories. . . ."

Pausing, he sipped his wine, his eyes veiled. After a moment's silence he straightened his back and spoke again.

"We retreated from Jerusalem when I discovered with my own eyes how impossible it would be to take it. It was one morning, very early. I had risen at dawn and ridden out to attack a band of Infidels at Emmaus—a surprise attack; I had been told they would be there. They were, and we killed twenty of them. We captured their horses, mules, three camels, and a load of spices and silks, but Saladin's herald and the rest of his men escaped and fled over the hills. I galloped after them, riding as I have never ridden before, seeing nothing but the horsemen ahead of me.

"I caught one of them when his mount stumbled. I drove my lance through him; then, for the first time, I looked around me. The hilltop on which I stood was surrounded by early morning mist. Suddenly the mist parted and I saw the minarets and towers of Jerusalem, all gleaming white and unbearably beautiful in the soft rosy light that follows the sunrise. Yes, there it was, my Holy City!

"I saw it—but I saw, too, the bleak almost bare hills that lay beneath it, patched with jagged, cruel grey rocks, and I knew that if we climbed into those hills we and our animals would surely die of thirst. So I looked again at the city of my dreams, then I raised my shield and hid it from my eyes. 'Fair Lord God,' I prayed aloud, 'do not allow me to see the Holy City if I may not deliver it out of the hands of thine enemies.' "

His voice trembled, then stopped. I saw that his eyes were wet, and I felt my own fill and brim over.

"So—so." He sighed wearily. "The French did not believe me, of course. They thought we might send half our men to attack Jerusalem while the other half carried water from the river Tekora—a mad scheme! Saladin would have sallied out and cut us to ribbons. He has hundreds of fresh men waiting, and the city itself is filled to the brim with food and other supplies. No, no, we could not do it. We could not do it. And I have reason to think now that we were not meant to do it, for an odd thing happened."

He paused again, drank a little more wine, then went on in a steadier voice.

"That hilltop was called Montjoie, and, not long after I had returned to our camp, a holy hermit who lives on it sent me an urgent message, asking me to come back to him there. 'Come in God's name, and without delay' was what he said. I went. This time the city was hidden in the clouds, but the hermit was there waiting for me: naked, and covered with a filthy mat of hair. He took me immediately into his oratory, a crude little shelter, reached into a hiding place, and brought out a small wooden cross.

" 'On this Holy Cross,' he said solemnly, 'made from the Tree of Calvary, I swear that I am telling you the truth when I say that you will not, this time, take Jerusalem. I know this, my lord King, as well as I know that seven days from this day I will die. I stand here before you, strong and well—but I have only seven more days to live.' "

Berengaria gasped. "Did you seek him out again, my lord? Did he really die?"

"I did not need to seek him out. He returned to our camp with me—willingly. Just as he had prophesied, he fell ill and, although our physicians used all their skills to save him, on the seventh day he died."

I crossed myself and whispered a little prayer. Richard rose.

"Well, ladies, that is my story. And now, with your permission, I must be off."

* * *

We heard nothing all the following day, but early on the second morning after Richard's arrival Blondel came to the palace with an invitation for supper. "We plan to set out for Beyrouth at dawn," he said, "and my lord King hopes you will sup with him tonight at the encampment."

As he was on the eve of departure we did not expect, nor did we find, an elaborate banquet awaiting us. Many of our friends were there to greet us, however, and I found myself exchanging a few words with Raimond, who was seated nearby. I knew that he had already taken his leave of Bourgigne and that they had been heard quarreling, but what the trouble was between them we did not know. Now he and I merely chatted briefly about the impending campaign, and I did my best to sound as if there had never been any trouble between *us*. He followed my example, of course, but it seemed to me that his eyes, again, were hinting at many things he could not say.

We finished supping early and were about to make our farewells when Richard's chamberlain led a dusty, frantic-faced courier into our presence.

"My lord King! My lord King!" he gasped, falling to his knees. "You must return to Jaffa! Saladin is attacking the city and threatens to slaughter every Christian within its walls!"

Everyone froze and remained silent while Richard drew the messenger aside and conferred in undertones, his own face growing more strained and gaunt with each quiet word. Finally we saw him nod.

"With God's guidance," he announced loudly, "I will do what I can. Our ships are ready; we will sail at the turn of the tide. Our men-at-arms must set out immediately and travel on the road that parallels the sea. I assume that I speak for everyone here?"

Every Englishman present shouted assent, as did Henry of Champagne and Raimond.

"Do as you please, my lord King." To my astonishment I heard the Duke of Burgundy's voice rising over the others, insolently, arrogantly. "I, however, see no reason to take my men on such a fool's errand. I warn you that no Frenchman will stir one step with you!"

Then, before Richard could protest or even reply, he and his nobles bowed and strode swiftly out of the pavilion.

I moved to Berengaria's side. "I can't believe it," I whispered in her ear. "How can they allow all those sick and wounded men to be massacred? How *can* they?"

She shook her head and I saw her eyes flash. "It's shocking, shameful! If I were only a man—"

While she was speaking I had a thought. "Perhaps we could help, you and I," I said. "Why should we not go, too, and take our strongest ladies? If we reach Jaffa in time to save our men we could bring the ill ones back here to Acre and care for them on the way."

Her face lit up. "Come," she replied instantly. "Come to my lord."

* * *

I came out on the deck and saw Richard pacing up and down, his face grim as he looked first out to sea and then across the harbor toward Jaffa's towers.

"Where are they?" he asked as I moved to his side. "Where is the fleet? Why must we always be hampered by adverse winds when every minute counts? We've been anchored out here all night, Joan, waiting for my other ships, and I've been driven almost mad thinking of our friends in danger."

For a long moment we stood together in silence, watching the rosy light spread over the early morning sky. It was so beautiful and peaceful that I found it hard to believe that agony and death were close by and that Richard might be dead, too, before the sun set again.

"God have mercy!" he burst out again, impatiently. "Why dost Thou keep me waiting here when I am going in Thy service?"

A lively breeze blew my veil across my face, and when I pushed it aside I saw three sails—four—

"The fleet! At last!" Richard shouted orders, and up came our anchor and the beautiful red sails rose. We moved a little closer to the harbor, then into it far enough to have a good view of the city's ramparts.

"Saladin's banners!" said Richard, pointing. "The city is his!"

As I looked across the sparkling water I saw something dark, approaching us through the waves. I pulled Rick's sleeve. "Look!" I said. "Is that someone swimming?"

He leaned over the side, shading his eyes with his hand. "By God, yes!"

By the time the swimmer reached us a dozen of our knights and nobles had gathered. Two of them lifted the dripping man on board. I saw that he was a young priest. He was too exhausted to move or speak but lay there on the deck, his habit oozing water and his breath coming in great gasps.

Richard knelt beside him and lifted his wet head in his own hands.

"Quickly, sir! Our friends—where are they? Are they still alive?"

"Before—the tower. Awaiting—death!"

My lord brother jumped to his feet and called out to our oarsmen. Our galley moved forward so suddenly that I almost fell, and I clung to the rail, watching our other ships surround and follow us. Servants handed our friends their weapons and, as Richard stood, poised and ready in the prow, I heard him shout, "God sent us here to suffer death if need be! Shame on him who lags behind!"

As our keel grated on the sand, Richard was over the side and striding through waves that reached his waist. Our nobles and knights from our galley and from all those around us jumped after him, and with Richard leading, waving his great gleaming battle-axe, they swarmed up on the beach and began to hack their way through the band of Infidels drawn up and awaiting them.

The enemy scattered and fled. Some of our men set to work blocking off the land side of the harbor, and others, following Richard, disappeared toward the city walls. In an unbelievably short time I heard a shout from the ramparts and saw his red head towering over a man who was ripping down Saladin's banners. Another, wilder shout heralded the first flutter of England's silken pennant, its golden lions gleaming in the August sun.

I gave a deep sigh of relief, hearing, as I did so, a voice behind me ordering our galley back into the harbor. I did not mind now; in fact I was content to leave the hot and bloody scene, and Berengaria, who had come quietly out beside me during the foray, drew me off the deck and into the cooler shelter. . . .

Long before nightfall we, too, were on shore. Jaffa was ours again, and our tents and pavilions were raised on the very spot that, only that morning, had held Saladin's. I shall never understand how he could be routed so swiftly, nor could Richard, who invited one of Saladin's envoys to his pavilion to discuss the situation.

"You need not ask me how much I admire your Sultan," my brother said, after greeting him. "Islam has never had a greater or more powerful sovereign. But why did he run away at my first appearance? Why, after taking Jaffa in two days, did you retreat? By God, I was not armed or ready to fight! See, my lord, I am still wearing my boating sandals!"

There being no answer, he shrugged and spoke again.

"Greet the Sultan for me, if you will, and beseech him to grant me the peace I ask at his hands. My own country beyond the sea is being ruined, and there is no advantage to you or to me in suffering this futile struggle any longer."

CHAPTER

XXI

For the few days that we remained at Jaffa we lived in a pavilion again, as the conditions in the city itself were so terrible that Richard would not allow us inside its walls. We had not been in time to save the lives of many of our men, and the Infidels, after slaying them, piled them in the streets and left them there to rot in the hot August sun; then, as a final insult, they killed every pig they could find and threw those bodies onto the heaps of stinking, insect-covered human remains.

Excrement and other filth filled the narrow streets, and not long after Berengaria and I arrived at Acre with the survivors we received a message telling us that a virulent fever was spreading over the city and the encampment. This gave us both the gravest concern, and with good reason. My brother, already weakened by his intermittent attacks of a less violent fever, was one of its earliest victims and was soon very seriously ill.

The next few weeks were, I think, as harrowing as any I have ever spent. Reports about Richard's condition were discouraging at first, then frightening, and each contained an order for us to remain where we were. His physicians made it clear that if he was not to die he must leave Jaffa and its pestilential environs, and this, thank God, finally speeded up the turgid peace negotiations with Saladin.

While my lord brother was fighting death in Jaffa, the Duke of Burgundy, who had never left Acre, fell ill too. I should, I suppose, not tell this, but we heard later that when Richard learned of Burgundy's sickness he rallied instantly and from that moment began to regain some of his health.

"May God destroy him!" he said to our nephew Henry. "He and his men lived on our bounty for months and months and then refused, as you know, to help us save our men here at Jaffa."

Whether God was listening I do not know. I do know that three days later the Duke of Burgundy was dead.

* * *

On September second the truce was signed. We were to have Acre, Jaffa, Haifa, Arsuf, Caesarea, and most of their dependencies; Ascalon was to be dismantled and not refortified for the three years of the truce; and the Christians were to have access to Jerusalem and be free to trade anywhere in the Holy Land.

Although this was not what we had been fighting for, both sides rejoiced at the end of the futile, long-drawn-out hostilities. Most of our men dropped their weapons and went on pilgrimage to the Holy City, but my brother, still weak and now miserably unhappy at such an end to all his dreams, refused Saladin's invitation to visit it and, on the ninth day of September, set out for Acre and then home.

Having been informed of his plans, Berengaria and I readied our possessions and awaited his arrival, reminding each other, as each day passed, that he was not well enough to travel with his usual swiftness. I suppose that we, too, were worn by the interminable anxiety-ridden summer and that this made us the prey of unnecessary fears. Certainly when Raimond rode into the palace courtyard late one evening and asked permission to visit us, I felt my heart jump into my throat and saw Berengaria turn pale.

"He has come to take Bourgigne home to Toulouse," I said, recovering my senses before he entered our salon. "If Richard is—worse—Henry would come to us, not Count Raimond."

His face, as he bent over our hands, reassured us.

"My lord?" asked Berengaria immediately.

"Grows a bit stronger every day," he replied. "I left him in Haifa having his supper and revelling in the sea breezes that sweep over the promontory. The physicians insist that he remain for a week or so before venturing into this heat and taking on himself the exhausting task of loading the fleet for his voyage back to England. I am here, dear ladies, to tell you of this further delay and to ask your help with a problem of my own."

"Haifa is not more than five miles distant," I said. "Should we not join the King there?"

Dropping his eyes, Raimond hesitated and suddenly looked uncomfortable. "I think, your Grace," he answered slowly, "that your lord brother will recover more swiftly alone. He came very near death, and the terms of the truce were not to his liking. Just the effort of hiding his unhappiness from you would weary him."

"Yes. You are quite right, my lord Count." Berengaria spoke before I could, her voice understanding and firm. "We must allow him to lick his wounds in privacy. He will come to us when he is ready. And your problem, Count Raimond? How may we assist you?"

If he had looked uncomfortable a moment earlier, he was the picture of embarrassment now, and I realized that my presence must be distressing him. As I opened my mouth to excuse myself, Berengaria said gently, "It is something about the Lady Bourgigne, is it not? Speak freely, my lord. She is, despite your marriage, still in my care."

I rose, while she was speaking, and I now suggested that I retire to another chamber. "You do not need me, I am sure."

But Raimond put out a hand in protest. "No, no, your Grace!

Please stay. Mother of God, what a fool, what a stupid fool I have been—blind, stupid, miserable, ruining my life and perhaps Bourgigne's as well—"

"Come, sir," said Berengaria soothingly. "Matters cannot be so bad, surely? My ladies tell me you two have quarrelled. Well, this is most understandable, almost inevitable in the circumstance. The long separations after so sudden a marriage, the uncertainties of the future, the differences in your ways of life—why would you not quarrel? The early days of any marriage—" She faltered, and I saw her face flame.

"You are all that is generous and kind, my lady." Raimond sounded grim. "But unfortunately our marriage was a mistake from the very beginning, based on lies and misunderstandings and entered into by both of us for the wrong reasons. I shall not say what they were, nor do I make excuses for either my lady wife or for myself. We are almost equally culpable—and now we are equally wretched." His eyes sought mine, but I refused to meet them. It was difficult enough to listen and to hide the emotions his words were stirring in my heart.

"Even if all you say is true, my lord Count, the fact remains that you and Bourgigne are man and wife." It was Queen Berengaria speaking. "It will not be easy, but with patience and good will you may yet find your life together more tolerable. You must make the best of it, I am afraid, as many others have done and will continue to do."

Her words made my heart ache for her, too, as it was aching for Raimond and for myself. All three of us, doomed to unhappiness. . . .

"Had that been the only answer, your Grace, I would not have distressed you with my problem. But, you see, our marriage can be dissolved at any time, for we were not wed by a priest. We merely took each other as man and wife before witnesses, as is the custom in this part of the world, and our union can be set aside in the same manner."

We must both have looked at him with horror, for he reddened

225

and hastened to explain. "Understand me, ladies, *I* am not suggesting that we do so! It is Bourgigne who insists I must free *her,* and I do not know what to do. I do not know what to do!" He spread his hands wide in a gesture of helplessness and spoke directly to Berengaria.

"Will you think about this, your Grace, and advise me? She is very young, you know, and, as you said a moment ago, we are man and wife. Perhaps you would be even kinder and talk with her about the matter. I have told her many times that, although our marriage was entered into with distressing haste, we did exchange vows and we cannot break them lightly."

My sister sighed. "You place a heavy burden on my shoulders, Count Raimond, for the Lady Bourgigne and I are not the best of friends and I doubt that anything I could say would influence her. Have you discussed this with my lord the King?"

He shook his dark head. "I thought him much too ill to add another problem to his own."

"Then suppose we await his arrival and ask him to advise you. His should be the deciding voice, for it was he, after all, who took the girl from her home."

* * *

I tried, from that evening until the moment that Richard finally joined us at the palace, to put Raimond's distasteful problem out of my mind. I told myself that it did not concern me in any way, for even if his marriage were dissolved he would not dare approach me again—not after wooing me one day and wedding Bourgigne almost the next. No, he could talk of lies and misunderstandings, but what he had done was irrevocable and unforgivable.

These were uncomfortable days for Berengaria, too, and we diverted ourselves by discussing our future life. I refreshed all my old memories of England as we talked of it together—and it did help to pass the time. We were, however, more than ready to welcome Richard when he joined us one day late in September.

226

The comfortable days at Haifa had filled out his gaunt face and thin arms, and although he was still saddened by the failure of the Crusade he was apparently too occupied with the problems of the return home to brood over it. He had with him the Grand Master of the Templars, the order that had protected and watched over the travels of all Crusaders and pilgrims for many centuries, and, while the two men were drinking a goblet of wine with us, my lord brother asked Berengaria to dismiss our ladies.

"Now," he said, watching the last skirt tail disappear around the door, "we will tell you our plans. But first I must give you this letter, Joan, that has been months on its way to you. Read it, my dear, and then we will talk."

I thanked him, unrolled it, and scanned it hastily, giving a cry of delight. "It is from Walter! My dear old Walter, our Archbishop of Palermo. I was so afraid he might be dead, but he is home and longing to see me once more. But that, I suppose, will never be."

Richard, glancing over at his companion, raised his eyebrows. The Templar nodded.

"Why not, my lord King? You have said that Tancred is still friendly. A halt at Messina would not be out of their way."

In my happiness at the thought of seeing Walter I did not notice that he said "*their* way." "I have wanted you and Walter to meet for so long," I said to Richard. "You will like him, I know. And if we stop at Messina we need not necessarily see Tancred. Walter could meet us there quietly—"

"Ah, but I shall not be with you, Joan." My brother's voice was regretful and his face sombre. "I must make my way home secretly and in disguise, for Philip of France has spread such false tales about me that I could very well be waylaid and killed."

"You, King Richard of England? Who would dare?"

"Henry, the Emperor of the Holy Roman Empire, for one. Philip has won him over and made him my deadly enemy. When you hear the crimes I am supposed to have committed you will understand why he or Philip would dare. According to them I am a

227

monster, not a man, and there is no end to my villainy. They say that I helped Tancred take Sicily, that I captured Cyprus for my own enrichment and made a servant of the Lady Bourgigne, that I murdered both Conrad and the Duke of Burgundy—" Hearing us gasp at this, he smiled bitterly. "Oh, yes, both of them! I have just learned that the Bishop of Beauvais is back in France already and is telling everyone that I sent two assassins here to Acre to kill Burgundy. The whole city knows that he died of a fever, but my lord Bishop cares nothing for that. They also say that I betrayed the Holy Land by my truce with Saladin and that I personally insulted the Duke of Austria by tearing down his banner from Acre's walls with my own two hands."

"That is indeed a formidable list of lies," I agreed. "You are quite right, Richard. Any one or two of these tales would be a splendid excuse to slay you and make our brother John King of England in your place."

"I am proud to say that his Grace has placed himself in our care," said the Grand Master of the Templars. "No one will know when he sails or by what route, not even you two ladies, and you may be sure that we will do everything in our power to ensure his safety."

After we had thanked him, he left us alone with Richard. "You two will leave Acre first," he told us. "I have asked Stephen de Turnham to take charge of your household and establish you in Rome, where you will await word from me. If all goes well we may meet in England for Christmas, or I will join you in Rome and we will travel there together."

We discussed this plan for a few minutes; then Berengaria remembered to tell him about Bourgigne and Raimond.

"Oh, the poor fool! Well, I am very sorry for him, of course, and I wish now I'd wed her to Baldwin instead of agreeing to a betrothal. But I will not be responsible for dissolving this marriage—if it is a marriage. It would be called another crime by my enemies. No, they must find their own way out of the tangle, and I will tell

Raimond so. Take the troublesome wench to Rome with you. Raimond can join you there and, if they still wish to be free of each other, seek the Pope's advice on how to go about it."

* * *

Two days later Berengaria and I set out on our travels, Bourgigne with us; and Richard, who had spent the night before with his young wife, rode down to the harbor to see us safely on our way. It was just after dawn and a beautiful morning, a morning I shall never forget, for although the heat would be oppressive later the air, on that twenty-ninth day of September, was still fresh and sweet, the sands cool and damp under our feet, and the vessels of the fleet, anchored in the blue water, were looking very trim and bright.

Richard pointed to a huge, cumbersome dromond. "That is your ship," he told us. "See how busy they are!"

While we watched the crew readying it for our departure and saw the last of our boxes hauled aboard, the rest of our party gathered around us and many of our friends joined us to say a last farewell.

Leicester took my hands in his and bent his head over them, Henry of Champagne kissed me on both cheeks, and Raimond knelt before us and promised to meet us in Rome. "Your lord brother is right," he said to me. "I shall do as he advises."

He moved away then to where Bourgigne was standing, her face heavily veiled, and as I did not wish to witness their parting I turned again to Richard. Blondel was beside him now, with my lord brother's arm around his slender shoulders; as my eyes met Richard's, I was shaken by the unhappiness I saw in his.

He said something in the lad's ear. His arm tightened for a moment, then dropped away.

"Blondel sails with you, Joan," he told me. "I will have no time for music."

The little craft that was to take us out to our dromond was now ready, and Richard carried first Berengaria and then me through the shallow water. His kiss and farewell words brought tears to my eyes and I could say nothing but "Oh, Rick, dear Rick!" until he gently disengaged himself from my clinging arms and stepped away from the side of the small boat.

Instead of returning to the shore, however, he remained in the knee-deep waves while the others were carried out to join us, staring off toward the distant hills that hid Jerusalem.

"Oh, Holy Land," I heard him say, "I commend thee to God. If, in His goodness, He allows me to live so long, I pledge my word to return one day and succor thee."

XXII

As was to be expected, the long journey from Acre to Rome was difficult for all of us. My lord brother's bleak face and despairing words haunted me for days, and when Blondel described, only too vividly, how Richard had lingered between life and death in his tent at Jaffa and then went on to tell us of the tears that were wept by Jaffa's people when he departed and the way they gathered in sad groups, talking of his bravery and colorful exploits as they waved farewell, I found myself weeping, too.

Added to these emotions was my concern over our impending visit to Sicily. Eager as I was to see dear Walter again, I could not help fearing another quarrel with Tancred, and until we reached the harbor at Messina and learned that he was off at the other end of the island I was uneasy. This welcome news and a message from Walter informing me that he was on his way and would join me on board our ship made me feel quite safe while awaiting his arrival, and I spent most of the daylight hours watching the little supply vessels bring fresh food and water to us and to the other two dromonds that accompanied us.

When our stores were sufficiently replenished, we invited our friends over to dine and were astonished to find young Baldwin among them.

"I did not know that you were sailing with us," I said. "I heard that you were to follow with the rest of the fleet."

Giving me an odd smile, he shook his head. "I *had* planned to travel with the others but I changed my mind. I had a private talk with your lord brother and—well, here I am." He glanced over at Bourgigne, blushed, and smiled again.

Surrounded as we were by our other guests, I could not question him further; but I watched him from that moment and, long before their visit was over, thought I knew what he and Richard had discussed. I was so sure that I finally beckoned him to my side and asked him to stroll with me on the open deck.

"Do you think it wise, my lord, to be so attentive to the Countess of St. Gilles? She is in our care, you know, until her husband joins us at Rome, and we are answerable for her welfare both to him and to King Richard."

Turning a deep red, Baldwin answered me almost belligerently. "Of course I know that, my lady. But I know also that she is *not* the Countess of St. Gilles and never was, and when the Pope assures her that she is free, as I am sure he will, I shall wed her myself. Our betrothal took place before that infamous ceremony, and I consider it still binding."

"You have informed my lord brother of your intentions?"

"I have, and he approves. It was, in fact, his own suggestion that I sail on one of the dromonds and take advantage of any opportunity to seek out the Lady Bourgigne, tell her that I am eager to fulfill our contract, then await her decision and that of the Pope."

Neither Berengaria nor I could object to this, so although we considered Baldwin too gentle to be burdened with such a wife as Bourgigne, we allowed him to come and go at will while we remained at anchor in Messina harbor. As was only natural in the circumstances I wished Raimond free of the wench—for his sake, I told myself, not for mine—and it seemed to me that she welcomed this chance to discard one husband and secure another.

While Baldwin went about his second courting I had the joy and sorrow of seeing my dear old Walter Ofamillia: joy because the bond between us was as strong as it had ever been, sorrow because we both knew that it was unlikely we would ever meet again. I was, at first, too blinded with tears to see the stoop of his shoulders, the transparent skin drawn tightly over his cheekbones, and the shuffle that had taken the place of his brisk walk, but even as we embraced I noticed that his eyes had the dim, sad, patient look of a very old dog, and my heart sank.

What changes he found in me I do not know. We had much to talk about, of course, and Berengaria, after greeting him warmly for my sake, took the other ladies and gentlemen away and left us alone in the most comfortable corner of our living quarters. Here we sat for an hour or two while Walter told me all that had happened to him and I, in my turn, recounted our adventures.

"You know that my visit to Rome was a failure," he said, "and that Tancred still wears the crown. The surprising thing, however, is that our people seem content. I have come to wonder whether we were wrong in opposing him. After all, dear daughter, you and I are English-born, and not even most of a lifetime spent on this beautiful island can make us true Sicilians."

I sighed and nodded. "Has it been all quarrelling and hardship for you, Father?"

"Only during the first weeks that followed my return from the Vatican. I look after my people and carry out my duties, but I remain in seclusion much of the time. Tancred sits on his throne and, I am glad to say, rarely interferes in the affairs of the Church."

"Why not come with me?" I begged, on impulse. "Dear lord— leave Sicily and come with me! I am most unhappy, and I have no idea what lies ahead for me. I need your companionship and your counsel, your countenance and your grace—" My voice thickened and I said the rest with my eyes.

At first he made no answer. Instead he took my hand in his long, gnarled fingers and stroked it absently. "England," he said at last, more to himself than to me. "England."

Then he lifted my hand to his lips and kissed it gently. "No, no, dear child, my place is still here. While I can still serve my people I shall do so. It will not be for long."

When I protested he merely shook his white head. "Do not talk of me any more," he said firmly. "I want to hear why you are unhappy and to learn from you the true story of the Crusade and its failure. We hear so many tales that must be false."

Before discussing my own problems I told him all I could of my lord brother's victories and frustrations: the jealousies and troubles between him and the French, the loss of their men, the disease, Richard's own illnesses, the impossibility of laying siege to Jerusalem or attacking it, even when the army had come so close, and, finally, the frightening news from England.

"A heartbreaking end to his great quest," was Walter's only comment. "Thank you, daughter. And now, what of you?"

What of me? What could I tell him? That I had fallen in love like a silly serving maid—and with a man who turned from me to wed another woman without a word of explanation? I was certainly not proud of the part I had played, and I found myself reluctant to recount Raimond's.

"I face such a lonely future," I said. "Living, I suppose, at my brother's court. My inheritance from my dear lord is gone—the Crusade swallowed it all—and the long years ahead look bare."

"I can only repeat what I said to you after William died: you should marry again. And I am sure your lord brother will think so, too, when he is not so occupied with other matters."

I laughed a little grimly. "The thought has already occurred to him. In fact, he tried to wed me to Saladin's young brother." Then, while Walter listened in shocked silence, I told him all about Rick's wild plan to make me Queen of Jerusalem and the steps I had taken to prevent him from carrying it out.

"I thank God that you had the courage to stand against him," he said, "and that you could see how wrong he was. Most women would have been blinded by the thought of wearing the crown! It is obvious that I need have no more fears for you, my dear daughter. Continue to do only what you think right, and all will be well."

I promised to try and we drifted, after that, into comfortable talk of the past. When he finally rose and said he must leave me, I could see that he was looking very weary, so I made no protest; after we had parted lovingly and sadly, I stood on the deck and watched him set out for shore.

He was standing facing me, the sea breeze whipping his long robe so tightly against his body that I noticed how thin his legs were now, and how sharp his knees. We waved to each other again and again; the barge moved swiftly away but I remained where I was, crying a little, until long after it reached its destination. . . .

There being nothing to keep us at Sicily after that, we sailed the following day for Rome. Just before we left the harbor I found myself facing another sorrowful farewell, for Lady Caterina, after much prayer and many tears, decided that she was too old to travel any farther and should return to her family and friends in Palermo. I had to agree, of course, but her going left a sad gap in my household and in my heart.

* * *

Rome was a whole new world to me—and to Berengaria. For the first few weeks we could not see enough of it; indeed, for the first few weeks we lived in the long-ago past, trying to forget our problems and our anxiety over the safety of those we loved.

It was, in part, the wonder of the ancient Roman buildings. We had many in Sicily, of course, but they could not compare with these. And it was, I think, the bracing weather that we enjoyed most after the miserable heat and rain on Crusade. Certainly it seemed a Heaven on earth, to wander out into cool streets at any hour of the day, to sleep under covers at night, and to wake feeling truly rested in the early morning.

Then, too, Rome was a different world in that we were free to come and go as we never had been before, either of us. We were comfortably housed, it is true, and surrounded by our ladies and gentlemen and other attendants, but our spacious creamy stone palazzo could not be called a royal palace or our household a court; and although the Pope was kind, and many of the noble Roman families more than willing to visit the Queen of England and the widow of King William the Good of Sicily, where we went and how we passed our time was our own business—within reason, naturally, and as long as we behaved decorously.

If we wished to climb around the huge Colosseum, drift through the ruins of the Forum, or even go to the markets, choosing fresh foodstuffs for ourselves, we could set out at will, taking one tall manservant and perhaps a lady or two. It was, we discovered, a busy city, too busy to pause at the sight of two visitors; everyone came to Rome at one time or another, and a queen must ride through the streets with a crown on her head before she could interest the inhabitants. Even Bourgigne, who announced that she had decided to wed Baldwin if it could be arranged, was sufficiently interested in Rome's wonders to become almost pleasant, and except for the usual domestic problems we had little to worry us.

This peaceful interlude lasted from our arrival at the end of October until Count Raimond appeared about three weeks later. I shall always be grateful for its rest and refreshment, for I had come to Rome weary in body and sick at heart, dangerously near tears at one moment and falling into quarrelsome words the next. But by the time Raimond joined us I was in better health and spirits than I had been for many, many months, and I was able to face all that happened afterwards in a reasonable manner.

Raimond came on a rainy day when we were all gathered with our needlework around a fire in one of our smaller chambers. His garments were worn and travel-stained and his face so weary that

Berengaria made him sit down immediately and drink a goblet of wine.

"You have come to see your—wife—of course, my lord Count," she said, glancing over at Bourgigne, "but first we must hear something of your voyage and of our other friends."

"It was a long and a horrible ordeal," he said. "We ran into such heavy storms that many of our ships were wrecked and the rest of us were blown far off our course. Although our sails were ripped and we were leaking badly we managed to reach Brindisi—how I will never know!—and after a day or so there I came the rest of the way on horseback, riding over roads that I will not attempt to describe."

"And my lord? Have you news of him for us?"

"I wish I had, your Grace. We saw what looked like his galley approaching Brindisi, and that is why I remained there for a while. But it did not come into the harbor and, as you know, he kept his plans so secret that he may well not have been on board. I cannot tell you when he sailed from Acre, or on what ship, or what was to be his route home."

"He said he would try to join us here at Rome," said Berengaria slowly, "and that we might all spend Christmas together in England."

"We may very well see him any day then," was Raimond's cheering reply. "Perhaps he decided to sail farther up the coast and land at Chieti or Arpi. If so, he was wise—those roads!"

I said nothing, and I was quite ready to follow Berengaria when she rose and suggested that we leave Raimond and Bourgigne alone.

"You have much to discuss, my lord Count," she told him. "You will be warm and comfortable here and will not be disturbed. Sup with us tonight, if you will, and then you and I should have a word or two in private."

As we made our way to the adjoining room I gave Berengaria a grateful smile. Her manner with Raimond had been just as it should be, without a trace of her usual shyness or indecision, and by acting the queen she had made it unnecessary for me take part in this distasteful affair. Her concern for my unhappiness had, in fact, forced her out of her shell.

And that unhappiness was, unfortunately, not yet a thing of the past. Raimond's face, voice, the touch of his hand—even the sound of his footsteps on the marble floor—were still enough to set my heart beating fast. Just the thought of him alone with Bourgigne, either deciding to separate or, as she was as variable as the wind, to reunite, made me so miserable that I summoned Lady Elizabetta and walked in the streets around the palazzo until almost supper time.

I ate my evening meal in my own apartments, pleading weariness. Berengaria, bless her, accepted my excuse without question, saying that she would probably join me before we all retired.

My ladies were all in their beds when she appeared, and her visit was very brief.

"I just came to tell you that Raimond and Bourgigne declared in front of me and several other witnesses that they are no longer man and wife. This supposedly dissolves whatever tie there was between them, but Raimond is making sure by consulting the Vatican. Oh, and I wrested a promise from Bourgigne to remain in seclusion until we have the Pope's decision; she will not even see Baldwin in the meantime." Without giving me an opportunity to comment, Berengaria added, "That is all. Good night, Joan." And she was gone, leaving me to my own thoughts.

* * *

We did not refer to the situation in the week or so that followed, but I, alas, thought of little else. Berengaria and I were sitting alone when, at the end of that time, Raimond sought us out, and I knew immediately that he was free. This was the Raimond with whom I had laughed and sung, and as our eyes clung for a long dizzying moment, the sudden ardor that I saw in his brought the hot blood into my cheeks.

"I have just come from an audience with the Pope," I heard him tell Berengaria. "His Holiness assured me that the Lady Bourgigne and I were never man and wife and that there is no need for an annulment or dispensation."

"You have found an easy solution to your problem," replied Berengaria. "I think you both very fortunate."

"We are, your Grace, very fortunate indeed. We might well have paid for our mistake with a lifetime of misery—and perhaps deservedly so. I cannot blame myself enough for my share in it."

We were all quiet for a minute or two; then Berengaria rose. "I will go to the Lady Bourgigne and set her mind at rest. In the circumstances, my lord Count, I think you two need not meet again."

Raimond heaved a great sigh of relief. "I will be guided by you, of course, your Grace. But are you sure? I hesitate to place any further burden on your shoulders."

"I am quite sure. In my lord's absence her welfare is in my hands. Remain here, if you will, and I will return shortly."

Almost before the door had closed behind her Raimond was beside me, my trembling fingers in his.

"The Queen is more than kind," he said softly. "She must know that the one thing in the world I want now is a few moments alone with you, to try to explain and to beg your forgiveness."

This was what I also desired, but in the perverse way of a woman I drew my hand away and spoke coldly.

"It is not necessary, my lord. I had not made you any promises, and it was your privilege to seek elsewhere for a wife. I regret that your choice did not please you and I wish you better fortune next time."

"Stop!"

Raimond's instant protest was like a slap in the face. I looked at him, startled by his vehemence, and saw that he was staring at me intently, his mouth set in a determined line, his eyes stern.

"Listen to me, my lady, listen to me! May we not, at last, in this small miracle of time allotted to us by the Queen, put an end to these evasions and pretenses and tell each other freely and clearly what is in our hearts? Must we continue to create misunderstandings and misery? You are no frightened or foolish damsel, unable to think and speak for yourself, and I am not here to affront or harry you in any way, nor do I wish to disturb you with love-making. I want to set matters right between us, if I can, and to discover whether I have lost all hope of ever winning my true heart's desire."

There was something about the way Raimond said "Listen to me!" that made me obey. I listened to every word he said—and with my mind, not my senses. And as I listened, I realized that he was right. There must be no more misunderstanding between us.

"I would like to set matters right, too," I said quietly. "I quite agree that we should talk plainly while we have the opportunity. Tell me first how you came to wed Bourgigne. When I left you, that night in the grove, I thought it was me you wanted to marry."

"Let me say, first, that I knew nothing of your illness. I waited, the following evening, and you didn't come. But Bourgigne did. She came to me, in the dark wood, and said that you were sitting in your pavilion and laughing at me, that you were boasting to the ladies of how you had led me on and that you were keeping me waiting as punishment for my presumption."

"And you believed her? After holding me in your arms? You believed *her,* and thought *I* would behave in such a manner?"

"I thought she was lying, of course. But early the following morning your lord brother summoned several of us and informed us, in the strictest confidence, that he was arranging for you to wed Saphadin and become the Queen of Jerusalem. I called for my horse and spent the day in the saddle; I was so angry and heartsick that I rode blindly, recklessly, hoping I might be captured or even killed."

He stopped. I said nothing.

"At nightfall I returned to the camp and, without speaking to anyone, entered my own pavilion. There, in my bedchamber, was

Bourgigne. Alone, waiting for me. I, fool that I am, welcomed her. There seemed nothing to do, after that, but to agree to what she wanted, the secret ceremony that supposedly made us man and wife. And," he concluded bitterly, "until you rose in the presence of us all and announced that you would never marry Saphadin, I had had no reason to think you anything but delighted with Richard's plan for you."

"I see," I said. "I see." Some of Raimond's tale did not altogether surprise me; I had suspected Bourgigne of behaving more or less as he related, but the rest of it was a revelation; I suddenly remembered Raimond watching me while I dined with Saphadin, and his stiff words to me afterwards about my "new life."

"Mother of God," he said, more to himself than to me, "what a stupid fool—what a selfish animal I was, risking the future happiness of three people simply to ease my hurt! How, my dearest lady, can I describe my feelings when you faced everyone so bravely and asked for help in defying Richard? You looked so beautiful—and so alone." Giving me a smile I shall never forget, he shook his head. "I felt a great pride, and a great despair. I saw what I had lost and I knew that I had no one to blame but myself. How could I have listened to Bourgigne, or even Richard?"

"I think that much of this came about because I am a queen," I said. "If you and I had been free to meet openly as other people do, and if my future concerned only myself, these things would not have happened. So let us agree that this is so, Raimond, and put the past behind us. Let us be friends again."

"We will always be friends, but that is not nearly enough for me. My life will be empty, Joan, unless you share it with me as my wife." He was looking at me now with his eyes full of love, but he did not attempt to take me in his arms or even touch my hand. This, I think, made me believe in him as nothing else could have done.

Realizing that our future happiness might well depend on my reply, I hesitated.

"Come, my lady," he said at last. "Tell me what is in *your* heart. If I have ruined forever that small chance I had of winning your love, say so and I promise never to speak of it again. But, oh, Joan! If you could love me and trust me, how happy we would be!" His voice broke a little, and he fell silent.

"I must love you, Raimond," I said softly, "or I would not be listening to you. And I think, as you do, that we might be very happy together. But it is much too soon after your separation from Bourgigne for any exchange of promises between us, and I still need my lord brother's or my mother's consent before I may wed anyone. For decency's sake, my lord, return home to Toulouse. Wait for word of Richard's arrival and then, if you still want me, come to England or wherever he takes me and we will settle this matter at last. But remember, I make you no promises, nor do I ask any of you."

Before I finished my last few words, he caught me in his arms and gave me the kisses for which I had hungered so long. When I was ablaze from head to foot he groaned and released me.

"There," he said, "I'll go. But that, my sweet, is what I want *you* to remember!"

CHAPTER

XXIII

Although I had every intention of keeping my secret to myself, I soon found this impossible. Berengaria knew, from the moment that she saw my face, that something had happened. For the first time in our years together she questioned me, and once I had begun I could not resist telling her the whole story. To my delight she approved of all I had said and done, particularly my sending Raimond back to Toulouse.

"Then, when my lord returns, you will marry him," she said.

"I shall not give Rick a moment's rest until he agrees."

"Good. You would be a fool to throw away such happiness."

The wistfulness in her face and voice saddened me, for what happiness could she see ahead for herself? Why, I wondered, should I have so much and Berengaria so little? All those contented years with William, and now the hope of spending the rest of my life with the man who had shown me what love can be, while she and Richard—

There being nothing I could say, I asked her about Bourgigne.

"She wants to marry Baldwin immediately and travel with him home to Flanders."

"And good riddance," I said. "I hope you agreed, Berengaria. We know Richard favors their union, and any delay might end in her changing her mind."

Berengaria laughed. "I would church them tonight if it were possible."

It was not, of course, but we began making arrangements the very next morning, and before the week was out we stood in the beautiful church of Santa Prassede while they exchanged their vows. I marvelled at the rapture on Baldwin's face, wondering if he had any realization of the problems ahead of him; then I told myself that, as his love had been strong enough to weather Bourgigne's union with Raimond, it would surely carry him through the difficult task of settling even so spoiled and indolent a bride into the different kind of life she must lead in Flanders.

I was fond of Baldwin, however, and sufficiently concerned for his future welfare to return to Santa Prassede later and pray for his guidance. Then, before leaving the church, I made my way into the small vaulted chapel to see the mosaics that I had been told were very fine. They were, and they reminded me so vividly both of our chapel in the palace at Palermo and my own beautiful chamber there—the glittering gold, the enchanting lamb and pair of horses in one of the frescoes—that I sank to the stone floor and prayed for my dear William's soul.

A young priest who entered as I was rising from my knees told me that these particular mosaics were four hundred years old. I found this hard to believe, for the colors were as fresh as if they had just been placed there on the walls. Would the mosaics in Monreale be as beautiful in 1586 as they had been when our cathedral was finished in 1186?

* * *

With Bourgigne gone, Berengaria and I settled down peacefully to await my lord brother. Crusaders were arriving in Rome every day now, and when we heard that many others had already reached their homes in France, and even in England, we were confident that he would soon be with us. We were, in fact, so confident that we ordered his favorite food for supper each night and made sure there was always enough water heating to fill his wooden tub.

I am not sure just when we began to worry. I do know that we were terribly anxious all during Advent; at Christmas I feared, in my heart, that he had been shipwrecked and drowned. By all our figuring he was several weeks overdue, and each hour added to our apprehension. Because of this we spent the day quietly in the palazzo, and our Roman friends, understanding only too well, accepted without question our refusal to join in their festivities.

All our household shared our fears. Stephen de Turnham had been trying to hide his for some time, but his face was proof enough of what he was thinking. Blondel, however, talked of his concern quite openly and, even before Christmas Day, spent most of his time wandering around the city hoping to find some Crusader who had news of our lord's whereabouts. So many were returning by way of Rome that he set out each morning with fresh hopes and unflagging energy.

As he never let us see him looking discouraged, my heart sank when he returned early on the day after Christmas with a white, set face. He asked to see me in private, and this, too, frightened me.

"Tell me, Blondel," I said the moment we were alone. "I know you have bad news."

"It may be, your Grace," was his reply. "Or it may not—I cannot say. But I cannot hide it from you because I haven't enough money."

"Money? Money for what? Mother of God, Blondel, what can you want money for?"

"To buy my lord's belt and gloves." He had tears in his eyes as he spoke, and his voice trembled. "I saw them in a little shop, a shop that sells only beautiful things. And when the owner refused to answer my questions I thought that if I purchased them he might at least tell me where he found them."

"You are sure they are the King's?"

He nodded his pale head. "Of course, my lady. The gloves you and the Queen made for him and the belt he wore on his wedding day."

I rose. "Take me there. But we will not alarm the Queen. As you say, Blondel, this is not necessarily bad news. His Grace may well have sold them for some good reason. Travelling as he was, he could need money and have no way of procuring it openly."

After making sure I had a large sum of gold in my purse, I summoned one of our men-at-arms and we set out on our errand. The shop was close by, an easy stroll, and the moment my eyes rested on the gauntlets and belt I told Blondel he was right.

Picking up the gloves, I saw my own stitches and recognized the pearls that had once adorned William's leggings. There was no question. I turned to the shopkeeper, now hovering over me, and after saying I would buy them I asked how he came by them.

He hesitated, looking from me to Blondel and back again.

"Come, sir," I said sharply. "Answer my question! I am Queen Joan of Sicily, sister of Richard of England, and these are his gloves and belt."

He must have believed me for he knelt instantly, his face as white as the pearls on Richard's gauntlets.

"I am an honest man, your Grace," he quavered. "Everyone will tell you so. I bought them from a Jew who travels around the country purchasing articles of value—an honest man, also, I promise you."

"Where did he purchase these?"

"I don't know. There were other people in the shop, and I could not spare the time to talk."

Blondel interrupted him. "I will go to him now. What is his name and where will I find him?"

The Jewish quarter being some distance away in the oldest part of the city near the Tiber, I sent our man-at-arms back for horses and my litter. Blondel wanted to go on alone but I insisted, and after a short wait we were on our way.

Our route led us past the Colosseum and the Forum and then to the ancient portico of Octavia. Blondel, who was riding beside my litter, leaned down and pointed to the propylaea still standing at its entrance.

"Emperor Augustus built that gate," he told me, "and it was rebuilt in the year 205." When we had passed inside, he said, "Now we are in the Jewish quarter and must watch for a house with the figures of four men cut into its wall."

A strong smell of fresh fish—and some not so fresh—came from the stalls in the center of the square, but they were empty at this hour, and except for a cat or two the narrow streets around us seemed deserted. I remained in my litter with the curtains drawn back as far as they would go, and I was the one who first saw the building for which we were searching.

"There, Blondel," I called to him. "There it is!"

He was off his mount in a flash and into the stone building. A moment later he reappeared and hurried over to my side.

"The man we want is staying with his cousin in that other dwelling—there, two doors away. See, your Grace? That one."

The building he indicated was adorned with another bas relief; this one was of a lion, a dog, and a small hare. Under the lion was an open door through which I could see a steep flight of stone steps.

"Help me out," I said. "I shall go in with you."

Leaving our man-at-arms with the horses, we climbed the stairs and Blondel knocked loudly on the barred door at the top. It opened slowly to reveal a short, fat, frightened woman with a small, round-eyed boy clinging to her black robe.

"I would like to speak to your cousin the merchant," I said, smiling down at her.

She made no reply but took us immediately into a dim, sparsely furnished room. A bearded man rose from a seat beside the fire and advanced to meet us.

I held out the gloves and belt. "I have just purchased these from

247

your friend," I told him. "Will you tell me, sir, where you found them?"

"I did not, my lady," he replied courteously. "It is my cousin Isaac who buys and sells, not me."

"Then may I speak to him, please? These were my brother's possessions and we are eager for any word of his whereabouts."

He shook his head. "Isaac set out for England some days ago."

"England?"

"The city of York, where his parents live—or lived. He goes to discover whether or not they survived the massacre of our people there two years ago." Both his face and his voice were bitter, and I, ignorant of this grim business, did not know what to say.

Seeing me hesitate, Blondel spoke for me.

"Perhaps you can help us, then. Do you know where your kinsman bought these gloves and this belt?"

Again he shook his head. "He showed me a pack full of beautiful things that he purchased recently, but all he said was that he hoped they would sell for enough gold to take him to York and to help any of our people who were still living. I gave him what I could, and so did many of our friends."

There being no reason to question him further, I thanked him and we made our way back down to the street.

"A fruitless errand," said Blondel sadly, helping me into my litter.

"No." I gave him as hopeful a smile as I could. "Perhaps not, Blondel. I shall follow this Isaac to York and then carry whatever news he gives me of the King to our mother, Queen Eleanor."

CHAPTER

XXIV

In later years I often looked back on that journey of mine to York and wondered how it was possible to accomplish it in so short a time. From the moment of my return to our palazzo, when I wasted not an hour in telling first Berengaria and then Stephen de Turnham of my determination to set out after the Jewish merchant, we were all three of us occupied in plans and preparations.

Berengaria not only agreed instantly that I should go to England without delay but also made up her own mind to leave Rome with me. "I shall travel to Poitiers," she decided. "In the hope that you will return to me there. I feel I must not visit England for the first time as Queen without my lord, nor do I wish to remain here any longer."

Stephen, after protesting that winter was not the season for ladies to attempt journeys of such length, put his scruples aside and did everything possible to speed our departure. He was as concerned about Richard as we were and wanted to find and question Isaac without any unnecessary delay. He had, in fact, already agreed to my plan when I pointed out something else in its favor—that my half-brother Geoffrey should be in York and, as its Archbishop, was the best possible person to aid us in our inquiries. His quarrels with Richard were, I knew, all in the past. Richard had told me so himself.

An interview with the Pope quieted some of Stephen's other fears, for his Holiness, instead of merely providing us with a safe-conduct through the places where we might encounter hostility, suggested that we sail the following day with Cardinal Mellar, who had Papal errands in Marseilles; at Marseilles the Cardinal would either find us another powerful escort or would himself conduct us farther on our way.

We packed immediately and divided our household. A few of our people, including Blondel, remained in Rome on the chance that Richard might still arrive there, a few of the youngest and strongest prepared to journey all the way to England with Stephen and me, and the rest would accompany Berengaria to Poitiers.

While we were selecting the few possessions we thought necessary, I found myself remembering my royal father's progresses through England, Normandy, and Poitou, with his Lord High Steward, Lord Great Chamberlain, Lord High Treasurer; his poulterers, cooks, bakers, butlers, fruiterers; his Keeper of the Dishes and Usher of the Spithouse; his lawyers, clerks, chaplains, guards, huntsmen, archers, and hornblowers; not forgetting his own washerwoman and water carrier, and the crowds of actors and artists who straggled along the road behind the long line of wagons and pack animals!

And I remembered, also, my own journeys with William, accompanied by slaves, servants, and nobles.

When Berengaria and I met Cardinal Mellar on board his ship early the next day, he was surprised at our small retinue and our few boxes. I explained that if Stephen and I were to go on to York and then reach my mother in time to help her find Richard, we must travel as swiftly as our couriers—forgetting rank, forgetting even that I was a woman.

To my great relief he did not seem to think us mad. Instead, he assured me that while we were in his care we would proceed as speedily as the winds allowed. "You will not find me a laggard," he said. "The Holy Father sends me on his errands because he knows I do not dally along the way." Then he turned to Stephen. "I do think, however, that you would be wise to dispatch a courier from Marseilles with letters informing Queen Eleanor of what you have discovered and of your plans. If he reaches her first, she can then begin her own inquiries."

Stephen replied that we had already decided to do so. "I tried to persuade her Grace to send me to the Queen," he told the Cardinal, "and remain in Rome herself."

"My lady mother may be anywhere in England or Aquitaine," I broke in. "Or the courier could find her just gone from one place to the other. If we travel to York ourselves we may save many days in the hunt for Isaac." These were the arguments I had used to win Stephen over to my way of thinking, and he had agreed that I was right. Cardinal Mellar, I am glad to say, agreed instantly. "With a courier on the way, too, you will know that everything possible is being done."

*　*　*

The moment we dropped anchor in the harbor at Marseilles— and this time the winds were both strong and favorable—Cardinal Mellar hastened ashore both to attend to his own affairs and to discover whether there was anyone in the old town to take his place as our protector.

Realizing only too well that St. Gilles was only a short sail up the coast, I stood on the deck wondering whether it would be possible to arrange a brief meeting with Raimond. It had been on my mind constantly, of course, despite the fact that I had sent him away so firmly some weeks earlier. To be so very close and not see him was asking a great deal of my better self!

I was still there, enjoying the fresh air with Berengaria but not sharing my wistful thoughts of Raimond, when to our surprise we saw our barge returning with Cardinal Mellar. The moment we glimpsed his face we knew he had good news for us.

I said so to him. "Indeed I do," he replied. "But particularly for *you,* your Grace!" he added, turning to Berengaria. "Your kinsman, the King of Aragon is at this very minute with the Abbot of St. Victor. He is visiting his holdings in Provence."

Following his pointing finger, we saw a rambling old building on the south side of the harbor.

"I found him there in the abbey," he told us, beaming. "He was enchanted to hear of your arrival and will be most happy to take my place and sail with you on the turn of the tide."

Berengaria was overjoyed. "My dear Alphonso! You *have* brought me good news. I've loved King Alphonso since I was a small child!"

I saw why when he joined us on board a few hours later. The King of Aragon was gentle, kind, and quick to understand our problems, and he, like the Cardinal, agreed that we must travel as swiftly as possible.

"I keep hoping to hear some word of my lord on the way," said Berengaria. "I wonder if we should not put in at St. Gilles, Joan, and ask Count Raimond whether he learned anything of Richard's whereabouts while he was making *his* way from Rome to Toulouse? He must have encountered many fellow Crusaders."

Then, while I felt my cheeks grow hot, I heard her explaining to her kinsman that Raimond, unlike his father, was now Richard's close friend, and ours.

"If that is so," said King Alphonso, thoughtfully, "we will certainly halt there long enough to ask him a question or two."

* * *

As we approached the smaller branch of the Rhone that would take us up to St. Gilles, I was again at the rail of our deck, watching the changing coast line. We were quite close to shore, so close that, when Berengaria and Stephen joined me, I was able to point out to them the church and houses of "Our Lady of the Sea." This tiny village was built on the edge of a queer salt marshland that was actually an island, bordered by the sea and framed by two arms of the river Rhone; as Richard had taken me there years ago when I was waiting at St. Gilles to sail to Sicily and my stranger husband, I knew it and its fascinating history.

"Soon after Christ's resurrection," I told my companions, "many of his followers were so persecuted that they embarked in a ship without oars or sails and were guided here by providence. Saint Salome, the mother of the Apostles James and John, was with them, and so were Martha, Mary Magdalene, Lazarus, and Saint Mary, the mother of Joseph and James the Less. They say they lived, died, and were buried here."

For a moment we were all silent, staring at the church outlined against the sky. I was thinking of the days and nights it would take one of our swiftest sailing vessels to make the journey from the Holy Land to this lonely spot—yet that little band had neither sails nor oars!

"I have heard pilgrims talk of visiting here," said Berengaria. "Many of those who passed through Pamplona on their way to St. James's tomb at Compostela began their pilgrimage by worshiping his mother's resting place first."

After that there was nothing to see but waving sea grasses on the river banks and flocks of wheeling, screaming water birds diving into the water around us. I felt as restless as they looked and sounded, and longed for their wings to take me more speedily to St. Gilles's harbor, and Raimond. I was haunted, too, by the fear that he might not be there and that we would have wasted precious hours.

Stephen had protested against our halting, thinking it wiser to sail straight on to Narbonne, where we would begin our overland journey through France. I was not the one who overruled his protests—it was King Alphonso, I am glad to say—but, even so, I was well aware that Berengaria had suggested it for my sake.

For that reason I was doubly grateful when we reached our

destination and our barge, setting out for shore, returned in a mercifully short time with Raimond on board. Before I could catch my breath he was up the rope ladder and kneeling at my feet. I gave him my hand and bade him rise and, as our eyes met, I knew that all was still well between us. Stephen, who had gone into St. Gilles to fetch him, was right behind him; to my great relief he had lost the disapproving frown he had worn ever since we left Marseilles, and my first thought was that Raimond had good news for us.

"You bring us word of Richard?" I asked immediately.

"Alas, no, although I have questioned every Crusader I have encountered since I left Rome. I am here to discover whether I may not have the privilege of escorting you and Queen Berengaria and your people through my father's holdings. I have family business in the city of Toulouse, and I would be most happy to lead you there by the shortest route and to see to your comfort all along the way."

Hearing footsteps on the deck behind me, I turned and saw King Alphonso and Berengaria approaching us. After Raimond had greeted my sister and she had presented him to the King, he repeated his invitation, an invitation that left me speechless. For some reason this had not occurred to me, although I realized later that King Alphonso had had it in mind from the moment Berengaria told him of our friendship with Raimond. Who better, as he said now, to guide us safely through Toulouse?

Stephen, too, was completely in agreement. "If, my lord Count," he said to Raimond, "you understand that the ladies and I must not waste an hour on our way. They are not travelling as royalty."

"Thank God for that! With King Richard in danger I shall be as eager as you to help them reach their destination swiftly. I will arrange for horses and litters. Tell me how soon your party can be ready, Sir Stephen, and how many will be travelling with us; then leave the rest to me."

* * *

In a very short time we had said a grateful farewell to King Alphonso, who would now continue home to Aragon, and were nearing the shore in our barge. But, although our preparations had been concluded with remarkable speed, Raimond had apparently taken care of his share of the tasks even sooner, for there he was again, wading out through the shallow water to meet us.

For the third time I found myself being lifted in his strong arms and carried onto the sandy beach, and if they held me more tightly than was necessary, or proper, I made no protest. As he set me down, my eyes met Berengaria's, and I saw a smile in them that told me she, too, was remembering and was sharing in my happiness.

"It seems wrong to have you here in St. Gilles and not take you home to my castle," said Raimond, leading us to the waiting horses, pack horses, and litters—we were dispensing with baggage wagons and taking only what could be carried in saddlebags—and helping me mount a sturdy little mare.

"Never mind," I replied softly, so only he could hear. "Another time, perhaps."

This brought the color into his cheeks as he arranged the reins for me, and his hand touched mine in a secret caress. While the others were landing and lining up behind us, I looked all around the pretty, busy harbor, thinking of it as my home, too, if we should become man and wife. The same thought was very much in my mind as we rode through the town, and when we drew near the abbey church I slowed my horse to a walk. I still remembered its almost unbelievably beautiful stone façade, a glorious mixture of holy figures, delicate leafy tracery, and charming animals. It was unfinished when I saw it first, in 1176, and now, seventeen years later, I saw that the stone masons and sculptors were still at work.

They put down their tools to bow, replying cheerfully to Raimond's shouted words of encouragement and farewell.

"You must be very proud," I said as we left the church behind. "King William and I built many handsome edifices, but none of

255

our stonework can compare with that!"

"Our best men have spent their lives on it," Raimond admitted. "We bring them from Arles and Toulouse; we scour the country-side for them and pay them well. With luck, you and I will be here together when they gather up their tools for the last time."

* * *

The countryside along the coast was rather dull, but after we left Narbonne and turned farther inland, on our way to Carcassonne, it changed constantly, delighting us with its variety and beauty. At times we rode along between bare hills that reminded me of the hills surrounding and protecting Jerusalem; at others we traversed rich green valleys bounded by softer, mistier hills on the right and strange, bleak mounds on the left. I even remember a stretch when I fancied myself on one of our English moors, and another when our little cavalcade seemed all alone in a world of desolate, rocky peaks.

Having risen with the sun each day, spent every possible hour in the saddle, and passed the nights in simple hostelries, we were all glad to see the walls and towers of Carcassonne looming above us on its steep hilltop. We would be more than comfortable here, we knew, and Raimond had assured us that we would be welcome.

A messenger rode on ahead to announce our arrival. Raimond led us over the bridge that spanned the Aude River, through the stone gate that opened as we approached it, and into the courtyard in front of the castle; there we faced the twin towers and wall of the castle itself, guarded by another bridge and another great doorway set into its own stone arch.

The courtyard was crowded with the usual people that inhabit such places, some going busily about their tasks, others idling and watching us with curious eyes. The usual dogs, too, skirmished around our horses' hooves, some snapping, some barking in a friendly fashion and wagging their tails. As we made our way through them we heard a loud hail, and a slender lad ran through the arch and over the bridge.

Raimond answered his shout, jumped off his horse, and gave him a great bear hug. He took the boy first to Berengaria, who was riding beside Stephen, and I saw that he was about thirteen years of age, with dark hair and eyes, very like Raimond himself.

A moment later Raimond brought him to my side. "My young cousin, namesake, and godson," he said proudly. "Raimond-Roger Trencavel, your Grace, who will, one day, be the Viscount of Carcassonne and lord of all you see here."

"In my father's absence, my lady," the lad greeted me formally, "I bid you very welcome. He is off at Albi—and will curse the errand that took him from home at such a time. But come, come into the castle to my lady mother."

We alighted and followed him rather stiffly up the stone staircase and through the inner guard room to the great hall of the keep where we found the Viscountess, Raimond-Roger's mother, with her ladies and gentlemen behind her. After warm words of welcome, she led us through two more vast rooms and into a third, which at first sight seemed to be full of scurrying handmaidens; they were spreading coverlets on several great bedsteads, laying pallets beside them on the stone floor, patting cushions into shape on wooden benches, and placing silver basins and ewers of water on the heavily carved chests that stood against the walls.

"With a little more time to prepare for your Graces," she murmured, her gentle voice and sweet face showing concern, "we would have spared you this bustle. You are weary, I know, and will want to retire early. Tomorrow we shall ready other chambers, so that you and your ladies need not be so crowded together."

Dropping down on the nearest bench, Berengaria gave a tired sigh. "We will be more than content here, dear lady. And we must be on the road again soon after dawn."

The Viscountess looked both surprised and horrified. "But you cannot—you will surely remain with us a se'enight or so!"

I hastened to make what explanation I could. Raimond had told me that although the Trencavels had never entered into his father's strife with us the less we said to anyone of our real purpose in

257

hurrying to England the better. "There are urgent family reasons for reaching my mother's side just as soon as possible," I told her. "And we must consider the weather also. So far we have been fortunate."

She nodded. "We have snow, some winters. Carcassonne is beautiful then, but it keeps us all up here in our *cité* until it melts. If we are to have only this evening together we will make the most of it. Refresh yourselves, dear ladies, and come to me in the hall where we met."

While our ladies shook the wrinkles out of fresh robes—we were heartily tired of the heavy woolen cotes in which we had been travelling—I climbed into a windowed niche in the thick wall and sat on one of the stone seats there. Here I could look out over the surrounding countryside for many miles. Even at this bleak season, it was a breathtaking sight, stretching to the far-away hills. I was to discover later that, because the *cité* was so high, almost any aperture in its walls provided views equally rewarding.

Berengaria, following me there, gave another weary sigh.

"Why not rest here for a few days?" I suggested. "We could part company now and spare you any more of these long, long rides."

"No, Joan—please!" The very thought seemed to frighten her. "Not until we are closer to my lord's lands. Toulouse, without Count Raimond, would be full of dangers, and I suspect that if you set out ahead of me he will be a member of *your* party, not mine."

This I could not deny, and we sat quietly, thinking our own thoughts, I counting the days until Raimond would leave us, then savoring the companionship we had already enjoyed together. Even with the heavy shadow of Richard's disappearance darkening our hearts, I had the satisfaction of knowing that every hour in Raimond's company had drawn us closer; the inevitable strains of our mode of travel, which might well have weakened the love between us, had strengthened it instead. We fitted together, and when we should part at Bordeaux, or wherever he and Stephen decided we must say farewell, I knew now I would feel bereft.

Deciding finally to forget our parting and enjoy the evening ahead, I took more pains with my appearance than I had since we set sail from Italy. Here we were queens again, not just two dusty women halting at a plain hostelry, too weary to think of anything but supper and bed.

I must have been successful for, to my amusement, my Raimond's dark eyes were not the only ones that lighted up when I entered the great hall behind Berengaria. Young Raimond-Roger, whose privilege it was to lead my gentle sister to the high table and take the chair beside her, kept glancing my way, his boyish admiration apparent on his eager face.

"My godson and I seem to think alike," Raimond murmured in my ear as we were finishing our meal. "He has a weakness for red hair and blue eyes too, I see. How well I remember the first time a lovely lady stirred my senses! I wonder if he will sing for you, or if his voice is still uncertain."

It must have been, for the lad played the vielle for us instead, and with so great a skill for one so young that we all marvelled and called for more and more. When at last we allowed him to stop, he came right to my side.

"My lady mother suggests that we take you and the Queen to the top of her favorite tower," he said. "The moon is almost full and she is very proud of the view by moonlight."

Hearing me agree, Raimond insisted on our sending for warm cloaks, and while we waited for them I strolled around the hall and studied the fresh paintings on the walls, spirited scenes depicting, among other things, meetings between the French and the Saracens. The artist had used much of the same blue paint that covered the vaulted ceiling and I was charmed with the result; it was not as striking, of course, as our mosaics, but the figures were much more lifelike.

The Viscountess was pleased when I said so.

"I wish my lord could hear that," she said. "They were painted by a member of King Philip's entourage who halted here on his way home from the Crusade soon after the fall of Acre. It seems a long time ago."

I thought to myself that it was indeed a very long time ago. To me, certainly, almost a lifetime ago. Much had happened since that summer of 1191.

Our cloaks arrived a moment later, and we all made our way to the tower. The Viscountess would not let us pause on the lower floors or look over the countryside until we reached a room that covered the whole top of the tower, roofed, but with eight broad loopholes set into the walls at regular intervals. By moving from one to the other we could see in all directions, and the moon, dazzling bright, glimmered on the river Aude below the walled city, then spread its white light over the fields and woodlands and even on the far hills beyond, making us gasp with its beauty.

I was so enchanted that I was only vaguely aware that young Raimond-Roger was pleading with his mother for something, wheedling and coaxing in the way of a son with an indulgent parent. This time, apparently, she was not indulgent, for he came to wish us good night with a doleful face.

"I wish you would talk to my mother for me, sir," he said to Raimond. "Both she and my lord father have said that I should join your household now that the Crusade is over, and I cannot persuade her that this is the perfect time to do so. I want to set out with you tomorrow."

"I'm sorry, lad," said Raimond, shaking his head at the boy. "I would be taking you much too far from home. However, you have my promise to send for you the moment I return to St. Gilles."

After he left us, very reluctantly, the Viscountess asked if we, too, were ready to retire.

"I am," answered Berengaria immediately. Before I could reply, she added, "Will you discuss tomorrow's journey with Count Raimond for me, Joan? I am too weary to remember whatever it was we wished to ask him."

"Gladly," I said. "If you will remain a moment or two, my lord Count? I will not detain you long."

I was in his arms almost before the others had started down the staircase.

"Her Grace is kind," Raimond said between kisses.

"She is—but I do have a question for you, Raimond. I thought we were now only a short distance from the city of Toulouse."

"We are."

"Then you plan to accompany me as far as Bordeaux? That is where we will part?"

"No."

"But Raimond, you told Raimond-Roger you could not take him so far from home! Surely Toulouse is not far from home for the lad."

"Dear heart"—he sounded amused and very, very tender—"I am not leaving you at Toulouse or at Bordeaux. I am going all the way to England with you, my foolish one. In case you have forgotten, Richard's disappearance has given me an extremely important reason of my own for visiting your lady mother, the Queen Eleanor."

CHAPTER

XXV

I huddled into my warmest cloak and smiled over at my new companion, the Lady Amicia. She was watching our tiring-women pack up my few changes of clothing and her own seven or eight boxes and, as she returned my smile, her grey eyes lighting up her plain, bony face, I thought again how fortunate I was to have her with me on this rough, cold voyage. Never once had she complained; her cheerful acceptance of our many discomforts, her quiet companionship during the long days and nights when we were unable to move about the tossing ship, had all endeared her so to my heart that I was dreading our parting.

I was grateful, also, for her unswerving agreement that as long as the winter winds were taking us up toward York we should not make for land and ride the rest of the way. The master of our sturdy vessel, not liking his task of carrying a queen over the stormy seas, would gladly have put in at Dover, Yarmouth, Boston, or, indeed, any little port along the English coast. This I was most reluctant to do, knowing how slow our progress must be on shore at this season.

Had the winds turned unfavorable I would have agreed instantly to change our plans. But they had not, and we were sailing toward the mouth of the Humber River and small Wyke-upon-Hull, where we would disembark. From there it would be a two-day journey to York, after which I would go to my mother.

Lady Amicia had promised to remain with me as long as I needed her, but as her home was near Leicester I was determined not to take her too far off her road. By accompanying me from Bordeaux she had made it possible for me to send all my other ladies with Berengaria. This I had been very eager to do, for the farther north they travelled with me the more obvious it became that there was not one of them suited to the rigors of a rough sea crossing, followed by an English winter, and when Lady Amicia came to me at the castle in Bordeaux I saw immediately that my problem was solved.

"I am Lady Amicia Kibworth," she told me, "a cousin of the late Earl of Leicester and, until she returned to England after his death, a member of Lady Petronilla's household at Breteuil. As my husband wished me to remain on this side of the water while he was on Crusade, I then came here to Bordeaux, where I have many friends. But my lord fell at Jaffa—and I must go home. Would there be room on your ship, your Grace, for me and my tiring-woman?"

"There would indeed," I replied warmly. Then, because I liked and trusted her at first sight, I confided in her, telling her both why we were heading for York, and my hopes for the future with Raimond. She understood instantly my reasons for wanting a smaller entourage, and by the time we finished our talk it was decided that she would come to me as lady-in-waiting, companion, duenna, all in one, and that a few tiring-women would suffice to make up the rest of my household.

Both Sir Stephen and Berengaria were appalled at this plan, especially as Stephen had finally made up his mind that his duty lay with Richard's Queen. Eager as he was to find some word of his master's whereabouts, he had, after all, been left in charge of Berengaria, and he had found no one during our travels to take his place.

However, in the short interval before Lady Amicia and I boarded our ship with Raimond, she so won their respect that they declared themselves satisfied with my new arrangement, Stephen even admitting that he was glad I was not hampered by a larger suite.

As for me, I thanked God every day on our voyage that I had only Lady Amicia and our strong serving women with me, wondering whether I could again endure the irritations that are part of a queen's life when she is surrounded by ladies and gentlemen. And if I was grateful for our small retinue on shipboard, I was more so during our ride from Wyke-upon-Hull to York. We mounted our horses before midday, reached York just as darkness fell the following afternoon, and rode immediately to the Archbishop's palace, close by the Minster.

There we learned that Geoffrey was indeed within its walls, and he soon appeared, looking so much like Richard that I failed to see how anyone could doubt that he was my father's son. My father, certainly, had never questioned it, having acknowledged him as such at least ten years before I was born; in fact, one of the first things I remember is watching Geoffrey wrestling with my true-born brothers.

Even then, it seems, he was destined for the Church. While he was still a boy my father made him Archdeacon of Lincoln; then, three years before I left England for Sicily, he became Lincoln's Bishop; now, of course, he was Archbishop of York.

I must have been about seven years old when we last met, and Geoffrey a lad of twenty; despite this great lapse of time, however, we greeted each other as brother and sister, and although he was obviously puzzled by my appearance in York, unannounced and almost unattended, he asked no questions. After he had welcomed Count Raimond and Lady Amicia he took me aside for a word in private, and before he could say anything or raise an eyebrow I told him what had brought me here and why I was travelling in such a fashion.

He heard me out, his face growing more sober as he listened.

When I paused, at last, he rose and moved to the door. "Await me here," he said. "I will send someone to seek out this merchant for us."

He was with me again in a moment. "I suppose you know, dear sister," he said, "that England is full of rumors concerning Richard. Many of our people think him dead; others say he is shipwrecked on some distant isle. Our brother John, of course, hopes to hear the worst. But I need not tell you how his fingers itch to hold the scepter!"

"And my lady mother?"

"Is so concerned about Richard that only the need to protect his kingdom keeps her here in England. If it were not for that she would be searching for him herself—or so she told me when I attended her Christmas Court in London."

Geoffrey then changed the subject by asking me how I came to be in Raimond's care. "The Counts of Toulouse have been our enemies for many, many years," he said.

"I know," I replied. "But Count Raimond has never entered into his father's quarrels with my mother. He and Richard were friends long ago, and they renewed their friendship during the Crusade. But it was not Richard who placed me in Count Raimond's hands; it was King Alphonso of Aragon." I hastened to explain how that had come about, and I told him Berengaria's reason for staying on the other side of the water. "Sir Stephen remained in charge of her household, and Count Raimond was kind enough to escort me here."

From his dubious expression, I suspected that my story did not fully satisfy him. He said no more, however, and, after leading me back to where Raimond and Lady Amicia awaited us, sent for food and wine.

While we supped, I asked him to tell us about the Jewish massacre. "Were you in York when it happened, Geoffrey?"

"I was on my way to Normandy," he replied. "With the Queen, our brother John, and the Lady Alys. Richard had summoned us all there for a great council. However, I *was* in London at Richard's coronation at the time the trouble really began."

"What was the reason for the massacre?" asked Raimond. "Why did your people rise against the Jews at that particular time?"

"Because of money, I think, although it was Richard's refusal to have any Jews at his Coronation that brought everything to a head. They already held much of our wealth, and when our nobles were forced to borrow large sums from them to go on Crusade they instantly raised their interest charges. This made so much ill feeling that our people snatched at any excuse for a general slaughter."

"Why did my lord brother not welcome them to his Coronation and make them his friends? He was reaching in every pocket for gold for the Crusade. Why not theirs?"

"I don't know." Geoffrey sighed. "In any case, his order was strictly obeyed: no women and no Jews were admitted either to the Abbey or to the banquet afterwards, and this particularly angered Benedict and Josias, a pair of extremely wealthy merchants who had travelled down from York with large retinues to attend the ceremonies and bring gifts to the new King. They tried first to enter the Abbey, then the banqueting hall; in the ensuing scuffle Benedict was seriously wounded and dragged into a church, where he was baptized by force. They brought him, bleeding, before Richard—we were all there—and he shouted defiantly that he was still a Jew in his heart and would remain one until he died of his wounds, which he said would be soon. The guards drove him out of the hall and not long after he did die."

I shivered, remembering scenes in the past and wondering again how Richard could be so cruel. "What happened to the other one?" I asked.

"He escaped and came home to York. In the months that followed there were Jewish massacres and house burnings in Lynn, Stamford, and Bury St. Edmund's, but nothing happened here until March, when part of our city caught fire. Then, while many of our townspeople were occupied fighting it, others surrounded the by now well-fortified home of Benedict, forced their way in, murdered his widow, his children, and some friends, stripped it of everything of value, and burned it to the ground.

"This frightened Josias, who took his family and all his wealth to the castle and begged the constable for protection. It was granted. Then the townspeople burned Josias's house in Coney Street, which drove many more Jews into the castle—and then, by some unbelievable error, these frightened men refused entry to the constable himself! He, with the help of the Posse Comitatus, besieged his own castle, and the Jews, trapped inside, tried to buy their way to safety. When it was refused, a foreign rabbi who was with them suggested that they destroy their goods, set fire to the castle, and return to God by killing themselves."

"Oh, no!" I heard myself protest. "Oh, no, Geoffrey!"

"He must have been very persuasive, for Josias immediately slew his wife and children and insisted that the rabbi cut his throat for him. Others followed his example, but those who were not that brave put out the fire started by their dead friends, climbed up on the walls, and screamed the whole story to the constable standing at the foot of the mound. To prove it they threw the bodies over and pleaded for mercy."

"Surely the constable granted it?"

"I'm afraid he lied to them, Joan. Once the Jews opened the gates, our men marched in and killed everyone who was still alive."

"No wonder this Isaac was concerned for his parents," said Raimond quietly.

"They may well have perished with the others—or gone elsewhere. Very few remained here in York, although some, in the intervening years, have returned."

"I do remember Richard being angry about some trouble, and sending back orders that your constable be dismissed, many knights fined, and soldiers punished," I said. "We had just reached Acre, I think, and I never heard why."

We were going over and over the dreadful business when Geoffrey's messenger entered the chamber.

"The merchant Isaac was here in the city a few weeks ago," he told his master. "But when he learned that all his kin had fled to Lincoln, your Grace, he set out for there immediately."

"Ah," said my brother, "then with luck, and Hugh's help, we should find him. Hugh"—he turned to Raimond—"is our very holy Archbishop of Lincoln. During these troubled years he has made his city a haven for the oppressed."

Both Geoffrey and Raimond urged me to remain in York while they sought Isaac in Lincoln, but I refused. We would set out together early the next morning, I told them firmly, and, whether we heard anything helpful from the merchant or not, I would be that much closer to London and my lady mother.

When they finally agreed, I asked Geoffrey to take me to his beautiful Minster. "I will rest more peacefully if we pray for Richard and the success of our mission."

"Wrap up in your warmest cloak, then," was Geoffrey's reply. "There are few places colder in the winter months than our cathedrals. The short walk from my palace gates will seem warm by comparison."

He was right. Although a bitter wind whipped our thick garments around our legs and threatened to blow out the torches that lighted our way across the bleak close, the dank chill of the great vaulted edifice was much worse. It seemed to reach into my very bones, numbing my feet and limbs when I knelt on the icy stones and making my teeth chatter so violently that I found it difficult to compose myself for prayer.

Geoffrey made our pleas brief; then, before we returned to the palace, he led me to the north aisle to see a glazed window of which he was very proud. Unfortunately it was hardly visible in the dim light, but, while he was pointing it out to me, I saw a familiar ring on his finger: my lord father's own signet, that he had always worn. Should it belong to his baseborn son, I wondered? Should it not be Richard's?

Seeing my puzzled glance, Geoffrey raised it to his lips. "Our father the King bestowed this ring on me with almost his last breath," he said. "This and his promise that I should be Archbishop of York. It was my privilege to care for him at the very end—to rest his head on my shoulder, to fan away the clouds of July flies that swarmed around his deathbed, and to comfort him as best I could in the rare moments when his senses returned to him. We were almost alone; Richard had received the kiss of peace, but your father's curse followed it. And he had just discovered that even his beloved John had turned against him. On that sad, blazing-hot day, he had only one son at his side. His bastard son."

I was silent, not knowing what to say. "I have heard something of my brothers' quarrels with my father," I told him, at last, "but I cannot judge the matter. I only know that I love Richard dearly and that I am frightened for him."

"In justice to Richard, I must tell you that he hastened to carry out our father's dying promise. He saw to it that I became the Archbishop of York immediately, and we have been good friends ever since."

We turned, then, and walked back to the huge door. I compared the noble structure around us to St. Sernin at Toulouse, which I had visited with Raimond. "It was surprisingly plain," I told Geoffrey. "A painted fresco lent it color and the curved vaulting of its ceiling a feeling of grandeur, but there was no elaborate marble, no mosaics—"

Geoffrey looked at me in amazement. "You were in the city of Toulouse? There is something here I cannot understand. You, a daughter of Eleanor and Henry of England, were received in Toulouse by its Count, their sworn enemy?"

"No, no," I replied hastily. "Raimond's father was down at his castle of Crampagna, near Foix, or I should not have set foot in his city." Then, as he still looked at me with puzzled eyes, I shivered and suggested we walk more swiftly. "I begin to long for my warm bed," I said.

*   *   *

I thought of Geoffrey's comfortable beds often during our bone-wracking journey from York to Lincoln and I am afraid that Lady

Amicia did, too, for her face was quite grey when we finally clattered into the courtyard of Bishop Hugh's dwelling. This, to my surprise, was in Stowe, twelve miles north of Lincoln and not, as I had expected, near the city's cathedral.

"The Bishop's palace was damaged by the same earthquake in 1185 that brought about the collapse of the two main towers of the Minster," Geoffrey explained. "Hugh began rebuilding everything last summer, but he is, in the meantime, living at Stowe, the mother church of Lincoln. He is very devout, and a great man. He allows no one to influence him and does only what he considers right. And he is, I know, happier in quiet Stowe than he will be in the palace."

Stowe was, indeed, quiet; it could, I thought, be a monastery, with its long empty corridors and cell-like rooms. A strange contrast, certainly, to Geoffrey's richly appointed palace, bustling with liveried servants and noisy with the chattering voices and the laughter of visitors and townspeople.

A young priest made us welcome and led us to a cloistered garden. "His Grace walks out here every morning at this time," he told us. "Every dry day. Ah, there he is, coming down the path."

There he was indeed, moving swiftly toward us. A plain woolen cloak opened over a girdled robe like the one worn by our guide, and his bearded face was all but hidden by its hood. But I think I was only vaguely aware of his monkish garb; the thing that caught and held my eyes was the large white swan that pattered along beside him.

As they neared us, Bishop Hugh placed his hand on the bird's smooth head and kept it there. Then, while the young priest presented us to him and we exchanged greetings, his fingers slipped caressingly up and down the long curved neck, and the swan sidled closer and closer until he was resting his feathered head on the Bishop's cloak.

"You find me with one of my best friends," Bishop Hugh said, smiling at us. "Although I keep reminding him that he has a family on the moat, he seems to prefer my company to theirs. And when I cannot join him for our daily stroll, they tell me he grumbles around the garden, flapping his wings. But come, we must not stand here in the cold."

With one last pat he turned the bird about and ordered him off. The order was obeyed so reluctantly that we were all still laughing when Hugh took us to a chamber where there was food and wine. Our laughter was soon forgotten, however, for Hugh's concern over Richard's disappearance proved as great as ours.

"Many of our nobles and their knights have returned home in the last month or so," he told us, his face grave. "And every one of them expected the King to reach England around Christmas time. I don't know what to think about his belt and gloves appearing in Rome, but I agree that we should find the merchant immediately. This should not be difficult. Most of Lincoln's Jews live near the castle and the cathedral—I promised them that they would never be molested there—and, as you will see, they have built themselves some very handsome houses. While you rest, I will send someone to Aaron; if this Isaac is here, Aaron will know. He is our wealthiest, most respected Jew and has both family and business connections all over England."

As he finished speaking the same young priest who had escorted us to the garden entered the chamber with a letter in his hand.

"For you, your Grace," he told Hugh. "A royal messenger brought it from Newark Castle."

"A royal messenger? From Newark?" Taking the letter, the Bishop examined the seal. "This is Queen Eleanor's seal. Could she be at Newark Castle?"

He turned it over again slowly, and I wanted to scream at him to open it. I suppose it was only a minute before he did, but I had enough time to think of the many frightening things it might contain; my lord brother's death, of course, came first to my mind.

But his face, after he broke the seal and began to read, set that particular fear to rest. "Her Grace *is* at Newark. I am to join her there at the earliest possible moment. She is, she writes, visiting many of the royal castles and has urgent business with her barons and bishops."

"I hope she will be pleased to find the Bishop of York within such easy reach," said Geoffrey. "We will go to her together."

As for me, I felt as if a great load had rolled off my shoulders. My lady mother so close! I had been dreading another long journey down to London or Winchester or wherever she happened to be, and this solved several of my problems.

"I am happy for myself and for you, Lady Amicia." I went to her side and took her hand in mine. "Rest here for a few days; then either come to me again at Newark or, if you prefer, continue on your way to Leicester. You have worn yourself out on my behalf."

While I was speaking to her I heard Raimond telling the others that he, too, had business with my lady mother, and my heart began to pound. We had agreed to think of ourselves as little as possible, during our search for news of Richard, and to behave so discreetly that no one would suspect what lay between us. But now, of course, there was no reason why Raimond should not settle the question of our marriage with my mother while we were all together at Newark.

My hand trembled in Lady Amicia's, and she gave it a reassuring squeeze.

"I shall certainly not remain here without you," she said. "We have many hours of daylight still. Let us ride into Lincoln and seek out the merchant—all of us—then, if it is not too late, continue on to Newark and the Queen."

Seeing my face light up, Raimond added his voice to hers but made a suggestion of his own. "Rest for an hour, dear ladies," he said, "and some of us will ride on ahead to find Aaron and, with his help, Isaac. In this way you should be refreshed and no time will be wasted."

My Raimond's plan was accepted by everyone, and he, Geoffrey, and one of Hugh's young priests were long gone down the road to

272

Lincoln before the rest of us climbed into our saddles again. The day, fortunately, had turned warmer. A pale February sun broke through the clouds, and although the countryside was brown and bleak we galloped along in comparative comfort. We were all well mounted—Hugh had seen to that—and our good strong horses covered the miles in less time than I thought possible. In fact, before I could believe that we were much more than half way to our destination, Bishop Hugh was pointing to the towers of his city, high above us. Soon after that we crossed the river Witham, rode along the High Street, and started up the steep, narrow brick road leading to the castle and what remained of the cathedral.

As we proceeded slowly on our way, Bishop Hugh called my attention to a stone house on the left. "There," he said, "that house with the moulded doorway—see the basketweave pattern around its arch? With the chimney over it? That's the home of one of our wealthy Jewish families."

"Aaron?"

"No, Aaron lives on the other side of the hill, within the Bail."

We had reached the steepest part of Steep Hill, as it was called, the steepest and the narrowest, when we saw Raimond and Geoffrey emerge from a plainer house and wave to us to halt.

"Isaac is here," Geoffrey announced immediately. "He remembers the gloves and belt well. He bought them in December, he says, in Vienna, from a young lad who was English but first addressed him in German. They belonged to his master, a Crusader who needed gold for fresh horses. He knows nothing else."

Vienna. Richard in Vienna—and no news of him since December. Vienna, one of the most dangerous places in the world for him to be! He had told me himself that the Emperor Henry and Leopold of Austria were both his sworn enemies. . . .

"Ask him to accompany us to Queen Eleanor," I heard Bishop Hugh say. "Her Grace must hear this disturbing news from his own lips."

Hugh took us all into the castle at Lincoln for a hasty meal while they saddled fresh horses, but that interval and the ride from there to Newark are hazy in my mind. The truth is that I was suddenly convinced that Richard was dead, and the grave faces of the rest of our party did nothing to allay my fears. If my brother was in Vienna in December and had not been heard of since, I told myself, he must have been captured there by the Emperor and put to death.

Lady Amicia, I remember, tried to cheer me by whispering that he had probably fallen ill along the way, no doubt a return of his fever; that his messages to us could well have been intercepted; that any one of a dozen things might be delaying his return: snow, lack of money. Just because *our* journey had prospered, she argued, did not mean that everyone else would be so fortunate. The winter was a perilous time to be on the roads.

I suppose I agreed. I do not know. I know I saw Raimond looking at me with loving, worried eyes when we mounted our horses in the castle courtyard. But even that did not melt the ice that was gathering around my heart, and as we clattered down the hill and over the road that led to Newark every hoofbeat pounded the same words into my brain: "Richard is dead—Richard is dead—Richard is dead!"

I saw him in chains before Henry the Emperor and remembered Isaac of Cyprus on his knees at Limassol, begging for his daughter's safety. I pictured Richard, his red head high, flouting Henry and being dragged, shouting defiance, to some cold and rat-infested dungeon. I imagined him dying by the sword, strangulation, starvation. . . .

There was good reason for these fears. My lord brother had told them to me himself, when he had explained why he could not sail home openly with the other Crusaders. And here he was—lost—in the place that held the greatest danger for him. The fact that I was desperately weary made it easier for me to lose sight of hope, of course; I had, after all, been travelling for weeks as women rarely travel, at a pace that was unusually swift even for men, day after day after day, and with my great anxiety for my brother burdening my heart.

I saw little of the meres and marshes of the fenny country we rode through; I think my eyes were on the horsemen ahead of me, if they were anywhere. I do remember that it soon grew colder, for the sun had lost its warmth even before we left Lincoln, and as we drew near our destination the fading light failed and the air around us was very bitter.

Our attendants guided us by torchlight for the last mile or so, and I suspect that we were all numb and swaying in our saddles. I was, certainly, when I heard a shout and, looking up, saw Newark Castle just ahead, a great dark shape outlined dimly against the evening sky. Faint twinkles at the windows were heartening. We urged our mounts on more rapidly and were soon crossing the river that lapped against the high stone foundation. The lights were bright now, reflected cheerfully on the black water flowing by, and, as I walked my patient horse slowly over the bridge, loud voices hailed us from the gatehouse on the other side.

There was much shouting back and forth before the great portcullis was raised and we were allowed to enter, but this was as it should be, for Newark Castle, known as the "Key to the North," was always strongly guarded. Tonight, with England's Regent, Queen Eleanor, within its high walls, there was double reason for caution. I was glad that even one of her daughters and two of her archbishops must name themselves before being admitted.

Once inside, all was warm and welcoming. Our cavalcade was instantly surrounded by a noisy crowd made up of those who lived in the castle and members of my lady mother's retinue, and as they lifted us from our saddles and helped us over the rough cobbles we saw doors and windows being flung open and excited faces looking down on us.

The word of our arrival must have been carried to my mother while we waited outside the gatehouse, because she was standing just inside the castle entrance, her arms held out to me. After we drew apart she turned to greet Bishop Geoffrey and Bishop Hugh.

"I am more than happy to see you both," she told them, "and eager to discover how you and my daughter come to be travelling together in this part of the world." Then, seeing her eyes move to Raimond, I waved him forward and presented him to her.

She stiffened. "Count Raimond of St. Gilles? I am sure I need not conceal my surprise, my lord Count, in meeting you in England. What brings *you* here?"

"A private and very personal matter that I wish to discuss with your Grace," he replied quickly, "and something much more pressing—the disappearance of my very dear friend and companion, your son, King Richard."

My mother caught her breath and her face was suddenly that of an old, old woman.

"If you are here as Richard's friend," she said slowly, "I bid you welcome." Holding out a shaking hand, she spoke again. "You bring me news of my son?"

"I have escorted the Lady Joan here to tell you something that may possibly be of help in discovering his whereabouts. But it is a long tale, my lady, and she has ridden many miles since dawn with only two brief halts along the way for rest and refreshment."

"And now I keep her and all of you standing in this chill hall! Forgive me; my fears for the King have made me forget all else."

Any lack of thought for our comfort was soon remedied. While we retired to wash the dust off our hands and faces, she had a table just large enough for the six of us placed near a roaring fire in her privy chamber; when we joined her there, servants rushed up from the kitchens with platters of steaming food, served us, and disappeared.

We ate for a few minutes in grateful silence. My lady mother watched us closely, waiting until we had satisfied the worst pangs of our hunger before questioning me.

I began, finally, with Blondel's discovery of Richard's gloves and belt in Rome and then related all that had happened since. She interrupted me first to say that the courier we had dispatched from Marseilles had not yet reached her and, later, to ask why Berengaria had remained in France and how I happened to be travelling with only one lady.

When I had answered her questions as best I could and had come to the account of this day's events, I suggested that Geoffrey finish the tale, he having been one of those who talked with Isaac the merchant.

To my surprise, my mother seemed very little disturbed by what Geoffrey told her, merely saying that she would question Isaac further herself.

After that she rose, walked to a small chest on the other side of the room, opened it, and lifted out a roll of parchment.

"This," she told us, unrolling it as she returned to her seat, "is a copy of a letter from Emperor Henry to Philip of France. It came to me from the Archbishop of Rouen. Let me read it to you.

"Henry by the grace of God, Emperor of the Romans and ever august, to his beloved and special friend Philip, the illustrious King of the Franks, health and sincere love and affection. In as much as our imperial highness does not doubt that your royal mightiness will

277

be delighted at all things in which the omnipotence of the Creator has honored and exalted ourselves and the Roman Empire, we have thought proper to inform your nobleness by means of these presents that while the enemy of our empire and the disturber of your kingdom, Richard, King of England, was crossing the sea for the purpose of returning to his dominions, it so happened that the winds brought him, the ship being wrecked on board of which he was, to the region of Istria, at a place which lies between Aquileia and Venice, where, by the sanction of God, the king, having suffered shipwreck, escaped, together with a few others. A faithful subject of ours, the Count Maynard of Gortze, and the people of that district, hearing that he was in our territory and calling to mind the treason and treachery and accumulated mischief he was guilty of in the Land of Promise, pursued him with the intention of making him prisoner. However, the king taking flight, they captured eight knights of his retinue. Shortly after, the king proceeded to a borough in the archbishopric of Salzburg, which is called Frisi, where Frederic de Botestowe took six of his knights, the king hastening on by night, with only three attendants, in the direction of Austria. The roads however, being watched, and guards being set on every side, our dearly beloved cousin Leopold, Duke of Austria, captured the king so often mentioned, in an humble house in a village in the vicinity of Vienna. Inasmuch as he is now in our power, and has always done his utmost for your annoyance and disturbance, what we have above stated we have thought proper to notify to your nobleness, knowing that the same is well pleasing to your kindly affection for us, and will afford most abundant joy to your own feelings. Given at Creutz, on the fifth day before the calends of January."

My relief at knowing that Richard was still alive was followed by a feeling of deep regret that I had put so many people to so much trouble for nothing, and that I myself had overturned so many rules of royal behavior for the same result. My first thought was that, now we knew my lord brother had been captured by his enemies, a demand from us would bring his release.

This, I soon learned, was not so. My lady mother was dispatching letters to the Pope almost every day, but until we discovered just where Richard was imprisoned he continued to be in mortal danger. Many of our friends, she told us, were already seeking him: the Abbots of Boxley and Pontrobert were looking for him in Bavaria, Hubert Walter was combing Germany, and the Bishop of Bath—a kinsman of Emperor Henry—was on his way to visit the Emperor in the hope of bringing him to his senses.

When my mother finished telling us all this, she rose again and held out her hand to Raimond. "Come to me in the morning," she said, "and we will talk of the private matter that brings you to me. My people have orders to make you comfortable for the night."

Raimond took his abrupt dismissal gracefully, smiling at me as he bowed. My mother watched him go, her face impassive.

"I hope," she said, after the door was closed behind him, "that you have not brought one of Philip's spies into our midst, Joan. He is, after all, his father's son! I would have sent him hence long since, but there is now nothing secret about Richard's capture or our attempts to find him. Do you know what his business with me is?"

"I do, but I promised him that I would not reveal it." I felt the color rise in my cheeks and saw her lips tighten. Then she shrugged.

"Whatever it is, I am sure tomorrow will be soon enough to hear it. And now, my lords, if you will bear with me, I have other serious matters to discuss before you retire."

I made a move to leave, but she waved me back.

"No, no, Joan. You may as well hear this damnable problem from me. It will be better so. It is John and his treacherous conniving again! At the first hint of Richard's capture he sneaked off to Normandy, posed as the heir to the crown, and sought the support of our barons over there. Now, according to my informants, he is in Paris with Philip, promising him everything he wants in the way of our lands and suggesting again that he set aside his wife Isabelle and wed Alys. I also hear," she finished grimly, "that he has scouts in Flanders hiring bands of mercenary soldiers to bring here when he claims the throne."

Bishop Hugh gasped. Geoffrey and I were silent. We knew that John had been working behind Richard's back all during his absence, but it was hard to believe that he would so openly ally himself with France.

"Well, my lords, that is why I am here. Captive or free, Richard is King of England, I am his Regent, and until he returns it is my duty to defend his kingdom for him. My aim, at this particular time, is to make sure that all our royal castles are well manned and their wardens loyal to the King. I am also asking our barons and bishops to declare anew their allegiance to Richard—which is why, my dear Hugh, I sent for you today—and I am issuing orders that everyone who lives along the coast be prepared to defend it against possible invasion. If John brings troops from Flanders or France, he may plan to land them at any point between Dover and Bamburgh."

"But the Flemings are Richard's friends!" I said.

"Mercenaries fight for gold. They fight for whoever pays them," Geoffrey explained, his voice as grim as my mother's. "I think I need not tell you, your Grace, that I and everyone in my See are loyal to you and to the King. Rest easy about York and its environs; I will undertake its defense myself. Call on me, my lady, for anything at any time."

"I echo your words, Geoffrey, for Lincoln," said Hugh. "And, as you are not on good terms with Hugh of Durham, I will warn him to do the same. Then, with this castle strongly held, your Grace, I think you may consider the North well guarded."

"Thank you both. I shall sleep almost peacefully tonight! But work quietly, my lord Bishops. I do not want to drive John into open defiance, nor can I bring myself to declare my own son a traitor."

* * *

I slept very heavily that night, so heavily that Lady Amicia had to shake me awake. It was midmorning, for the chamber was full of light, and she was looking down at me with a regretful face.

"I'm sorry, your Grace," she said. "I hated to rouse you, but the Queen has summoned you to her privy chamber."

Still half asleep, I jumped out of the shallow, boxlike bed and called for my clothes and a bite to eat. Within a very few minutes I was speaking to the guard at her door and entering the room; she was alone and her face, when she greeted me, made my heart sink. Even before she spoke, I knew that Raimond had asked to wed me and she had refused him.

"I think you must be mad, Joan," were her first words, her voice icily cold. "Raimond of St. Gilles may profess to be Richard's friend, but that does not make him a suitable husband for a daughter of England or for the widowed Queen of Sicily. And even if I were willing to overlook all the other objections—which I am not!— there is still the distasteful matter of his marriage or whatever it was to Isaac of Cyprus's daughter. To choose such a time, too, to add to my problems! . . .

"No." She spoke even more sharply as I tried to interrupt. "No, I do not want to argue this further, either with you or Count Raimond himself. In fact, I suggested that he leave England immediately, before it becomes more widely known that he escorted you here with only one lady of rank to lend you countenance. Thank God you had Hugh and Geoffrey with you when you arrived last night, or I would be much angrier than I now am."

Suddenly I was angry also, very, very angry. I remembered the story of my mother's marriage to my father and wondered how she could criticize *my* behavior. They had rushed to the altar a bare six weeks after her divorce from Louis of France—and many people said that Louis could have won that divorce for adultery instead of merely claiming consanguinity.

Then I recalled her casual question, when we were reunited in Sicily, as to whether I had taken any lovers during my years with King William. As long as you presented the appearance of virtue, apparently, you were behaving royally; take lovers in secret, but do not travel with only one lady-in-waiting and a few tiring-maids!

I restrained myself with difficulty, for my impulse was to say all the things that were seething inside me—to accuse her, to demand her consent to my marriage, to point out that Richard had spent my inheritance from William and that she should be grateful I had found a way to provide for my own future. Somehow I forced myself to answer her quietly.

"As you refuse to discuss the matter with me," I said, "I will, with your permission, retire."

Without waiting for her to answer I bowed and climbed down the steep, circular staircase to the hall, hoping to find Raimond there. I could not see him at first, for the great room was filled with people: lords and ladies chatting in groups, servants preparing the tables for the midday meal.

I moved just inside the entrance, trying to find his dark head. There, in a far corner, stood Bishop Hugh and Geoffrey, but Raimond was not with them, and I had a sudden fear that he might already have obeyed my mother's orders and set out for home without bidding me farewell.

While I was telling myself not to be a fool, I heard a familiar footstep in the corridor and swung around to see Raimond walking swiftly toward me. I wanted to run to him and throw myself into his arms. Instead, only too aware that the guards leaning on the walls nearby were watching me, I strolled to meet him and gave him a nod and a casual word of greeting.

"Her Grace tells me you are returning home," I said.

"Not *home*, perhaps," he replied, stressing the word, "although I shall soon cross the water again. If you have talked with your mother, my lady, you know that she was unable to help me—and that I must therefore seek the answer to my question elsewhere."

"Elsewhere?"

He nodded. "My search may take me far, and to places where I will not be very welcome. However, if I find my friend I am sure all will then be well."

Two ladies were wandering slowly by, which was why Raimond could not answer me more directly. He was trying to tell me, I was sure, that he was going to look for Richard himself, a plan that both elated and frightened me. I glanced around, seeking some place where we could talk freely without setting tongues wagging. Halfway down the corridor was a deep window embrasure with the usual stone seats built into the walls; the two castle guards were standing opposite, too far away to hear anything we might say to each other. I pointed to it.

"Sit there with me for a few moments," I suggested loudly. "All that chatter and clatter in the hall makes my head ache. . . ."

"Tell me quickly," I said when we reached it and sat down. "You mean you are going to Vienna to seek Richard?"

He nodded. "I have made up my mind to sail from Boston to Flanders, then go first to Cologne. If I hear nothing of him there, I will travel along the Rhine, then the Danube. At some place I hope either to discover him or to join one of the other groups already searching for him."

"And now I shall worry about your safety, too," I said slowly.

"I shall take care, be sure of that. With you waiting for me, my heart, I have every reason to take care." His eyes, meeting mine, sent a warm glow over me that was most comforting. "But where will that be, Joan? With your mother's household?"

"I had planned to join it, of course; now I am not so sure. I might be happier elsewhere—in Leicester, perhaps, with Lady Amicia, or in Poitiers with Berengaria. If she had been even a little understanding about you and me, Raimond, or willing to listen—"

"Her whole concern is Richard, my sweet. She brushed me aside as she would an annoying insect and ordered me out of England. I think, in the circumstances, you might well be happier somewhere else. But I shall be setting out for Boston within the hour, and I must know where to find you."

A sudden daring thought took possession of me. Could I? Should I? Would I?

"I shall need more than an hour to decide. Who knows? My mother may be sorry and want to be friends again. Could you wait in Boston for a message from me?"

"I will not sail until I hear from you. But the Queen made it very clear that I am not to linger."

I was so absorbed in my own thoughts after leaving Raimond that I remember little of dinner. I know that I chatted with some of my mother's ladies after we rose from the tables and learned from them, without asking any actual questions, that the royal entourage would move down to Norwich Castle in a day or so, then return to London. Having found that out, I summoned Lady Amicia to our quarters.

I told her quite frankly what had happened between Raimond and my mother and my mother and me. I did not mention Raimond's plan to seek for Richard, but I did say that I might be happier in Leicester or Poitiers than at Court.

Her grey eyes lit up, making her bony face almost beautiful.

"Oh, come to Leicester! How happy the Countess would be— and I was dreading our parting! Later, if you changed your mind, we might both travel to London with you."

Her warm response made me feel guilty, but I quieted my conscience by reflecting that should my secret scheme go awry I would certainly visit the Lady Petronilla at Leicester Castle for a while.

"Shall we set out early tomorrow?" I asked her.

She laughed. "I could be ready within the hour."

"Tomorrow, then." I made myself smile back at her. "An early start will be nothing new for us, will it?"

While our women gathered up our belongings, I called for pen and ink and spent most of the afternoon writing letters. Two of them were to my lady mother and I weighed every word, every sentence, in each, crossing out, beginning again and again, copying and recopying before I was satisfied. One I put away; she might see it later, or she might not. The other I scanned for the last time. It was short, and it was not conciliating.

Your unfeeling refusal to further my happiness, or even to discuss the matter with me, has disturbed me more than I can say. I am bone weary from my long journey and heartsick over Richard's capture by our enemies. I think, and perhaps you will agree with me, that we might be better apart at this time. If you do, I shall set out for Leicester early in the morning with my good Lady Amicia. Whether I then come to you in London or join Berengaria's household can be decided later; at the moment I prefer not to look too far ahead.

It would do, I thought, so I sealed it and dispatched it to her privy chamber. After that was done I penned notes of thanks and farewell to Geoffrey and Bishop Hugh and a letter that I might be sending on to Raimond in Boston. I had just laid down my pen when my lady mother entered unannounced, her face flushed with anger and my letter in her thin hand.

She threw it on the floor at my feet. "By all means, go!" she said. "Go to Leicester or wherever you wish! I am too old and too tired to quarrel with an infatuated daughter at a time when I have one son in danger of his life and another trying to steal the throne. Mother of God, I have all England to guard and you call me 'unfeeling' because I refuse to let you wed one of my most encroaching and aggressive enemies! Until you come to your senses I agree that we will be much better apart."

Before she had finished her tirade I was trembling so that I could hardly stand or speak. In my overwrought state, everything she said added to my anger and deepened the chasm between us. I did not realize, certainly, that I would one day remember her words and see that if I had been in her place—seventy-one years of age and carrying her burdens—I might well have spoken them myself.

As it was, I steadied my voice with a great effort and gripped the table behind me with both hands. "Then shall we say farewell now? If the Lady Amicia and I are to begin our journey early tomorrow I will sup here, with your permission, and retire immediately to snatch what sleep I can."

A chilly word of agreement, and I was watching her disappear through the door, her head high as always. But I saw, for the first time, that her back was slightly bent and that she looked much shorter than she had in Sicily.

I turned to Lady Amicia. "You see?" I said, my voice rising. "You see?"

Instead of answering me she stooped and picked up the letter my lady mother had thrown at my feet.

"You see?" I asked for the third time, even more urgently.

"I see that the sooner you have some hot food and a night's sleep the better. I see, too, that her Grace would be wise to follow your example. What you both need is an opportunity to rest, to find some peace of mind and regain your composure."

My quiet evening and early night gave me at least the appearance of composure the next morning, but it certainly did not add to my peace of mind. Instead of falling asleep, I found myself going over and over my quarrel with my mother; I thought of Raimond setting out on his dangerous quest and counted the various things that might keep us apart forever; I frightened myself by thinking of the reckless plan I had made for the following day and by seeing only too plainly where it might fail.

I decided, during the darkest hours, to abandon the whole dangerous scheme, but an interval of deep slumber refreshed me so much that I awakened with enough courage to spur me on, and when I received no farewell message or word of any kind from my mother my hesitation passed.

After that I never looked back, and from the moment I arose and donned my warmest travelling garments, until the time when I finally reached my destination, all went with a smoothness that was almost unbelievable.

Our small cavalcade trotted out of the castle courtyard even earlier than I had hoped, long before anyone but the servants had left their beds. The guards who raised the portcullis for us were heavy-eyed and yawning, the straight Roman road ahead was deserted, and we soon seemed to be alone in a sleeping world. As we rode swiftly along in the direction of Leicester, everyone in our entourage was quiet: I, for many good reasons of my own; the others, I suppose, because they were not yet fully awake. I saw Lady Amicia eyeing me anxiously from time to time, but I said nothing to her until we reached the small village of East Stoke, perhaps three miles from Newark Castle. Then I reined in my mount and waved her closer to my side.

"Forgive me," I said, "but I cannot go any farther. I find I am too anxious about my lord brother, too unhappy over my quarrel with the Queen, too unsettled and miserable to be comfortable in Leicester, even with you. I want to turn back here with one of our tiring-women, the pack horse that carries most of my possessions, and just two of our men." I named Maria, a strong woman we had brought from Rome who spoke only her native tongue, and my most truthworthy knight and his squire.

To my great relief and, I must confess, secret guilt, Lady Amicia said she understood when I refused to allow her to return with me, and we parted with a few tears, kisses, and many promises to meet again. I then bade the others farewell, sent orders for my small escort to follow me, and, with one backward glance and a wave of my hand, swung my horse around and galloped back along the road toward Newark.

After a few minutes I resumed a slower pace. Sir John Airlies, whom I had selected to escort me, caught up with me, and we rode side by side for a mile or so, then, Lady Amicia and her party now being out of sight, I halted again.

"What I did not tell you, Sir John," I said, "is that I want to go to Boston, not Newark, and by the shortest possible route. Take me safely there, ask me no questions, and you will earn my everlasting gratitude."

For a long moment, he stared at me. He opened his mouth to speak—probably to protest—and closed it again. Finally he nodded. "Then we should cut across country and find the road to Sleaford. We cannot hope to go any farther by tonight, and there is a priory near the town there that shelters travellers."

* * *

287

I need not describe our journey except to say that Sir John more than justified my faith in him, guiding me to Boston without incident and without revealing my identity to anyone along the way. We decided, before reaching Sleaford, to say that I was his widowed sister, and this seemed to satisfy the monks at the priory. I was too weary after my day's hard ride and sleepless night at Newark to lie awake again, and the good rest enabled me to continue on to Boston at the same swift pace. I had my anxieties, of course: would Raimond be there, would we find him, and would he, if I *did* find him, think me quite mad?

By sheer force I put these worrying thoughts aside until we were actually at the port itself. Sir John had asked no questions, but when we drew rein in front of the old church of St. Botolph, for whom Boston was named, I could no longer remain silent.

"My errand here is with Count Raimond of St. Gilles," I told him, attempting to sound as if there was nothing unusual in this. "He is in Boston seeking a ship to carry him home. Where do you think we could find him?"

I avoided his eyes, so I don't know whether he looked startled or not. His voice, when he replied, revealed nothing and I thanked God, again, that I had chosen him to accompany me.

"Dismount and wait for me in the church, your Grace," he suggested. "I will surely find him at the waterfront or in one of the better hostels."

Only too happy to leave the search in his hands, I obeyed, taking Maria in with me. The damp chill in the small stone building was worse than the brisk wind that had buffeted us as we rode across the flat fens, and that, added to my private fears, soon had me shivering. My maidservant was miserable, also, her nose red and dripping and her hands, when she pinned my cloak tighter around my throat, like lumps of ice. The church around us was empty; after I had tried, unsuccessfully, to lose myself in prayer, I walked up and down to bring some feeling back into my numb feet.

I was near the entrance when the door opened and Sir John stepped inside.

"We found Count Raimond concluding a bargain with a ship's master," he said immediately. "He will follow me here, then bring you to me at his hostel, where I shall be arranging for dinner for us all."

I tried to express my thanks; then, after he had gone again, I remained where I was, my heart pounding. Would Raimond agree to my plan—or would he send me back to Newark? As I went over and over what I would tell him, the heavy door swung open a second time and a pilgrim entered, his wide hat shading his face and his ash stick tapping on the stone floor.

I half turned, meaning to join Maria; then I turned back, looked at him more closely, and ran to meet him.

"Raimond, Raimond!" seemed all I could say. And "Joan, Joan!" his only reply.

We laughed. Before he could ask the questions I saw in his eyes, I pointed to his dull brown chape and pilgrim's hat. "You did not tell me you would be travelling as a pilgrim, Raimond. Nothing could be better!"

"I thought of it only today," he said. "A ship had just set sail with a band of them on board, and I learned that many pilgrims use these ports when they take the northern route; they land at Antwerp, then journey to Venice by way of Cologne where they halt to worship the relics of the three Magis. As you say, nothing could be better for my purpose! And, as you see, I even found a merchant in the town that sells pilgrims' goods."

"Then go right back to him," I told him, smiling into his eyes, "and purchase a hat and stick for me. I am going with you, Raimond, and it will suit me very well indeed to travel as a pilgrim."

Several hours later, when I climbed on board the small ship and followed a rough seaman to the tiny enclosure that was to be my home for the voyage, I wondered whether Raimond would have agreed to my coming with him had he not thought of his excellent disguise. Fortunately for me, it answered his first and strongest objections, for who would question the identity or morals of a widow making a pilgrimage?

As for his other objections, I answered them by telling of my own doubts and indecisions and how they had melted away, one by one, as I surmounted the difficulties that lay in my way.

"From the moment that the thought of accompanying you first entered my mind," I said, "I was prepared to put it aside as both mad and impossible. And had my lady mother shown me by even a word or a glance that she might be willing to think more favorably of our marriage after her present great problems are solved, I would have been more than ready to remain with her and share those problems. In fact, after I wrote her that she and I might be better apart, I penned a letter to send on to you here, saying that she and I were friends again and that I would await word from you at her Court."

I then repeated to Raimond what I could remember of that last bitter meeting with my lady mother, telling him that after it was over I still waited for some conciliating message from her. "But when she allowed me to set out the following morning without one further word, I saw no reason why I should not join you. If you will think it over, Raimond, you will see that I am, for the first time in my life, free to go wherever I wish. With my own household scattered there is no one to miss me or care where I am. Lady Amicia thinks me with the Queen"—here I confessed how I had turned back toward Newark, allowing her to assume that I was rejoining my mother—"and, of course, my mother and everyone at her Court think me with Lady Amicia."

Raimond had listened quietly to my story. Now he interrupted.

"Perhaps at this moment no one is concerned about where you are. But someone will soon discover that you are neither at Leicester nor with the Queen."

"Yes, of course," I agreed swiftly. "And before we set sail I shall give Sir John a letter for my mother, explaining just what I am doing, and why, and suggesting that she inform anyone who asks that I am on my way to rejoin the Lady Berengaria. That will not be a lie, Raimond, for after we find Richard and gain his permission to wed, I would like to go to Berengaria and be married at her Court."

He looked at me rather despairingly. "My darling, you must not be so sure that I shall find Richard—or that he will favor my suit. I don't want to frighten you, but he may be hidden away in such a remote castle that neither I nor the others who are searching for him will ever discover it, some castle deep in Germany where travellers never venture."

"I do know that, Raimond," I replied. "I am not a fool."

He was silent, then, and for so long that my heart sank. Perhaps

I *was* a fool, after all. Perhaps we were both fools and I should better ride back with Sir John and make up my quarrel with my lady mother. Perhaps Raimond was regretting the day that had brought us together and placed us now in this dangerous situation. He might even be wishing he could return home and forget the whole matter.

While these dispiriting thoughts turned me to ice, Raimond began pacing up and down the stone floor of the old church. Finally he halted and took my hands in his.

"Joan." His voice was urgent and his fingers trembled around mine. "Joan, my dearest, let us marry now! Let me find a priest here in Boston, and we will cross the water as man and wife. I could then send you down to Berengaria and go seek Richard myself, knowing that nothing can part us. What could he or the Queen do then?"

"Many things," I replied grimly. "Have our marriage set aside, or lock me up in a nunnery for the rest of my life. I would not be the first royal lady to suffer so, I assure you. We could, perhaps, defy them—hide in Toulouse and wait for their anger to cool—and if this proves to be the only answer to our problem I will do it, but first, Raimond, let us try to find Richard! He will listen to us, I am sure he will, and so will my mother then; she would be so grateful to you and so happy."

For another long moment we were both silent, but this time I could feel our love for each other pulsing warmly between us.

"So be it, my darling," he said. "Come, fellow pilgrim, and I will buy you a hat and stick. It shall be as you wish—and we *will* find Richard!"

* * *

This was the beginning of our great adventure. I had no time, during the busy hours that followed, to think much about the voyage that lay ahead, and when we finally boarded the sailing vessel I was too weary to do anything but curl up on the straw-filled sack that was to be my bed and pull the heavy, odorous coverlet snugly around me. I was vaguely aware of running feet on the deck over my head, voices shouting orders, the slap of waves against the side of the ship, and the usual creaking and groaning of its timbers, but I believe I must have fallen into a deep sleep even before the anchor was raised and we slipped out of the dark harbor.

Maria, my strong and loyal handmaiden and now my only companion and attendant, slept on a second sack close to my side. She greeted me cheerfully when I opened my eyes, and we laughed together as I looked around the tiny cupboard that, as we were the only women on board, had been reluctantly allotted to me as my private quarters. What could have been its original purpose, I do not know. It contained one long, low sea chest and that was all. That chest was, however, to serve us in many ways; at this moment it held my sack and me as my bed, our belongings were already stowed away inside it, and after I rose we used its top for many other purposes. While I washed it was a wash stand, holding a bowl and ewer; at mealtimes it was a table for our salt meat, bread, and wine; during the rest of the waking hours it was my seat. There was just enough space between it and the door for Maria's pallet, her bed at night and her seat when she was not otherwise occupied.

The tedium was indescribable, for I was a virtual prisoner during the whole rough voyage. Heavy rains and strong winds kept me off the deck, and, as there were always some of the crew asleep in the one cabin that housed everyone else on board, I knew I was not welcome there. Raimond would come and chat from the doorway, but except for those breaks in the monotony there was nothing to do but look at the rough walls and the clumsy beams close over my head.

When I felt most trapped I would think of Richard. Was he living in a dungeon smaller than this tiny retreat? While I could count the hours until I would be freed from my voluntary incarceration, was *he* sitting in chains on a damp stone floor, suffering perhaps from his intermittent fever and with no hope of leaving his prison alive? Indeed, *was* he still alive? My old fears, arrested by Emperor Henry's letter to Philip, returned to haunt me and I controlled my thoughts with difficulty.

The voyage, of course, was much shorter than our trip from Bordeaux, and before too long there came the welcome moment when we dropped our anchor at Antwerp and I left that tiny closet forever. Oh, the delight of breathing in the fresh salty air! The joy of setting foot on the damp sands of the beach, the satisfaction of that first simple meal at the pilgrim hospice! Never before had food tasted so delicious or a humble chamber seemed so spacious.

Raimond, the beginning of his pilgrim's beard a dark stubble on his cheeks and chin, ate his fresh fish and rough dark bread with an appetite that matched mine, and the other men and women seated at the bare trestle table smiled as we both reached for more. They were friendly people, and before the meal was over we were all talking freely together and Raimond and I had accepted their invitation to join their little band.

They were, we discovered, the pilgrims who had sailed from Boston just before we did—three merchants and their wives from Nottingham—and were now eager to be on the road. The usual visit to a money-changer had delayed them, they told us, and they had not yet purchased their horses and mules.

Money-changers! This was a danger I had not anticipated. All Raimond's money, I knew, had been struck off for him at St. Gilles and bore his arms. As I looked at him with what I suspect were frightened eyes, he reached into the escrepe that hung around his neck, drew out a coin, and handed it to the nearest merchant.

"I obtained some of these in Boston before we sailed," he said. "Will I receive fair value for them here?" This both answered my unspoken question and led to a lively discussion among the men of the hazards of changing money as one moved from country to country. When that subject was exhausted, Raimond announced that he, too, must find sturdy horses for us and our servants, and left me with the women while he and the men went into the town together.

I rushed out with the others when the men rode back to the hospice with their purchases, and, after admiring the low, broad-backed Spanish-bred mare with a beautiful mane and tail that Raimond had found for me, I strolled off alone with him for a private talk.

What he had to tell me was disappointing. "There is no word of Richard here," he said, "although as a pilgrim I felt quite easy about asking questions wherever we went. There were rumors in England, I said, that the King might have chosen this route home. But no one has heard anything."

"Did you think they would? Were you expecting news of him here?"

"No, just hoping. No, Joan, we may never hear anything, as you know, and we are a long, long way from Vienna. If we do hear, it is more likely to be at Cologne."

＊　＊　＊

I determined, after that, to continue on our journey without show-ing any further anxiety, for fretting would not help either Raimond or me, and as our companions were as eager as we were to cover every possible mile each day it was to our advantage to remain with them.

They expressed themselves as quite willing to set out by Prime, halt for dinner at Tierce, then be in the saddle again two hours later instead of resting, as more leisurely travellers do, until Relevee. By thus cutting our nooning in half we could add eight or ten miles to our afternoon's ride and, with luck, reach Cologne in four days instead of five.

This, we discovered from the helpful, brown-habited brothers who served us our supper, was the way most of the pilgrim parties planned their days, and he advised us to break the journey at Diest, Maastricht, and Jülich, where we would find either suitable hostels or pilgrim hospices.

We did as he suggested and found his advice good. At Diest we were the only pilgrims in the small inn, but at Maastricht, where we were told that the hospice, an abbey that was once a royal palace, was across the Meuse at the village of Meerssen, we fell in with a large band from Norwich. They were a merry group, and we all lay awake on our pallets much too late that night singing and laughing.

A pleasant evening at Jülich, another day in the saddle, and we were at Cologne, our carefree interval at an end. Here, in this busy walled city, its towers high on the banks of the broad Rhine River, where travellers came every day on foot, horseback, or in the small boats that, even in March, made their way up and down the murky, sullen water, we had great hopes of discovering some word of Richard. Here Raimond would go into all parts of the town, asking questions and, as this might take some days, we would part here from our new friends.

Our band, of course, was no longer the intimate little group that had set out from Antwerp, and when we entered the great hall of the hospice we found it already crowded with other pilgrims, some on their way to the Holy Land, others returning. It was so full, in fact, that we saw we would either have to wedge our pallets between those of strangers on the straw-covered floor or find some other shelter for the night. A few of our friends decided to look for a hostel, but Raimond thought it wiser for us to remain and lose ourselves in the large company.

The day's journey having been a short one, he waited only until Maria and I had begun to settle our belongings before taking his leave and beginning his quest. I, having little to do, fell prey to my old anxieties and so was actually pleased when two women, a short distance away, began a lively quarrel over some of their possessions. This took my mind off my own worries for it was a good quarrel, beginning with low-voiced protests and much headshaking, then moving on to a loud altercation that included descriptions of each other's characters and habits and, finally, to face slapping and hair pulling. By the time their husbands had jerked them apart, I was laughing with my new neighbors and awaiting Raimond's return in a more tranquil mood.

Supper was being spread on the long bare tables when he finally entered the hall and came to my side.

"You have news for me," I said instantly. It was written all over his face, but whether it was good or bad I could not tell.

"I do," he replied softly. "Is there any corner in this madhouse where we can talk?"

As he spoke a bell sounded and there was a rush for the tables. More than half of the pilgrims found seats, including all those who had been standing near us, and while we waited our turn to eat we could talk freely.

"Tell me," I said.

"Do not expect too much, Joan," Raimond warned me. "But I did hear something, for what it is worth. I was in the cathedral, at the marble casket that holds the relics of the three Magi. There were many people there, among them two English Crusaders who are visiting all the shrines they can find on their slow way home. It was the natural thing to question them about Richard, and they told me that he was first imprisoned at Durrenstein, on the Danube near Vienna, but that Duke Leopold of Austria took him to Ratisbon early in January for a meeting with Emperor Henry. There Henry charged him with betraying the Holy Land, murdering Conrad, and conspiring with Tancred, then ordered him thrown back in prison. Where, they did not know. It might be Durrenstein again—the castle there is high on a rocky crag and should be impregnable— or it could be anywhere in either Henry's or Leopold's domains."

"At least we can assume he is alive," I said slowly. "But think of the miles between here and Vienna—and the castles!"

"First we must discover just where Henry and Leopold are. I feel that Richard will not be too far away, and that some member of their households could be made to talk. In any case, we will now continue on our journey, following the pilgrim route along the Rhine to Mainz, then turning east to Frankfurt."

"By ourselves?"

"Not until we reach Mainz. I encountered a group of our friends in the town arranging for a boat to take them up the river, and we shall travel with them as long as possible."

We found seats at the table soon after that and ate a hearty meal. After everyone was finished and the tables carried away I saw three gaily garbed jongleurs and a bold-faced dancing girl enter the hall, draw up stools, and prepare themselves to entertain the more than willing company. I had heard that minstrels made a good living by travelling from one pilgrim hospice to another, but these were the first that we had seen.

Any real music was welcome, and although they were only moderately skillful almost everyone in the hall joined in the singing of a familiar *chanson de geste,* stamping their feet when it was finished and shouting for more. But it was the girl's turn now, and her lively contortions soon had the men pushing their way closer. To me, accustomed to the more seductive movements and gestures of the hot-blooded women who had entertained us in Sicily and Acre, this jongleuresse, with her untidy, unbraided flaxen hair and her shoddy gown of some streaky red fabric dotted all over with white spots, was stiff and clumsy.

Raimond, close beside me, seemed more interested in the three men. I saw him watching them even while the girl was whirling around wildly, his face so earnest and thoughtful that it made me curious, but his only reply, when I queried him, was that he planned to talk to them before they left the hospice. "I should have remembered that these itinerant trouvères often go from castle to castle, too, and are the most likely people to hear any whisper of Richard's hiding place. Everyone talks to them, from the lord down to the kitchen maids."

Some time later he left me; I saw him chatting with the little band of musicians, but I had retired to the women's side of the hall and was asleep before he finished what became a long conversation. When we were on the river boat the next morning, moving up the Rhine, I asked him what he had learned.

"Nothing," he said, shaking his head. "Nothing of Richard, I mean. But they told me of many castles they have visited and much of the life they lead."

It was bitterly cold on the river, so we were wrapped in our warmest fur-lined, hooded chapes, the wide-brimmed pilgrim hats (which would have blown off) packed away in one of the canvas bags that held our scanty possessions. Despite the chill, the water journey was a restful change after the more strenuous days on horseback and we found ourselves enjoying what our boatman said was the most beautiful stretch of the long river. Almost all the way from Cologne to Mainz, which we reached some days later, the banks were high and wooded, and we passed many a castle looming above us among the craggy rocks. The Rhine was narrow here, and the current swift, and the road that we would have travelled was, when we glimpsed it from time to time, only a track, steep and winding.

It was hard to see those castles and wonder if Richard might be behind their walls, perhaps looking down on the water as we glided by. However, it was most unlikely that he would have been brought this far away from Ratisbon. To leave nothing to chance, of course, Raimond made his usual inquiries at every stop along the way.

At Mainz we said farewell to the other pilgrims, having told them that we had business in the city that might keep us there for a while. After they had continued on their southern route we hired another river vessel for us and our two servants and headed east for Frankfurt by way of the smaller river Main. We sailed rapidly through the broad valley, seeing little of interest around us but the dim outline of the Taunus Mountains to the north, and arrived at the city as darkness was falling that same night.

Here, just inside the walls, we found a small but clean hostelry. Having left the pilgrim route we were no longer travelling as pilgrims, and I heard Raimond explain to the innkeeper that we were brother and sister, seeking word of my Crusader husband. This was what I expected him to tell people, but I was completely un-prepared for the question he suddenly put to our host as he led us to the supper table.

"Is there a nunnery here or on the road to Aschaffenburg where I might leave my sister and her maidservant for a few weeks? She has journeyed far and is weary, and I would like to proceed alone and return for her when my quest is ended."

Before I could protest the innkeeper replied that there were several, the best being a Benedictine nunnery at Seligenstadt, beside the old church and the castle. I held my tongue, with an effort, until he returned to the kitchen; then I turned indignantly on Raimond.

"I am *not* weary," I said hotly. "I am coming with you, Raimond!"

"Please, Joan." He took my hand under the scarred board and held it warmly. "Please listen to me. I brought you this far because I could, because you could travel as a pilgrim in safety. Now, if I am to find Richard, I must assume another disguise, one that will take me into the castles that lie between this city and Vienna. When I tell you that I persuaded those jongleurs at Cologne to sell me some of their clothes and one of their vielles, you will understand. From now on I shall make my way as a minstrel."

I did indeed understand and I saw instantly that he was right. When I admitted it, he told me that he would begin the very next evening at the castle in Seligenstadt. "And it will comfort me to know that you are comfortable and well looked after only a short distance away."

We said nothing of the nights that would follow, each one taking him farther from my side, and, after we finished our meal he fetched his vielle and sang for me. I was able, during that short interval, to put aside the thought of our separation, but later, when we had parted for the night, I found I could neither sleep nor think of anything else.

As we were the only guests in the inn, Maria and I had a chamber to ourselves, and Raimond, I knew, was alone on the other side of the thick wall, his servant quartered elsewhere. I wanted him, suddenly, as I had never wanted him before, and I lay there in darkness, with waves of desire sweeping over me, calling myself a fool for having refused to wed him secretly in Boston as he had suggested.

I also asked myself why I was not now in his arms, marriage or no marriage. I was not a young maid—and his travels, after tonight, would be full of danger. I might well never see him again.

I sat up and looked around the dark room, identifying the dim outline of the door and the lump in the corner that was Maria, snoring on her pallet. I threw back the coverlet and rose to my feet, standing quite still for a long, long moment. Then, moving as quietly as possible on the thickly strewn straw, I crept through the darkness to the door, held my breath as I pushed it open, and slipped out into the corridor.

There was no light out there; I could not see even the wall beside me. Putting out my left hand I found it, then tiptoed along until my fingers touched the door into Raimond's chamber. Again I held my breath, opened it silently, and stepped inside, my heart beating so fast that I could almost hear it.

Another step and I felt something soft under my foot, the edge of his coverlet on the floor. I knelt and took it in my hand. He was breathing softly, deeply asleep. Should I waken him by whispering his name or lift the coverlet, creep in beside him, and waken him with a kiss?

While I knelt there, trembling, Bourgigne's dark face, smiling maliciously, flashed into my mind. Bourgigne! This was the way *she* had entrapped Raimond, by coming uninvited to his tent, by offering him her soft, hot, little animal body—

A slap in the face would not have brought me to my senses more effectively. All I wanted, suddenly, was to reach my chamber without rousing Raimond, for the thought that he might compare me with Bourgigne was unbearable. I pulled myself to my feet and groped my way out. I was shivering when I crawled into my own pallet and drew up the green woolen cover, but Bourgigne's hated face was gone, and as the blessed warmth returned to me I fell comfortably asleep.

CHAPTER

XXVIII

The journey to Seligenstadt was so short that we did not leave Frankfurt until after our midday meal, and Raimond, thinking to make our last morning together a pleasant one, took Maria and me to the market place. It was market day, and the vendors were offering everything anyone could possibly want, both old and new. He, seeing a booth of musical instruments, said he would try and find a better vielle than the one the jongleurs had sold him, and Maria and I drifted over to where a merchant was selling worn garments.

Something bright caught my eye and, before I could shake my head, the man was holding up a vivid green cote fashioned like the one worn by the jongleuresse at Cologne. It had even larger white spots, and it was, perhaps, not quite as shabby. As I stared at it, wondering who would buy it, another mad plan took possession of me.

Raimond and I had been able to travel together as pilgrims, and no one had questioned our doing so. That dancing girl was accepted by everyone at the hospice as a member of the minstrel's party; why should I not disguise myself, too, and accompany him as a jongleuresse?

Without taking the time to decide whether such a thing would be possible, I made a bargain with the merchant—he seemed more than content to take a few of the coins I was carrying—and I turned back to join Raimond. He had discovered just what he wanted, he told me, and it was not until we were on our way from the market place to the hostel that he noticed the bundle Maria was carrying.

"It's a new cote," I said, when he questioned me. "Green, with white spots. To shock the nuns." I laughed as I said it, and he laughed with me.

We were still in a gay mood as our boatman began to take us on up the river, but the nearer we came to our destination the quieter Raimond became. Everything was arranged for our parting; I was carrying all the gold I would need for Maria and me during his absence—enough, in fact, to pay for our journey to Poitiers should that be necessary—and our belongings were stowed away in two canvas bags.

Raimond's servant was riding to Seligenstadt on a horse for his master and they, too, would part there when Raimond, his jongleur's costume hidden under a long chăpe, went to the castle. The servant, Raimond told me, would remain in Seligenstadt, prepared to serve me should I need him.

Suddenly there seemed nothing to talk about, and we sat in silence until the towers of the small town loomed ahead of us. There was no one to carry our bags from the river to the nunnery, so after Raimond had paid off the boatman he shouldered ours and Maria trotted along behind us with his smaller one.

When we reached the great wooden door set in the forbidding high walls I put my hand on Raimond's arm. "Let us say farewell here," I said. "I would prefer to make my own arrangements with the abbess. If you take me to her, Raimond, we will have to tell so many lies!"

He hesitated, looking miserable, then swung his burden to the ground and reached for his bag, the one Maria had been carrying.

"If you want it that way, my heart. But I will wait here for some time; I must be sure that all is well with you. And you must promise to send Maria to me at the inn before nightfall if you are not comfortable. After that it will be too late. I shall be at the castle in my jongleur's guise."

I agreed and he raised my hand to his lips. "Remember, my darling, that I shall be calling myself Blondel de Nesle now. And remember that I shall return for you at the first possible moment!"

*　　*　　*

The abbess, to whom a silent little nun took me, spoke just enough French for us to understand each other and was quite willing to shelter Maria for an indefinite period of time. I kept my explanation simple, merely saying that I was travelling on urgent family business and that my brother found her a burden. She would make herself useful, I assured the gentle woman, and I would leave enough gold to pay for her keep for some weeks.

After we had agreed on a sum, she asked if there was anything she could do for me. "A glass of wine, perhaps, or some food, madame?"

"You are very kind," I replied. "The inn is noisy and I am weary. If I could rest for a little while before I return to my brother?"

"One of the sisters will show you and your servant to our guest house. Remain there as long as you wish."

Again, as when I was planning to join Raimond in Boston, everything seemed so easy that I persuaded myself I must be doing the right thing. Here, in the secluded guest house, I was able to eat, change into my gaudy green gown, comb out my red braids, and paint my face. Maria, who attended me until I was ready to set out alone for the castle, packed the few possessions I must carry with me in the smallest sack, helped me hide my strange appearance under her own shabbiest hooded chape, and bade me a tearful farewell. I had explained what I was about to do, swearing her to secrecy, and her great fear was that I might leave her here among strangers for the rest of her life!

The guest house, fortunately, was situated at the farthest possible point from the rest of the abbey, well beyond the kitchens. A door in the walls at this end of the enclosure was unlocked until bed-time for the use of the guests and those bringing supplies to the kitchens nearby, and after a final word of reassurance to Maria I slipped out unobserved.

The moment I closed the door behind me, however, I felt lost and frightened, realizing that for the first time in my whole life I was truly alone. My impulse was to turn back, take off the threadbare gaudy cote, wash my face, braid my hair, and seek out the abbess again to make the arrangements that Raimond expected. I think I might actually have done so had not a group of ragged but merry beggars passed by on the other side of the road, obviously on their way to the castle too.

I knew they were going there to beg for a share of the broken meats distributed each evening to the poor—a custom in every country I knew of—and so I hurried along in the shadows behind them and followed them through the castle gate. We all crossed the drawbridge together and, passing the lowered portcullis that guarded the main entrance, entered the open arch leading into the kitchen court.

We were not the first; the noisy dirty enclosure was crowded with men, women, children, dogs, and cats. While they pushed and fought to be near enough to the kitchen door to catch the scraps that would soon be tossed out, I looked around me. The castle was so small that the gatehouse and round keep that housed the kitchen appeared to be its only buildings; so, as I could not seek admittance through the main door, I realized that I must wait and try to reach the hall by climbing the kitchen stairs.

Everyone was too intent on gaining their supper to notice me, and when two servants came out with loaded baskets of food I crept behind them and slipped inside. The steep little staircase wound up the rough stone wall right beside the open door, and I was on it and around the first turn before the clamor below had quieted. Pausing to catch my breath, I began to hear music and laughter above me; then, as I climbed another few steps, I actually recognized Raimond's voice, singing the tuneful chanson he had sung to me the night before.

With a heart beating faster and faster I mounted more swiftly and found the entrance to the hall unguarded and empty. I peered in. Everyone was down at the far end, listening to Raimond. The tables were cleared and only a few servants remained, one throwing more wood on the fire, a second replacing a candle, a third taking a clutching, chattering monkey from the shoulder of one of the ladies.

As they all seemed to be occupied I stripped off my chape, placed it and my bag on a chest that held other garments, tossed my hair over my shoulders, and walked boldly over the rush-covered floor. The servant holding the angry monkey saw me first, but before he could do more than gape I reached the cleared space where Raimond was perched on a stool, and, moving my hips to the music, I swayed out in front of the surprised company and began to dance in the eastern manner.

Raimond's horrified face should have frightened me. Instead, I was swept by a surge of strange elation and, laughing delightedly into his eyes, I circled around and around him, posturing, dipping, whirling as if I had been born to dance and had been dancing all my life.

For just a moment his fingers faltered on the vielle strings; then I heard him change the familiar melody of the chanson to one of the haunting, sense-stirring songs of Acre. Now, when our eyes met again, he laughed back at me, and I knew that we were sharing this wild joy that bubbled up in me with every step and every gesture.

As he drew the last, throbbing chords from his vielle, I sank down on the floor and bent my head until it touched the cold stones. All was silent for the blink of an eye; then the people around us shouted for more. Raimond raised me to my feet, we bowed, our fingers entwined, he led me to the stool and whispered to me to sit down.

Standing close beside me, he played the first notes of Bernart de Ventadour's "Whene'er Green Leaves and Grass Appear," and we sang it together as we had at St. Gilles when I was a small girl on my way to wed William and later at Cyprus for Richard and Berengaria. My eyes were wet by the time we finished, and instead of taking my hand Raimond placed his arm around my waist and took me to where the lord and the lady of the little castle were sitting.

A little shaken and more than a little frightened by what I had done, I heard Raimond refuse the lord's pressing invitation to remain and amuse his household for a few days; we must, he said, set out on our travels early the following morning. Some coins found their way into Raimond's hand, and a servant, obeying his master's orders, walked ahead of us to the door, waited while Raimond gathered up our belongings, then beckoned us down the steep stairs, across the kitchen court, and over to the gatehouse.

A surly voice replied to his hail and loud knock, the wooden door swung open, and we faced an ugly little guard with a lantern in his hand and an angry frown on his countenance that changed into something I liked even less when he saw my flowing hair and painted cheeks and lips.

After exchanging a few words in their own tongue, our guide returned to the castle and the guard led us inside the small gate-house. He pointed to a bench beside the fire and then to Raimond, indicating, I suppose, that there was where he should sleep; then, while Raimond was putting down our bags and his vielle, the horrible man, with a leer, grabbed my arm and began to push me toward what seemed to be a second inner room.

Before I had stumbled more than a step or two Raimond jerked me free, thrust me behind his back, and faced the guard with such a menacing glare that the man mumbled something, shrugged his shoulders, and backed into the adjoining chamber. A muffled thud and loud rustlings indicated that he had flung himself down on a pile of straw or a pallet, and for a few minutes I could do nothing but cling to Raimond, trembling and whispering his name. He held me, smoothing my hair with gentle fingers.

"Well," he said softly, when I had regained some of my composure, "what shall I do with you now? Beat you, as you deserve, or wash your face and take you back to the abbey?"

"You can't," I whispered back, telling him how I had arranged matters. "I'm travelling with you from now on, whatever you say, and dancing as I did tonight."

"By Our Lady, Joan!" To my great relief, he began to chuckle. "I shall never forget that dance. Their faces, when you began wiggling around!"

"I was not 'wiggling,'" I protested indignantly. "I was good, very, very good, and furthermore I enjoyed it!" Now it was my turn to chuckle. "Do you know, Raimond, I don't believe I ever enjoyed anything more in my whole life?"

"Truly? Perhaps not, Joan, but something tells me you will."

This reply, and the way he said it, brought the blood up into my cheeks and, for a moment, we both fell silent. I was realizing something that I had not remembered when I planned this bold venture: dancing girls do not sleep with the women in a castle.

A snore sounded loudly from the other room; another followed, another and another. Raimond looked at me and smiled. Then, very deliberately, he removed my chape and his own, arranged them into a sort of pallet in front of the fire, and, coming back to me, took me into his arms.

I was shaking again, but for another reason now, and as his lips found mine I gave a little moan and closed my eyes. His kiss was deep and savage, and his hands, so gentle a moment before, were demanding and possessive. My body welcomed them, urging them on, and my trembling mouth, under his, opened.

Suddenly Bourgigne's face returned to jeer at me, and I think I tried to move away. I know I opened my eyes and met Raimond's, fierce and insistent. Pulling me even closer with one hand, he wound the fingers of the other in my long hair and, bending my head back, buried his lips in the hollow at the base of my throat, kissing it until the blood pounded in my ears.

When I swayed, my head swimming, he released my hair, lifted me up off my feet, and carried me toward the fire. "Beloved!" I heard him whisper. "*My* beloved!"

CHAPTER

XXIX

I settled myself more firmly on the pillion, tightened my arms around Raimond's waist, and rested my cheek on his back, so happy that the clopping of his horse's hooves sounded like music. The bare trees on one side of the road looked as beautiful as if they were in full leaf, the grey river Main, flowing by on the other, no longer seemed cold and forbidding, and even the chill morning air felt different. Instead of shivering and huddling into my chăpe I breathed deeper, glorying in being alive.

"Content?" Raimond glanced over his shoulder, his dark eyes so tender that my heart leaped into my throat.

"Content!" I gave an exultant laugh. "I am *far* from content! I am happy, Raimond, happy happy, happy! So happy that nothing else seems to matter—my shameful behavior, finding Richard, not even the dangers that may lie ahead because I have thrust myself on you."

"I know." I saw him nod and heard a new note in his voice, a note I cannot describe. "I know, my heart, because I feel the same way. I'm in a dream, Joan, and I don't want to wake—ever."

"We are dreaming together," I replied. "You are Blondel, seeking your master. I am Joanne, your woman: a woman who has one shoddy cote, tangled hair, painted cheeks; a woman who dances shamelessly, makes love even more shamelessly, and revels in both; a woman who has forgotten that she was once a king's daughter, a king's wife, and finds it difficult to believe that she is still a king's sister!"

Then, tightening my arms again, I pressed closer against his tall back.

"Feel my heart beat!" I told him. "Oh, Raimond, it is such a happy dream! We must waken from it some time, I know, but pray God not too soon. And until we do, and I become Queen Joan again, let us be Blondel and Joanne, and savor every day, every night, every hour—every sweet, fleeting moment!"

*　　*　　*

We did just that. In the blissful interval that followed we allowed only one concern to darken our life together, and that, of course, was for my lord brother. We forget all else, but not our quest, the great purpose that had brought us so far and freed us from the chains of our lives and responsibilities. Almost, but not quite, I succeeded in shutting my ears to the scolding of my conscience; I refused to listen, but the small voice was there. Later, I told it. I will listen later.

And it was no longer necessary to exhaust ourselves by travelling from dawn to dark, for a pleasant ride each day took us from castle to castle. Raimond's strong mount carried both of us and our saddlebags without tiring, we were never too weary for our evening's task and our evening's play, and, except for the occasional need to protect me from lechery, all went smoothly.

Minstrels here, as in other countries, led an easier life than most underlings. Many were scholars; some were noblemen seeking amusement and adventure; all brought so much diversion that they were warmly welcomed, never seated too far below the salt, and given generous *pourboires*.

We chose larger castles, after that first night, castles where Richard might lie hidden. Once inside we shared in the business of seeking him: discovering when it was safe to wander here and there, listening at keyholes, peering through windows, and looking for any closely guarded doors. Raimond, already accomplished in the art of asking questions without arousing suspicion, always talked to everyone possible, his ears alert for any hesitation, evasion, or lies.

This I could not do. No one, except perhaps the lowest kitchen maid, would demean herself by chatting with a dancing girl, and I despaired of ever learning much of their gutteral tongue. Had I been willing to visit the bed of the seneschal or one of the visiting noblemen I might have asked a few questions too, but failing this I helped in other ways and left the talking to Raimond.

Every night, after we had entertained the household and found a remote corner where we could sleep alone—and this was not always easy—we first discussed what we had seen and heard. Only then, when we were satisfied that Richard was not a prisoner in this particular castle, would we feel free to enjoy the delights of love or the comfort of sleep.

Had we not been so rapturously happy together we might well have grown discouraged. These rambling old castles, usually perched high on the river banks, often had enough dungeons to hide a dozen kings. I know because I saw so many of them. Their occupants, however, seemed to be mostly rats, beetles, and spiders, and only twice, in our searching, did we find a locked door. One was at Obernburg, the other at Miltenberg, and both times Raimond, waiting until there was no one near, knocked on the door and called out until he received an answer and knew the captive was not my lord brother.

Soon after the middle of March, we realized that if we continued to visit every likely castle along the way it would be summer before we reached Vienna. The day that we faced this fact was, for me, the end of my happy interlude, for my fears for Richard took possession of me again and I began, that very night, to suffer over my unhallowed relationship with Raimond. I do not mean that his kisses were less sweet or that my response to them less fervent, but I did often lie awake wondering how it would all end. I will not relate the doubts that tortured me until dawn; many of them disappeared with the light of day, but the rest rode along with me to Wertheim and, when I looked up and saw the castle, I found I was for the first time dreading the evening ahead.

Fortunately the Count and his lady and most of their household were not at the castle, and the seneschal and the small group that sat down for supper were very grateful for any diversion. They made much of us and, after we finished playing, singing, and dancing, provided us with a small chamber near the kitchen that actually held a real bed.

The moment we were alone Raimond took me in his arms and looked searchingly into my face. "You are weary, my heart," he said. "Thank God for that comfortable bed. Climb into it now and sleep; I shall return and drink a few goblets of wine with the seneschal. If he talks freely there will be no need to search the castle—and in any case, I cannot think that the Count would be absent if the King of England was here in his care."

I must have fallen deeply asleep very soon, for I did not awaken until Raimond walked into the chamber the next morning, holding a flagon of wine in one hand and a crusty loaf in the other.

"News at last, my darling!" he said. "Leopold and Emperor Henry met at Würzburg on the fourteenth day of February, and no townspeople have been admitted to the Marienburg Castle since. Again this may mean nothing, but we should be up and on our way as soon as possible."

Würzburg being almost thirty miles distant, we had a long day in the saddle, halting only long enough to rest our sturdy horse. During these intervals, and while we were riding along the winding river road, we talked of the problems that lay ahead.

"Who knows?" Raimond warned me. "They may welcome us. There could be several reasons why the townspeople are not allowed in the castle. We must not assume that it is because Richard is there—the Emperor and Duke Leopold may be meeting again, or perhaps they are just keeping the rooms clean for a future meeting."

Remembering the trail of filth that was left behind when the people of Palermo were free to wander around William's palaces, and how difficult it had always been in England to prevent the common folk from crowding into my lord father's banquet hall when we were dining, I had to agree.

I agreed, too, that we would be fools to try and plan ahead.

"We are Blondel the minstrel and Joanne the dancing girl," Raimond said firmly, "seeking a night's lodging and some silver for our pockets. If that does not serve us this time, we will think of something else."

He was, as I realized later, saying all this to keep me from worrying, and while he was talking cheerfully to me he was secretly considering one scheme after another for gaining access to Marienburg Castle.

Like the others, it was situated on a hill overlooking the river, a black pile silhouetted against the evening sky. We saw a tall keep and a round tower glooming above the walls and, despite Raimond's confident words, I felt my heart beating faster as we neared the narrow road leading up the steep slope. But so it had been every night, and although tonight we had more reason for hope—and fear—I knew that tomorrow we would probably be riding up another hill to another stronghold, these particular hopes dashed and new hopes and fears in our breasts.

Our horse was so weary, after our long journey, that I was very glad when Raimond dismounted at the foot of the incline and led him off the road into a thicket.

"Wait here," he said to me. "I will walk up to the gatehouse and, if all is well, return for you."

"No," I replied instantly, holding out my hand. "Help me down and we'll go together. We can tie the horse to a tree."

"But—"

"We'll go together," I repeated firmly and swung myself to the ground. "I shall follow you—Blondel—so you may as well save your breath. I will not be left here alone."

I saw him frown and throw up his hands. After tethering our mount to a good stout sapling, he shouldered the bag that held the vielle and we returned to the road.

A few minutes climb found us under the walls, the gatehouse dark and forbidding. Raimond strode forward and knocked loudly. We waited, he knocked again, and the door opened. While he spoke to the guard I stepped back into the shadows; there was much headshaking at first; then, after Raimond had twice reached into his money bag, the man grinned, said something in a more friendly voice, and let us inside the walls.

Well, we *were* inside the walls, but we were still some distance below the tall square keep, and as we climbed the rest of the way Raimond told me that the man at the gate had been sure we would not be admitted tonight. "The money I gave him convinced him that it was just barely possible," he said. "And because his orders to keep everyone out did not specifically mention minstrels, he decided to risk his master's displeasure."

We reached the top and stood there in silence, looking all around us. It was unusually quiet and strangely deserted for a castle court-yard, and if I hadn't glimpsed a little light in a few of the lower windows, I would have thought the keep empty. Then, when we moved a bit closer, I heard the distant sound of voices, laughter, and music drifting down from what should be the dining hall.

"Supper is over," I told Raimond. "If we are to enter it must be now."

There was no moat, no drawbridge, just a great, heavy, nail-studded door through which we hoped to pass. Again I waited in the shadows while Raimond knocked, and again I saw a head emerge and shake, and shake. It continued to shake as Raimond's hand went in and out of his money pouch; then the door closed with a loud crash and I could hear a key turn in the lock and the grate of bolts being drawn on the inside.

Raimond stepped to my side, his face grim. "Come," he said. "He ordered me off but we'll try the kitchens first."

The kitchen court was dark also, and, except for a few dogs, unusually quiet and deserted. This time no one even answered Raimond's knock, although he pounded until his hands must have been bruised.

When it was apparent that no one heard him, he turned to me and we moved away, our feet dragging. "Perhaps a little later," said Raimond. "They must be busy cleaning up after supper. I suppose, with no one allowed inside the walls, they have locked all the doors and relieved the guards."

"At least no one is chasing us away." I smiled at him as cheerfully as I could and drew my chape more closely around me.

"No, but it's too cold to stand here, Joan. We'll walk around and then I'll knock on that door again."

My arm in his, we went around the castle, hugging the walls. It was warmer in their shelter and, as Raimond pointed out, we were less likely to be seen from the windows above us.

"What is so dreadful to me," I said, looking up at the one slit over my head where there was light, "is that Richard may be in there, staring out! And if he *should* see us, he would think us just a courting couple."

A thought struck me.

"Why not sing, Raimond? You're a minstrel. Why not? You've asked to go in and entertain the company and been refused. So you sing for your supper out here!"

Raimond took his vielle out of his bag immediately. "I can certainly try," he replied, handing the bag to me. "Richard might recognize my voice, Joan. And the worst they can do is send us away."

We moved out from the wall now, he struck up a tune, and his voice rang out in the still night. When he finished one verse and paused, a woman's head appeared at the lighted window and a coin dropped on the ground not far off. We stood there a moment longer, then took up a new position nearer the corner of the building. As Raimond lifted his vielle to begin again, I reached over and tugged at his sleeve.

"Wait!" I said urgently. "Not that song, Raimond—sing one of Richard's."

"By God, yes! Why didn't I think of that myself? But do I remember the words?"

He strummed softly, humming to himself; then, while I filled in a word here and there, he quoted the first verse of the chanson Blondel had taught Berengaria and me. "That's good enough," I told him. "Sing!"

He did, and this time every word was clear and distinct over the muted tones of his vielle. I listened, my heart pounding, seeing and hearing first Blondel and Berengaria singing it for my lord brother, then Rick joining in, with his arm around Blondel's slender shoulders.

All was silent again. A dog barked fitfully, but we heard nothing else. Without saying anything more we walked back to the side of the castle that opened into the kitchen courtyard and Raimond, after another futile attempt to rouse someone by knocking, took up a position a little distance away and sang as loudly as he could.

When he had finished, the discouraging silence remained unbroken; by listening carefully I could hear a clattering inside the thick stone walls that probably came from the scullery—but that was all.

"On we go," Raimond said at last, and on we went around another corner of the tall, square tower. A colder wind met us as we turned it, and the moon, almost full tonight, came out at last from behind a mass of clouds, lighting our way and making a silvery path on the wide river flowing below us.

I shivered and stared up at the dark windows. There was something frightening about them in the moonlight. What was it? I shivered again, realizing what it was. They reminded me of blind eyes, gazing sightlessly down at me. What, I asked myself, were we doing in this grim, lonely place? A sob rose in my throat, but I fought it back and moved closer to Raimond.

Putting his free arm around me, he drew me into a dark shadow and I clung to him, my cheek against his. Comforted and warmer, I drew away, gave him a tremulous smile, and pointed to a spot where the light was brightest.

"We'll stand there," I said, walking toward it.

He followed me, lifted his vielle, and sang again. Before he had finished, a gutteral shout sounded above us and I saw a man lean out and shake a menacing fist. He shouted something else, then disappeared.

"He's off to fetch the guards," Raimond told me. "Well, my darling, we've done our best. Once more, together, then we'll go meet them!"

He laughed into my eyes and as we raised our voices in a great burst of defiance, shouting to the moon the first verse of Richard's song, I was Joanne, the jongleuresse, he was Blondel, my lord and master, and nothing else mattered. When we came to the last few notes a small dark shape hurtled around the corner, loped toward us, froze, threw back its head and added his voice to ours in a wonderful hound's bay that must have reached the ears of the people in the town below.

I opened my mouth to say something to Raimond, then closed it again. He had tossed his vielle on the ground and was staring fixedly up at the castle.

I stood absolutely still, hardly daring to breathe. He had heard something; that was apparent in every line of his body. I strained my ears, listening, listening. Then, from the very top of the keep, a laugh drifted down to us, a hearty, joyous laugh, a laugh I knew well.

And my lord brother's voice took up his own song where we had left off, and Richard finished it for us.

The End

The story of Joan and her royal brother was far from ended, and for those readers who want to know what happened next, here, very briefly, are the facts: the Abbots of Boxley and Pontrobert now insisted on seeing King Richard, and on Palm Sunday, the twenty-first day of March, a meeting was arranged at Ochsenfurt, some ten miles from Würzburg. Two days later he was openly placed in the Emperor's custody, and when the Easter Court convened at Speyer he was at last allowed to refute his enemies' charges.

But although the Lion Heart did this so convincingly that friends and foes alike shouted aloud in sympathy and the Emperor himself wept and kissed him on both cheeks, it was still many more months before Philip of France sent a messenger to Prince John saying "The Devil is loose!" King Richard had been held captive for one year, six weeks, and three days.

When he was free at last, he saw to it that his favorite sister had her heart's desire, and Joan, with his blessing, became Raimond's wife. Berengaria was not as fortunate. She and Richard lived apart until some time in 1196, when Hugh of Lincoln shamed his royal master into resuming at least the appearance of a joint household.

It is doubtful, however, that she was happy, and she was the only Queen of England who never set foot on England's soil.

In telling this tale I have needed to invent very little, for the truth, in this case, is much stranger than fiction. The few liberties I have taken with time and space occur mostly after the end of the Crusade; and in using the Blondel legend—however charming, it is only a legend—in my own way to further my romance, I have followed a well-established precedent.

MOLLY COSTAIN HAYCRAFT